Notable British Trials

Adelaide Bartlett

NOTABLE BRITISH TRIALS SERIES.

General Editor—HARRY HODGE.

Wm. Hodge & Co., Ltd., Edinburgh and London.

ann [~~1913~~]

5/ 10/8

Mr. Edward Clarke, Q.C., M.P.

Trial of
Adelaide Bartlett

(1886)

EDITED BY

Sir John Hall, Bart.

EDINBURGH AND LONDON

WILLIAM HODGE & COMPANY, LIMITED

MADE AND PRINTED IN GREAT BRITAIN
BY
WILLIAM HODGE AND COMPANY, LTD.
GLASGOW AND EDINBURGH
1927

PREFACE.

STRANGE stories have been unfolded at the Old Bailey, but no stranger one has been heard than that of Mrs. Bartlett. Apart from the dramatic incidents of the trial and the curious medical questions which came under discussion, " the whole story," to quote from the *Times* leading article, " whether on the theory of guilt or innocence, is marvellous."

My task as editor has been lightened by the fact that a verbatim report of the trial with a preface by Sir Edward Clarke was published in 1886. In addition, I had the inestimable advantage of several personal interviews with Sir Edward, who kindly allowed me to see his case-book and other documents bearing on the trial. For this and for his great courtesy on all occasions, when I have invoked his help, I beg to tender him my best thanks. I desire also to take this opportunity of expressing my gratitude to Mrs. Norton for sending me a photograph of her father, Sir Alfred Wills, a copy of which appears in this volume.

JOHN HALL.

August, 1927.

CONTENTS.

LIST OF ILLUSTRATIONS.

ADELAIDE BARTLETT.

INTRODUCTION.

I.

THERE is a peculiar fascination about a case of poisoning. It is generally mysterious, the evidence is always circumstantial, and, if a woman be concerned in it, there is almost invariably a love story in the background. All these elements were present at the trial of Mrs. Bartlett, and, in addition, there were curious problems of medical jurisprudence and the question of the strange relations alleged to have existed between the different parties.

The history of the affair opens on 9th April, 1875, with the marriage at Croydon of Adelaide Blanche de la Tremoille and Thomas Edwin Bartlett. The bride was born at Orleans in 1855, and was therefore in her twentieth year. She was the natural daughter of an Englishman of good position. The name of her mother has never been disclosed, nor is anything known about her early life. Her familiarity with the English language suggests, however, that she was brought to this country as a child; but all that can be said with certainty about the matter is that, at the beginning of 1875, she was living at Kingston-on-Thames, in the same house as Charles Bartlett, who introduced her to his brother, her prospective husband. According to her own story, she only saw him once before her marriage, which was arranged by her father. No money seems to have been settled upon her, but it is supposed that her husband received a considerable sum, which he employed to great advantage in his business.[1]

The bridegroom, Edwin Bartlett, to give him the name by which his family and friends addressed him, was a prosperous grocer and provision dealer, about thirty years of age. So successful was he that at the time of his death, eleven years later, he and his partner, Mr. Baxter, were the owners of no less than six shops in the Herne Hill and Dulwich districts. It was afterwards said of him that he was a man of peculiar views about matrimony. But at this stage of the narrative it is only necessary to mention one of his characteristics. Like many successful

---

[1] *Cornhill Magazine*, December, 1920. "Leaves from a Lawyer's Case Book," by Sir Edward Clarke.

Adelaide Bartlett.

men whose education has been no more than rudimentary, he had a great respect for learning,[2] and no sooner was he married than he took immediate steps to remedy the defects of his wife's education. Almost from the church-door she was sent off to a boarding school at Stoke Newington, where she remained for two years, during all of which time she only lived with her husband in the holidays. There is no reason to suppose, however, that she resented this arrangement and was not a consenting party to it. Be that as it may, after a third year spent at a convent in Belgium, her education was considered to be sufficiently advanced to admit of her return to England. In 1878, accordingly, she took up her permanent abode with her husband, in the first instance in Station Road, Herne Hill, in rooms situated over one of his principal shops.

In her new home Mrs. Bartlett appears to have lived on the most affectionate terms with her husband. He was, however, too absorbed in business to have much time to devote to her amusement. With her neighbours she seems to have had no social intercourse, nor does she appear to have kept up friendly relations with any of her former mistresses or schoolfellows. Her work, her music, and her dogs, of which she was very fond, sufficed apparently for her entertainment. Had she and her husband been the only occupants of their home she would, as far as can be judged, have led a contented existence. Unfortunately, very soon after her arrival in Station Road, her mother-in-law died, and her husband thereupon suggested that his father should come to live with them. Old Mr. Bartlett was a builder who had not been very successful, and was, in consequence, largely dependent upon his son, whose invitation he accepted, notwithstanding that he disliked his daughter-in-law and disapproved of the marriage. Entertaining these sentiments, he could hardly fail to bring an element of discord into the peaceful atmosphere of Station Road. And so it proved. After several minor disputes old Mr. Bartlett made some very serious allegations against his daughter-in-law and his son, Frederick. Whether or not there was any truth in these charges, Edwin Bartlett stood by his wife and insisted upon his father withdrawing them. The old man, having no desire to quarrel with his son, agreed to sign an apology drawn up by a solicitor, in which he acknowledged that his statements were unfounded, and expressed his regret that he had made them. A reconciliation

---

[2] *Lancet*, 22nd May, 1886. Article by Dr. Leach. "He had a reverential regard for advanced learning."

Introduction.

followed, but it was upon the surface only. Henceforward old Mr. Bartlett and his daughter-in-law were to all outward appearances on friendly and even affectionate terms, but, as will be seen, they continued in their hearts to regard each other with as much dislike as ever.

After this incident nothing worthy of record seems to have occurred until the autumn of 1881, when Mrs. Bartlett, for the first time, was expecting to be a mother. About a month before the event, a nurse, Annie Walker by name, was called in and installed in Station Road. The circumstances which led to the selection of this woman must be noted, because they afterwards assumed some importance. The Bartletts possessed and appear to have closely studied a book entitled "Esoteric Anthropology; or, the Mysteries of Man." It dealt with the subject of birth control, and professed to be as "pure in morals" as it was "true in science." Thus abstention was prescribed as the only proper and effectual way of avoiding the consequences of the sexual act. But, having laid down this principle, it went on to explain, for the benefit presumably of those who were disinclined to exercise so much restraint, how the consequences of this same act could be averted. Now, when she found herself in the condition which has been mentioned, Mrs. Bartlett's thoughts seem to have turned towards Dr. Nichols, the author of this work. She was aware that he lived in Fopstone Road, Earl's Court, and was an American doctor who had no degree entitling him to practise in this country. But she knew also that, quite independently of him, his wife, Mrs. Nichols, was in the habit of seeing patients and giving consultations. Accordingly, she either went to see this lady, who died some two years later, or communicated with her by letter, and it was on her advice that Annie Walker was engaged.

Mrs. Bartlett was not attended by a doctor. When Annie Walker, who seems to have been an experienced and skilful nurse, spoke to Mr. Bartlett on the subject, he merely inquired whether she was apprehensive on his wife's account, and, on learning that it was the life of the child, not that of the mother, which would be endangered, begged her "to take the case through," as he would "rather not have any man interfering with her." The nurse's fears proved well founded. After a most painful confinement Mrs. Bartlett was delivered of a dead child, the doctor whom, at the last moment, Annie Walker insisted on calling in arriving too late to save it.

For another three weeks, until she was once more up and

Adelaide Bartlett.

about, the nurse remained with Mrs. Bartlett. The two women undoubtedly became much attached to each other, and, when her professional attendance was no longer necessary, Annie Walker continued from time to time to visit her former patient. On one occasion, indeed, she seems to have stayed with her for several days. Both Mr. and Mrs. Bartlett treated her with the utmost confidence, and never hesitated to discuss with her their most private affairs. Later on, in consequence, when all these matters were investigated, she was able to give much valuable information about their relations to each other and generally about their mode of life. According to her, they were a united and affectionate couple. Nevertheless, Mrs. Bartlett did once speak to her with regret about her husband's failure to appreciate either her musical talents or her work, although, in Annie Walker's opinion, " she worked beautifully." She also on several occasions complained of Mr. Bartlett's testamentary dispositions. He had left everything to her, but only on the condition that she should never re-marry. She would often revert to this matter, and, to the best of the nurse's recollection, had once mentioned the subject in her husband's presence.

In 1883, a little more than a year after these events, the Bartletts left Station Road and went to live over another of Mr. Bartlett's shops in Lordship Lane, East Dulwich. Here Mrs. Bartlett became very friendly with a neighbour, a Mrs. Matthews, the wife of a silk salesman in the city, who was doubtless a business acquaintance of Mr. Bartlett. During the whole of her married life this lady and the nurse, Annie Walker, seem to have been the only persons of her own sex with whom Mrs. Bartlett can be said to have been on intimate terms. After remaining for about twelve months in Lordship Lane, the Bartletts again changed their place of domicile, this time to The Cottage, Merton, some two miles from Wimbledon. At Lordship Lane and at Merton Mrs. Bartlett seems to have led very much the same kind of life as in Station Road. But there was one important difference. When they left Herne Hill old Mr. Bartlett did not accompany them to their new home. Neither at Lordship Lane nor at Merton was the accommodation sufficient, he afterwards explained. Be that as it may, the old gentleman ever afterwards lived apart, and contented himself with occasional visits to his son's house. He was in the habit, however, of seeing him nearly every day at one or another of his shops.

The Bartletts remained at Merton until the autumn of 1885. Before that, however, a man had entered into their lives who

Introduction.

was destined tragically to affect their future existence. One Sunday, at the beginning of their last year's stay at Merton, they attended divine worship at a Wesleyan chapel in the village street. The Rev. George Dyson, a young man about twenty-seven years of age, with " closely trimmed whiskers and a heavy black moustache,"[3] conducted the service. There was nothing very striking either about his appearance or his address, and neither Mr. nor Mrs. Bartlett was particularly attracted by him. A few days later he paid them a formal call, and was received by Mrs. Bartlett, who, when he took his leave, does not appear to have expressed any wish to see him again. The Bartletts, however, continued to attend his chapel, and, in June, 1885, some five months later, he repeated his visit. On this occasion both husband and wife were at home, and entertained the reverend gentleman at tea. He was about to go to Dublin for a few days to take his degree at Trinity College, and talked about his studies. Mr. Bartlett, whose profound respect for a classical education has already been mentioned, was greatly interested, and, when Mr. Dyson went away, he pressed him warmly to return at no distant date. The young man complied, and a considerable intimacy soon sprang up between them. The Rev. George was certainly not possessed of deep learning or of wide mental attainments, but he was probably a more-cultivated and better-educated man than anybody with whom Mr. Bartlett had hitherto associated on terms of equality. That he was impressed by him and derived a keen pleasure from his companionship may be gathered from the fact that he suggested, before long, that his wife should resume her studies under his able tuition. Mr. Dyson readily undertook the task, and henceforward came nearly every day to The Cottage to " coach " his friend's wife in Latin, history, geography, and mathematics.

Mrs. Bartlett's lonely days were over. Instead of long hours in which she had to depend for amusement upon her own resources, her afternoons and, sometimes, even her mornings were passed in Mr. Dyson's company. With the exception of the Matthews, who stayed for a week at The Cottage in July, there were no visitors to intrude upon their privacy. From eleven o'clock, when the daily servant finished her work and went home, they had the house completely to themselves. About six Mr. Bartlett generally returned from business, and, if Mr. Dyson had not yet gone, he would insist upon his remaining and devoting another hour or

---

[3] *Daily Telegraph*, 20th February, 1886.

two to his entertainment. Thus matters went on until the end of August, when the Bartletts' tenancy of The Cottage expired. Before selecting a new residence they proposed to spend a month at Dover. But by this time Mr. Dyson had become so necessary to their happiness that they felt that no holiday would be worthy of the name without him. Mr. Dyson was a man of small means, being wholly dependent upon his stipend of £100 a year. A journey to Dover was, therefore, to him a serious matter. Mr. Bartlett, however, would not allow any consideration of that kind to stand in the way, and offered to supply him with a first-class season ticket.[4] Mr. Dyson's clerical duties, unfortunately, prevented him from taking full advantage of his friend's generosity, but, while declining a season ticket, he promised to run down and see them whenever he could. And he was as good as his word. On two different occasions during the month of September he stayed with them at Dover, the cost of his return ticket being defrayed by Mr. Bartlett.

Although the Bartletts were in the habit of alluding to the month which they spent at Dover as a holiday, it was in point of fact a period of strenuous activity for Mr. Bartlett. Nearly every day he went up to business, not infrequently catching the boat train at three in the morning and sometimes not returning until ten o'clock at night. And on one of the first days on which he thus went up to London he gave Mr. Dyson a proof of the confidence which he reposed in him, although his acquaintance with him had lasted for little more than two months. On the afternoon of 3rd September, while at one of his shops in Herne Hill, he requested two of his assistants to witness his signature. The document which he asked them to attest was a will leaving everything he possessed to his wife unconditionally, and appointing his solicitor, Mr. Wood, and his friend, the Rev. George Dyson, his executors. And, having made these dispositions, he made no secret of them to his wife and Mr. Dyson, both of whom, in consequence, became aware that his new will contained no objectionable stipulation that she must not re-marry.

Having seemingly determined to live in the heart of London, the Bartletts, on leaving Dover, went to a hotel in the Strand, in order to seek for lodgings. These they found in Claverton Street, and thither they removed on 3rd October. Claverton Street runs from Belgrave Road to Grosvenor Road, on the river embankment. It begins under the name of Denbigh Street, but,

---

[4] Inquest, 11th February, 1886.

Introduction.

after crossing Lupus Street, it widens out and becomes Claverton Street. It is a street like many others in this part of London. The houses are three storeys high, and each has a portico supported by Doric pillars, which forms a balcony for the first-floor windows. And it was the first, or drawing-room, floor of No. 85 which the Bartletts proposed to occupy. It consisted of only two rooms, divided from each other by folding doors—one in front looking on to the street and one at the back which was to serve as their bedroom. In discussing their arrangements with Mrs. Doggett, the landlady, Mr. Bartlett, bearing in mind that Mr. Dyson would doubtless be a frequent visitor, was careful to warn her that a gentleman would dine with them once a week. "It is only a clergyman," interjected Mrs. Bartlett. But whether this remark had reference to their guest's appetite or was intended to guarantee his respectability can only be surmised. In view of what happened afterwards, it may perhaps be considered ominous that Mr. Doggett, the landlord, held the post of Registrar of Deaths for the district.

Life at Claverton Street followed the usual routine. Every morning, soon after eight, Mr. Bartlett started off to business, returning as a rule at six, at which hour he and his wife generally dined. Long before that, however, Mr. Dyson, who had been thoughtfully provided with a season ticket from Putney to Waterloo, generally appeared at the house. By this time all three of them had discarded in speaking to one another the ceremonious "Mr." and "Mrs." Whether her husband were present or not, Mrs. Bartlett was "Adelaide" to Mr. Dyson, and he was "George" to her. It may be that in these days there would be nothing extraordinary about such familiarity, but, forty years ago, especially in the rank of life to which these people belonged, it was most unusual. When Mr. Dyson arrived in the morning, as he sometimes did, he and Mrs. Bartlett always had luncheon together, and far more often than the "once a week" mentioned by Mr. Bartlett to the landlady he ate his dinner at Claverton Street. That he made himself thoroughly at home may be gathered from the fact that, on arriving, he generally discarded his clerical attire and put on an old jacket and a pair of slippers which the Bartletts kept for his use in their sitting-room. If the real purpose of his long visits was the supervision of Mrs. Bartlett's studies, it is strange that he never brought any books with him to Claverton Street. And Alice Fulcher, the maidservant, who supplied that information, could recollect other matters which suggest yet more strongly that he and Mrs. Bartlett devoted very

7

Adelaide Bartlett.

little time to "Latin, history, geography, and mathematics." One day, after Mr. Dyson's departure, she noticed that the window curtains had been pinned together, and, on another occasion, when she entered the room, she found him seated in a low chair, while Mrs. Bartlett reclined upon the floor at his feet with her head upon his knees.

Although he often suffered from his teeth, Mr. Bartlett, throughout his married life, enjoyed excellent health. In November, 1880, while at Station Road, he was examined and accepted by the British Equitable as a first-class life. Once only, owing to overwork, he was compelled to take a rest, but a sea voyage to Scotland soon put him right, and, at the end of a fortnight, he was back again at business. On 8th December, however, when he had been living in Claverton Street for about two months, he felt so out of sorts that he abandoned work for the day and returned home. He had arranged the following morning to go with his wife and Mr. Dyson to the St. Bernard Dog Show, and, when at half-past nine that gentleman arrived, he still adhered to his intention of accompanying them. But in the evening, after a long day spent at the show, he complained of fatigue, and the next day was so clearly very ill that Mrs. Bartlett went out to fetch a doctor. Dr. Leach, whom she saw, was quite unknown to them both, and was only selected because he lived in Charlwood Street, less than a quarter of a mile away.

Dr. Leach found his patient suffering from a severe pain in his left side, from sickness, diarrhœa, and hæmorrhage of the bowels. His pulse was weak, and his condition one of extreme nervousness and prostration. He complained of sleeplessness, and said that he had overworked himself. On looking at his mouth Dr. Leach observed a blue line round the edge of the gums, which pointed unmistakably to mercury. Having diagnosed the case as one of mercurialism or sub-acute gastritis, he prescribed a lotion for the mouth and a stomach and sedative mixture, and recommended that the patient should be kept very quiet and see no one connected with his business. In the evening he called again, and for the next two or three days came in twice a day to see him. Being still at a loss to account for the symptoms of mercurial poisoning which he had observed at his first visit, he took the opportunity, when Mrs. Bartlett was out of the room, of suggesting to him that he must have taken mercury. But this he denied, and the only light which he was ever able to throw upon the matter was that, some few days previously, he had swallowed a pill of unknown strength. Dr. Leach could discover no

8

Introduction.

signs of the disease which is generally associated with the taking of mercury, and, in default of a better, was inclined to accept his patient's explanation as correct. Probably, he reasoned, the man had what he described as " an idiosyncrasy for the drug." His physical symptoms soon yielded to treatment, but the mental depression and the sleeplessness proved far more difficult to overcome. Bromides only made him more restless, and, on 13th December, Dr. Leach was forced to inject morphia. But even this failed of its object, and, on 15th December, he came to the conclusion that his patient's teeth, which were once again painful, were the cause of the trouble. He arranged, accordingly, for the attendance of Mr. Roberts, a dentist, practising in Charlwood Street. Some ten or eleven years earlier, Mr. Bartlett had been very badly treated by another dentist, who had sawn off his teeth and supplied him with a plate without extracting the " subjacent stumps."[5] It is not surprising, therefore, that Mr. Roberts found them loose, decayed, and, in the words of Dr. Leach, " in a horrible condition." He now lost no time in doing what should have been done long ago. On 16th December he removed two, on the following day eleven, and, on 21st December, yet another four of these stumps.

After Dr. Leach's first visit Mrs. Bartlett converted the sitting-room into a sick-room by moving into it from the back room the small bed in which her husband had hitherto slept. Throughout his illness she watched over him with unremitting attention, and performed, without assistance, the most disagreeable duties of a nurse. At night she was content to obtain what rest she could either in an armchair by her husband's bedside or upon a sofa in his room. Never once could Dr. Leach persuade her to go to her own bed in the back room. Visitors when they came were received by her in a small room on the ground floor, known in the house as the " back smoking-room " or the " ante-room," which the Doggetts placed at her disposal. Here she saw Mr. Dyson, who called as regularly as ever, but, after talking to her, he generally went upstairs and sat for a time with the sick man, whose partner, Mr. Baxter, also came every Sunday to see him. Old Mr. Bartlett, directly he heard of his condition, hurried round to Claverton Street. On this first occasion he was admitted to the sick-room, but after that his daughter-in-law generally refused to allow him to go upstairs. Her husband was too ill, she assured him, to receive visitors, and during

---

[5] *Lancet*, 22nd May, 1886.

Adelaide Bartlett.

the whole of his son's illness the father was only permitted to see him three times. His daughter-in-law, however, wrote him several short notes. These were afterwards produced in Court, and can be more conveniently dealt with later. For the moment suffice it to say that in one of them she intimated very plainly that she had neither forgiven nor forgotten the quarrel at Station Road. The old man greatly resented his exclusion from his son's room, and on one of his visits, when he was talking to his daughter-in-law in the ground-floor room, he professed to be disappointed with his progress, and offered to send in another doctor. She, however, declined to entertain the suggestion on the score of the expense it would involve, a plea which the old man scouted as ridiculous.

Nevertheless, old Mr. Bartlett's words were not without effect. It is plain from a very remarkable conversation which took place with Dr. Leach that she must have talked over his father's suggestion with her husband. "Doctor," said Mrs. Bartlett to Dr. Leach in the course of his visit on 19th December, "will you excuse me for what I am about to say," and, after some complimentary remarks about his skilful treatment of his patient, she proceeded to tell him that her husband's relations and friends were desirous of sending in a doctor of their own selection. "These people," she continued, "were most unfriendly to her." "We intend," exclaimed Mr. Bartlett from his bed, "to manage our own affairs in future, and not to be interfered with by my friends or relations. I am sorry to say that they are not kind to my wife." Dr. Leach begged them to call in whom they pleased; he had no objection, he assured them, to any number of consultations. "No," replied Mr. Bartlett, "I will not have a consultation in the ordinary sense of the term. I will not see any one they send. I will see any gentleman you choose to bring. I am getting better, and I will not submit to any other treatment. I will see any gentleman once. I do this for the protection of my wife." "Doctor," added Mrs. Bartlett, "Mr. Bartlett's friends will accuse me of poisoning him if he does not get out soon." Before Dr. Leach left the house it was arranged that he should invite the attendance of a neighbouring practitioner, Dr. Dudley, of 71 Belgrave Road.

That same day, 19th December, Dr. Dudley, in conjunction with Dr. Leach, made a thorough examination of Mr. Bartlett. He complained very much of sleeplessness, and appeared to be depressed and lacking in energy. Dr. Dudley, however, saw no reason to suggest any alteration of his treatment, of which he

10

Introduction.

expressed his complete approval. In his opinion there was very little the matter with him. He was, he assured him, a perfectly sound man, and the best advice he could give him was to rouse himself and go out for a walk or a drive every day. Mrs. Bartlett was present throughout the interview, and replied to certain questions about her husband's previous health and habits. Already, before this, Dr. Leach had urged him to show some energy, shake off his lethargy, and go out of the house. But he either replied that " it would kill him " or begged to be allowed " to lie still and feel happy." So obstinate was he on the point of remaining indoors that Dr. Leach was almost inclined to fear that he might have " overlooked something serious in him." The only suggestion to which he responded was that, after Christmas, he should go to Torquay. To give him confidence Dr. Leach promised to accompany him and place him under the care of Dr. Dalby. By this arrangement he hoped that he would consent to go alone. He was now, Dr. Leach considered, a " hysterical patient," and it was very necessary to induce him to leave his wife, who " petted him too much." He only wished it had been in his power to order him off on a sea voyage, " with no one to nurse him."

Christmas that year fell on a Friday, and on Monday, 21st December, Mr. Dyson went down to Poole on a visit to his father, who, like his son, was a Wesleyan minister. On Saturday, the 26th, however, he returned to London, and spent the afternoon in Claverton Street. Mr. Bartlett seemed " brighter," and was apparently in good spirits. The next day, Sunday, the 27th, he came again, but only reached Claverton Street about nine in the evening. As he approached the door he met Mrs. Bartlett, who was going out to post a letter, and, turning back, accompanied her. As they walked along she told him that she wanted to obtain some chloroform, in order to soothe her husband and make him sleep. He suffered from an internal complaint which produced violent paroxysms, and when in that state it was only chloroform that quieted him. It would have to be sprinkled on a handkerchief, and, being volatile, she would need a considerable amount, about as much as would be contained in an ordinary medicine bottle. Hitherto the nurse, Annie Walker, had supplied her with it, but she was now abroad in America, and she therefore proposed to ask him to procure some for her. Mr. Dyson very naturally suggested that she should apply to Dr. Leach. She demurred to that, however, saying that, not knowing she was skilled in the use of chloroform, he would be afraid

11

Adelaide Bartlett.

to entrust any to her. Mr. Dyson seemed satisfied and expressed his readiness to help her, whereupon she handed him a sovereign to pay for the purchase of the drug. Both then returned to Claverton Street, and both went into the house together. Before departing that evening, Mr. Dyson had a talk with Mr. Bartlett, who was once more very depressed, but he omitted to say anything about the commission which Mrs. Bartlett had given him to execute.

That same night, as soon as he reached his lodgings at Putney, Mr. Dyson appears to have written to a friend, a medical student, asking him to send him some chloroform. To that letter he never received an answer, either because it was wrongly addressed or because his friend was not disposed to comply with his request. The next morning, however, thinking possibly that he would do well to have two strings to his bow, he set about procuring the drug himself. In the course of this Monday, 28th December, he went to three chemists' shops—one at Putney and two at Wimbledon—and asked for chloroform. At two of them he bought a 1-ounce bottle, and at a third two bottles containing the same amount, making about 4 ounces altogether. All the bottles which he thus procured were labelled " Chloroform—Poison," and, on returning home, he removed one of these labels and stuck it on to a 6-ounce medicine bottle which he obtained from his landlady. Into this larger bottle he poured the contents of the four small bottles which he bought that morning. To each of the chemists whom he visited he seems to have intimated that he required chloroform for the purpose of taking out grease spots. But, although he saw fit to practise this piece of deception, his proceedings in other respects were open and straightforward. One of the shops was within fifty yards of his chapel, and the other two were kept by men who were members of his congregation.

The next day, Tuesday, the 29th, Mr. Dyson took the chloroform with him to Claverton Street, but he did not at once pass it on to Mrs. Bartlett. A visitor, he afterwards explained, was present, and it was only later on, when he and Mrs. Bartlett went out for a walk by the river, that he actually placed the bottle in her hands. Mr. Bartlett's recovery had been somewhat retarded by an unpleasant complication which made its appearance in Christmas week. It had obliged Dr. Leach to administer certain powders, followed by strong purgatives, which for several days failed to produce the desired effect. It was this which had caused the renewed depression which Mr. Dyson had observed in him on Sunday. But after a drive in a hansom on Monday, the 28th,

12

Introduction.

he felt better, and on the following day Dr. Leach was able to tell him that he should henceforward discontinue his daily visits. But, unfortunately, his teeth once more became troublesome, and Dr. Leach perceived signs of incipient necrosis of the jaw. There was every hope, however, that the prompt extraction of one of his few remaining teeth would prevent the disease from spreading. Not wishing to alarm him, the doctor arranged privately with Mrs. Bartlett that he should visit the dentist on the following Thursday.

On Thursday, 31st December, Mr. Bartlett, who was seemingly by now aware of what was in store for him, had, about noon, half a dozen oysters. A light meal of that kind should surely have sufficed for a man who was to have a tooth extracted under gas in the afternoon. But at three his dinner was placed before him, consisting of jugged hare, of which he partook heartily. Shortly afterwards, Mr. Dyson paid him his usual visit. In view of his excellent appetite it is surprising to hear that that gentleman found him " nervous " and suffering great pain from his teeth. At five Dr. Leach, who was to accompany his patient to the dentist, arrived, and Mr. Dyson took his departure. A cab was called, and the two Bartletts and the doctor set out for Mr. Roberts' house in Charlwood Street. In spite of the decidedly prosaic character of their expedition, Mrs. Bartlett was in a somewhat romantic frame of mind. Addressing Dr. Leach, she said that so many of their friends had lately been married that she and her husband were saying that morning " we wished almost we were unmarried that we might have the pleasure of marrying each other again." " That is very flattering to you, Mr. Bartlett," observed Dr. Leach. Mr. Bartlett was closely muffled up, and his reply was inaudible, but, to the best of Dr. Leach's recollection, he said, before they reached their destination, something to the effect that " we suit one another very well ; we agree in our views." Hitherto Mr. Roberts, when removing Mr. Bartlett's loose teeth, had applied a local anæsthetic, but on this occasion Dr. Leach was to administer gas. The operation was quickly and successfully performed, and was attended by no untoward incident. The rather long time—about four minutes—which elapsed before the patient became unconscious was the only feature of the business which was in the smallest degree unusual.

Mr. and Mrs. Bartlett returned to Claverton Street in a hansom. Not long after their arrival Mrs. Doggett came up stairs to inquire how Mr. Bartlett had stood his visit to the dentist.

Adelaide Bartlett.

He seemed, she afterwards related, in good spirits, saying that "he thought the worst was over, and that he would now get better." It was his intention, he gave her to understand, to go to Torquay for change of air. Under the lead of Mrs. Bartlett, the subject of anæsthetics was then discussed. Had Mrs. Doggett, she asked, ever been under chloroform, and was not the sensation of taking it rather "nice and pleasant"? Mrs. Doggett had taken chloroform ten years before, but at that distance of time her recollection of whether it was "nice and pleasant" was rather vague. She was in the habit, said Mrs. Bartlett, of administering sleeping drops to her husband; "ten was a strong dose, but she did not hesitate to give him twelve." This seems to have brought the conversation to an end, but, before Mrs. Doggett went away, Mr. Bartlett told her how greatly he had enjoyed his jugged hare; "he would gladly eat three such dinners a day." At nine o'clock this remarkable invalid had for supper half a dozen oysters, bread and butter, some mango-chutney, cake and tea, all of which he ate with great relish. Not content with that, while Alice Fulcher was clearing the table, he ordered a large haddock for his breakfast, adding that "he should get up an hour earlier at the thought of having it." About half-past ten the girl brought up the coals for the night. Mr. Bartlett was by that time in bed, and Mrs. Bartlett, holding up her finger to intimate that she did not wish to be disturbed again, directed her to place a basin for his beef tea on the landing outside.

Downstairs the Doggetts were seeing the New Year in, and it was not until past midnight that they went to bed. At four Mr. Doggett was aroused by a sound of knocking, and, going to the door, found Mrs. Bartlett, who told him that she thought her husband was dead. Prior to this she had awakened Alice Fulcher and sent her out for Dr. Leach. As soon as he had clothed himself in a dressing-gown, Mr. Doggett went down to the first floor. Mr. Bartlett was in bed lying upon his back, with his left hand reposing upon his breast. He was quite cold, as Mr. Doggett ascertained, and had probably been dead for two or three hours. "I had fallen off to sleep," said Mrs. Bartlett, "with my hand round his foot, and I awoke with a pain in my hand and found him lying on his face. I put him in the position in which you saw him and tried to pour brandy down his throat." This was the only explanation which she had to offer. Before that, on first entering the room, Mr. Doggett noticed a peculiar smell, which he ascribed to chloric ether. The fire, he observed, was burning brightly, and appeared to have been attended to recently.

14

Introduction.

On the mantelpiece, within reach of the bed, was a tumbler half-full of brandy, which also had about it a smell of ether or paregoric. His investigations went no further, for at half-past four Dr. Leach arrived.

At a glance the doctor perceived that his patient was dead. Mrs. Bartlett, on hearing the fatal verdict, " burst out crying bitterly," but when she inquired the cause of death Dr. Leach could give her no definite answer. It might be that he had ruptured some small vessel, or there might be an aneurism which had been overlooked. For her part Mrs. Bartlett could only repeat what she had already told Mr. Doggett, with the addition, however, that before she found her husband dead she had heard him snoring in a peculiar manner. The whole affair was so inexplicable that Dr. Leach began to wonder whether the deceased might not have taken some rapidly acting poison, such as prussic acid. But Mrs. Bartlett, when he suggested that possibility, was positive that he could not have obtained anything of the kind without her knowledge. Nevertheless, assisted by Mr. Doggett, he made a thorough search of the room. They found nothing, however, which arrested their attention, except a nearly empty bottle of chlorodyne. Being aware that even as small an amount as one drachm of this medicine had been known to have a fatal effect, Dr. Leach attached considerable importance to this discovery, notwithstanding that Mrs. Bartlett assured him that her husband was not in the habit of taking it internally, and only used it for rubbing on his gums or for rinsing out his mouth. Before leaving the house the doctor was obliged to tell her that he could not give a death certificate. She seemed disturbed, and asked, " Will there have to be an inquest?" Dr. Leach was not prepared to say as much as that, but he assured her that it was absolutely necessary that a post-mortem examination should be held. He did not propose to perform it himself, and already in his mind had fixed upon an eminent pathologist, Dr. Green, as the most suitable person to conduct it. To that Mrs. Bartlett offered no objection, and appeared genuinely distressed when, later on in the morning, she learnt that Dr. Green could not attend until the following afternoon. Indeed, whenever the matter was mentioned, she expressed the utmost anxiety that the examination should take place as soon as possible, and, to quote the words of Dr. Leach, " chafed at the delay."

Some two hours after Dr. Leach's departure, Mrs. Bartlett telegraphed to Mr. Bartlett, senior, her deceased husband's partner, Mr. Baxter, and her friend, Mrs. Matthews, to inform them

15

Adelaide Bartlett.

of what had happened, and to ask them to come round to Claverton Street. Mr. Baxter and Mrs. Matthews shortly afterwards arrived. Mr. Bartlett had gone out before the telegram was delivered at his address, but Mr. Baxter, knowing that he was engaged upon some work in Berkeley Square, went to find him, and presently returned with him in a hansom. He was greatly distressed, and from the moment that Mr. Baxter imparted the news to him seems to have made up his mind that his son had been the victim of foul play. On entering the room in which he lay dead he went up to him, and, after kissing his forehead, smelt his lips to see whether he could detect the presence of prussic acid. Then, turning to Dr. Leach, who was once more back in the house, he exclaimed, " Doctor, we must have a post-mortem ; this cannot pass." Dr. Leach agreed, and told him that the matter was already engaging his attention. The necessary arrangements were then discussed, Mr. Bartlett giving it plainly to be understood that he wished the inquiry to be left to medical men who had not been concerned in the case. That, again, met with Dr. Leach's approval, and it was finally decided to ask Dr. Green, of Charing Cross Hospital, his assistant physician, Dr. Murray, and Dr. Dudley to perform the examination, and to invite Dr. Cheney, of Mandeville Place, to attend on behalf of Mr. Bartlett. Mrs. Matthews remained with Mrs. Bartlett until the evening, and accompanied her when she went out to purchase mourning. Prior to that Mrs. Bartlett wrote to Mr. Dyson and to Mr. Wood, the solicitor.

The next morning, 2nd January, Mr. Dyson presented himself at Claverton Street about half-past eleven, and stayed to hear the result of the post-mortem. It was to take place at two o'clock in the first-floor back bedroom, and thither the doctors were conducted as soon as they arrived. While they were engaged upstairs Mrs. Bartlett, Mr. Dyson, and Mr. Wood sat together in the little room on the ground floor. Old Mr. Bartlett declined to join them, preferring to spend the time in the street outside. There he remained until about four o'clock, when he saw Dr. Green come out of the house and drive away. Shortly afterwards Dr. Leach, whose part in the proceedings had been confined to taking notes, came down and invited every one to go upstairs to the front room, where the doctors awaited them. Then, having been requested by his colleagues to act as their spokesman, he communicated to all present the following declaration :—" These gentlemen wish me to state that we have carefully examined the body of the deceased, and we are unable to discover any patho-

16

Introduction.

logical lethal cause—that is, any natural or obvious cause—of death. The contents of the stomach are suspicious, and we have preserved them." It was plain that the doctors, with the possible exception of Dr. Leach, took a very grave view of the case. " He has no business to be lying there, a strong man like that," said Dr. Dudley, placing his hand upon old Mr. Bartlett's shoulder. The rooms, it was announced, were to be locked up and sealed and handed over to the coroner, and in the meantime nothing must be removed from them. One of the doctors said that Mrs. Bartlett must not take away her bag, and another that she must leave her cloak behind her. But to this Mr. Bartlett, who had seemingly been making some quiet investigations on his own account, demurred, saying, " Yes, Adelaide may take her cloak; there are no pockets in it. I will be answerable for it." It had been arranged that she should seek the hospitality of the Matthews, and presently, bereft of her handbag and escorted by Mr. Dyson, she left the house. Old Mr. Bartlett bade her " Good-bye," and kissed her, a mark of affection which he might well have dispensed with, seeing the nature of his suspicions.

Neither Mrs. Bartlett's nor Mr. Dyson's knowledge of what the doctors had discovered was confined to the bald announcement which Dr. Leach had been charged to make to them. When that gentleman came downstairs to summon them to the first floor he had seen fit to enter into certain explanations. Thus he confided to them that the doctors on opening the body had noticed a pungent smell which Dr. Green attributed to the presence of chloroform in the stomach. Dr. Leach, however, thought it very probable that he was mistaken, and that the smell was due to chlorodyne, not to chloroform. But to Mr. Dyson the mere mention of the word chloroform in connection with the death of Mr. Bartlett came as a most unpleasant reminder of his purchases on the previous Monday. No sooner, therefore, was he alone with Mrs. Bartlett than he inquired anxiously about the bottle which he had given her. " I have not used it," was her reply. " I have not had occasion to use it. The bottle is just as you gave it me." Mr. Dyson was not satisfied, and returned to the subject so persistently that she soon began to display some annoyance. She reminded him that it was " a very critical time " with her, and she hoped, therefore, that he would " dismiss from his mind " the fact that he had bought chloroform. She " must not be worried about it." Mr. Dyson, after expressing his intention of calling on Dr. Leach and asking for further particulars, allowed the matter to drop for the moment. On arriving at the Matthews he

c

Adelaide Bartlett.

was introduced to Mrs. Matthews, after which he at once returned to his lodgings at Putney. That his reflections that evening were of a disquieting character may be inferred from his subsequent conduct. On the morrow, Sunday, 3rd January, when he went out to preach at Tooting, he took with him the four small bottles which had originally contained the chloroform and threw them into the gorse bushes as he walked across Wandsworth Common.

The next morning Mr. Dyson went into London and paid a visit to Dr. Leach, who read over to him some of the notes which he had taken at the post-mortem. All he heard only tended to confirm his worst apprehensions. Dr. Green, he learnt, was of opinion that death was due to the contents of the stomach, the lining of which was unnaturally red and inflamed. Both the stomach and the intestines emitted a smell of chloroform, and, to add to Mr. Dyson's disquiet, no mention was made of any traces of the mysterious internal disease from which Mrs. Bartlett declared that her husband was suffering. On parting from Dr. Leach he determined to seek her out forthwith and hear what explanation she had to offer. Having taken the train from Victoria to Peckham Rye, he found on reaching Friern Road that Mrs. Bartlett was out, but on Mrs. Matthews' invitation he went into the house and waited. Before long she returned, and Mrs. Matthews left them alone together. That lady, however, soon heard sounds which led her to re-enter the room. Mrs. Bartlett appeared to be very angry, and in her indignation was stamping upon the floor. In answer to her friend's inquiry about the cause of the trouble, she explained that " Mr. Dyson was bothering her about a piece of paper." Presently Mrs. Matthews again left them alone, but only to return very shortly. As she went in she heard Mr. Dyson say, " You did tell me that Edwin was going to die soon," and, on Mrs. Bartlett denying that she had said anything of the kind, he " bowed his head on the piano and said, ' Oh, my God ! ' " Mrs. Matthews suggested that he should go, and he went, exclaiming as he reached the door, " I am a ruined man." Nevertheless, that same evening he returned to Friern Road, and again saw Mrs. Bartlett alone. She asked him, in reference presumably to the inquest which was to be held on Thursday, to say nothing about the chloroform. But he refused, and avowed his determination " to make a clean breast of the affair."

On the following day, Tuesday, 5th January, Mr. Dyson transacted some business with Mr. Wood, the solicitor, and did not see Mrs. Bartlett. But the next morning he went to Friern

18

Introduction.

Road, and found both ladies on the point of starting for London, where Mrs. Bartlett was to see Dr. Leach, who, in view of the approaching inquest, wished to be placed " in possession of any facts which would enable him to make a clear statement before the coroner." It was snowing hard, but Mr. Dyson procured a cab, in which all three drove to Peckham Rye Station and there took the train to Victoria. From Victoria the ladies went on to Charlwood Street, leaving Mr. Dyson to buy some cord which Mrs. Bartlett required for her boxes. Later on all of them were to meet at Dr. Leach's. But when Mr. Dyson arrived he learnt that the ladies had missed the doctor and had gone on to Claverton Street. By this time, however, Dr. Leach had returned, and, coming out, handed him a key, with instructions to give it to Mrs. Bartlett and to tell her that the coroner " had done with the rooms." Nevertheless, at Claverton Street he was refused admittance, but Mrs. Bartlett came out into the street and took the key from him. After that they all returned to Dr. Leach's, where Mrs. Bartlett was shown into the consulting room. Finding himself alone with Mrs. Matthews in the doctor's waiting room, Mr. Dyson took the opportunity of questioning her about the matter which was troubling him so greatly. Was it true, he asked, that Mr. Bartlett had had several severe attacks of illness? She remembered, replied Mrs. Matthews, that he had once been laid up for a fortnight, but, with that exception, she had no re-collection that he had ever been ill. Mr. Dyson then confided to her how he had bought the chloroform and how he was resolved to acknowledge what he had done to the coroner. Before that, suggested Mrs. Matthews, he would do well to talk the matter over with her husband, and with that their conversation appears to have ended.[6] Mrs. Bartlett, having concluded her business, presently came out of the doctor's room and returned to Claverton Street to collect her boxes, while Mr. Dyson accompanied Mrs. Matthews back to Dulwich. Mr. Matthews had not yet reached home when they arrived, but Mr. Dyson went out to meet him, and in the road between Peckham Rye Station and the house poured out his troubles as they walked along together. He was in a state of great agitation; in fact, Mr. Matthews, when he afterwards described the interview in the Coroner's Court, applied the word " panic-stricken " to his condition. He had been " duped," he said, " by a wicked woman." Her husband had deliberately thrown her into his company, and he had in conse-

---

[6] Inquest, 11th February, 1886.

quence found himself " attacked upon his weakest side." He then explained how he had been induced to procure the chloroform, and how he proposed to make a statement to that effect at the inquest. Mr. Matthews, however, pointed out that it was not yet certain that chloroform was the cause of Mr. Bartlett's death, and in these circumstances he recommended him to keep silence and await the report of the Home Office analyst.[7]

On the following day, Thursday, 7th January, 1886, Mr. Braxton-Hicks, the deputy-coroner, began his inquiry at the parochial boardroom in Buckingham Palace Road. On this first day the proceedings attracted no public attention, and were of brief duration. Old Mr. Bartlett deposed that, until he was taken ill, shortly before Christmas, his son always enjoyed excellent health. His daughter-in-law objected to his visits, because she said that they tired her husband. The suddenness of his son's death caused him to insist upon the post-mortem examination being carried out by an independent medical man. At this stage the coroner announced that he should adjourn the proceedings until 4th February, by which time Dr. Stevenson,[8] the Government analyst, would have delivered his report. After the Court rose Mr. Dyson and Mrs. Bartlett had a meal together in the private room of an adjacent confectioner's shop. Their talk was confined exclusively to the post-mortem, the inquest, and kindred matters. Mrs. Bartlett told him that he " was distressing himself unnecessarily," to which Mr. Dyson replied that he had " reason to be alarmed." In the course of the discussion which followed she uttered these words, he afterwards related, " if I did not incriminate myself she would not incriminate me."

Two days later, on the evening of 9th January, Mr. Dyson had a final interview with Mrs. Bartlett in Friern Road, in the presence of both the Matthews. The chloroform was the principal subject of discussion. Mr. Dyson, who displayed considerable emotion, complained that his career was at an end, and that he would be forced to resign his ministry. Turning to Mrs. Bartlett, he said, " supposing it were proved—that you——" " Do not mince matters," interrupted Mrs. Bartlett indignantly, " say that I gave it to him." " He was puzzled," said Mr. Dyson,

---

[7] Inquest, 15th February, 1886. The conversation of these men out of the hearing of Mrs. Bartlett was, of course, inadmissible as evidence against her at the trial. The same remark also applies to what passed between Dyson and Mrs. Matthews in Dr. Leach's waiting room.

[8] Stevenson, Sir Thomas (1838-1908); lecturer on chemistry and forensic medicine at Guy's Hospital; senior scientific analyst to the Home Office; author and editor of various books on forensic medicine.

Introduction.

" he was anxious to know what really had become of it.'' This question seems for the first time to have elicited from Mrs. Bartlett a definite statement on the subject. She poured the chloroform, she now asserted, out of the railway carriage window on the evening of Wednesday, 6th January, and threw the bottle itself into Peckham Rye Pond. Mr. Dyson departed in due course, and after this Saturday evening, 9th January, held no further communication either by word of mouth or by letter with Mrs. Bartlett.

Mrs. Bartlett did not prolong her stay with the Matthews beyond the following Monday, 11th January, on which day she moved into lodgings in Weymouth Street, Portland Place. She went away, declared Mrs. Matthews at the inquest,[9] because she insisted on paying for her board and lodging and they refused to consent to this arrangement. Whether that were the real reason of her departure may well be doubted. When she gave that explanation of her friend's departure, Mrs. Matthews admitted that she had said to her husband that she " did not feel comfortable about Mrs. Bartlett because she told lies.'' Nevertheless, whatever the truth may be, they maintained friendly relations and continued to see one another from time to time. Mrs. Bartlett, while awaiting the analyst's report in her lonely lodgings in Weymouth Street, also kept in touch with Dr. Leach, whom she consulted about her own state of health. Thus it was that, on 26th January, she learnt from him that Dr. Stevenson had sent in his report to the Home Office. " I have good news for you, Mrs. Bartlett,'' said the doctor when she entered his consulting room, and he then went on to say that he understood that Dr. Stevenson had found that chloroform was the cause of death. " That,'' he explained, " should set your mind at rest. Had it been one of those secret poisons which could be administered without the patient knowing it, you would most certainly have been accused of poisoning him by some people.'' But to his surprise Mrs. Bartlett displayed no satisfaction. On the contrary, she declared that she wished that anything but chloroform had been found, and, in reply to his questions, told a remarkable story which was in substance to this effect.

Mr. Bartlett had strange ideas. One of them was that a man should have two wives, one for companionship and the other for what he termed " use.'' It was with the intention that she should act in the former capacity that he married her when she was an ignorant girl of sixteen. The compact between them, to

---

[9] 15th February, 1886.

21

Adelaide Bartlett.

which she gave her consent without understanding anything about
the conditions of the married state, was that they should be
affectionate and loving friends, but nothing more. On those
terms they lived together happily for six years, her father-in-law
being responsible for the only quarrel which arose between them.
But at the end of that time her longing to be a mother had become
so intense that the rule which they had hitherto strictly observed
was broken on one occasion only. Unfortunately, the child was
born dead, and she in consequence was disheartened. Their
platonic relationship was resumed, and was adhered to ever afterwards. Her husband liked to surround her with male friends,
and was pleased by the attentions which they paid her. Thus her
position was often trying and difficult. Then they made the
acquaintance of Mr. Dyson, into whose company her husband
threw her deliberately, as though anxious to promote between
them an affection which was " more than platonic, but not criminal." He told them to kiss, and gave her, or affianced her, to
his friend. Nevertheless, after making her over to another man
in this fashion, he began during the later stages of his illness to
show signs of a desire to assert his marital rights. She endeavoured to make him realise the impropriety of his conduct.
" Edwin," she said, " you know you have given me to Mr.
Dyson, and it is not right that you should now do what during
all these years of our married life you have not done." It was
" a duty which she owed to her womanhood and to the man
to whom she was practically affianced " to protest strongly against
his behaviour. He agreed with all she said, but, as he grew better,
he became so urgent that she procured chloroform, intending to
sprinkle some upon a handkerchief and wave it in his face whenever
he should be too pressing. She did not, however, ever attempt
to put her plan into execution. " I never kept a secret from
Edwin," she explained, " and the presence of that chloroform
in my drawer troubled my mind. On the last day of the year,
when he was in bed, I brought the bottle to him and gave it to
him. He was not angry; he looked at it and placed it on the
corner of the mantelpiece close to his bed." She concluded her
story by repeating how, having gone to sleep with her hand upon
his foot, she had been awakened by a cramp in her arm, and found
her husband lying dead upon his face.

Beyond assuring her that chloroform used in the manner
which she described would not have had the effect which she
apparently expected from it, Dr. Leach made little comment upon
this extraordinary statement. He did, however, ask her how she

22

Introduction.

obtained the chloroform, but, as she seemed reluctant to tell him, he did not press the matter. He also inquired what became of the bottle. She was positive that it remained upon the mantelpiece throughout the night and the early morning. About eight o'clock, however, she took it away and placed it in one of her drawers in the back room, and there she left it until the afternoon of Wednesday, 6th January, when, having received permission to remove her effects, she carried it away with her, and, after emptying it out of the railway carriage window, threw it into a pond.

By 4th February, 1886, public interest in what the newspapers now termed " The Pimlico Mystery " was thoroughly aroused, and it was in a crowded room that Mr. Braxton-Hicks resumed his inquiry. The two persons principally concerned were both legally represented, Mrs. Bartlett by Mr. E. Beal, barrister-at-law, and Mr. Dyson by Mr. Lickfold, of the firm of Lewis & Lewis, of Ely Place. Mr. Dennis, a Croydon solicitor, attended on behalf of Mr. Bartlett and the relatives of the deceased, and Detective-Inspector Marshall, who had charge of the case, watched the proceedings for the Commissioner of Police. In reply to a question by the coroner, Mr. Beal announced that, until Dr. Stevenson had been heard, he could not advise Mrs. Bartlett to give evidence. But the coroner refused to consent to that arrangement, and again called upon Mrs. Bartlett to tender herself as a witness. Mr. Beal, however, maintained his objection. It were idle to pretend, he explained, that she was not under a considerable amount of suspicion, and questions of an incriminating character might not improbably be put to her in the course of her examination. He could not, replied Mr. Braxton-Hicks, compel her to come forward, but her counsel should understand that the jury would draw an unfavourable inference from her refusal. Dr. Stevenson was then called, and ascribed the cause of death to chloroform, a fatal amount of which he had found in the stomach of the deceased. Dr. Leach spoke of his attendance at Claverton Street and of the treatment which he had prescribed for Mr. Bartlett, but when it came to repeating the story which Mrs. Bartlett had told him, on 26th January, he begged to be given time to consult his recollections. After some discussion, it was arranged that he should at his leisure write out an account of what Mrs. Bartlett had said and have it ready for the next sitting of the Court, on 11th February. As soon as that had been settled Inspector Marshall gave the coroner a copy of Squire's " Companion to the British Pharmacopœia,"

Adelaide Bartlett.

which had been found among Mrs. Bartlett's effects at Claverton Street. On receiving it, Mr. Braxton-Hicks drew the attention of the jury to the significant fact that it appeared to open naturally at the very page on which the drug chloroform was described.

On 11th February, Dr. Leach's statement was read, and Mr. Dyson gave evidence. So effectually did he carry out his often-repeated intention of " making a clean breast of it " that, when he had finished, the foreman of the jury announced that they were all of opinion that Mrs. Bartlett should no longer be left at liberty. Mr. Braxton-Hicks concurred and gave Inspector Marshall the necessary warrant, which that officer proceeded to execute with as little fuss as possible. Mrs. Bartlett, who was present in Court, made no observation when the inspector took her aside, and, having cautioned her, explained the nature of his instructions. She was at once conveyed to Rochester Row police station, and, on the following day, was charged before Mr. Partridge at Westminster Police Court with causing the death of her husband by poisoning him with chloroform. Formal evidence of arrest was given, after which she was remanded.

The same fate speedily overtook Mr. Dyson. On 18th February the coroner's jury returned a verdict of " wilful murder " against Mrs. Bartlett, and found that the Rev. George Dyson had been an accessory before the fact. He was at once arrested, and in due course took his place in the dock at Westminster Police Court alongside Mrs. Bartlett. It was noticed that they met as complete strangers, and that neither addressed a word to the other. The proceedings before Mr. Partridge lasted until Saturday, 20th March, when both prisoners were committed for trial at the Central Criminal Court.

II.

The trial of Adelaide Bartlett and of the Rev. George Dyson was opened before Mr. Justice Wills[1] at the Old Bailey on Monday, 12th April, 1886. In view of the enormous interest which the case evoked, special arrangements had been made for the seating of spectators. Close to the dock and blocking up one of the principal entrances to the Court a kind of stand or hustings had been erected, in which many persons, the majority of whom

---

[1] Wills, Right Honourable Sir Alfred (1828-1912); judge of High Court, 1884; one of the founders of the Alpine Club, of which he was the third president; editor of "Wills on Circumstantial Evidence."

Introduction.

were women, found accommodation. Mrs. Bartlett, who appeared perfectly composed, was dressed in black, but she no longer wore the heavy widow's mourning in which she had been attired at the Police Court. Among the counsel engaged were some of the most distinguished members of the bar. The Attorney-General, Sir Charles Russell,[2] afterwards Lord Russell of Killowen and Lord Chief Justice of England, led for the Crown, assisted by Mr., now Sir, Harry Poland, Mr. R. S. Wright,[3] and Mr. Moloney. Of these Mr. Poland, when he retired in 1895, had been prominently concerned in almost all the great trials of his time, and Mr. Wright, not long afterwards, was knighted and appointed a judge of the High Court. Mr., afterwards Sir, Francis Lockwood,[4] Q.C., and Mr., afterwards Sir, Charles Mathews,[5] appeared for Mr. Dyson. For the defence of his client, Mrs. Bartlett, Mr. Wood had retained Mr., afterwards Sir, Edward Clarke, Q.C., M.P., Mr. Mead, now a metropolitan magistrate, and Mr. E. Beal. Nine years before Mr. Clarke had earned for himself a great reputation by his defence of Patrick Staunton in the Penge murder case and of Chief Inspector Clarke in the trial of the detectives. It was his skilful handling of the medical evidence which saved the Stauntons from the gallows, and when he undertook to defend Mrs. Bartlett he perceived at once that in her case also the issue would probably be decided by the testimony of the experts. Accordingly, for a fortnight before the trial, he declined all other briefs and put aside his Parliamentary work, while in the reading room of the British Museum and in his own library he devoted himself exclusively to the study of everything of importance which had been written on the subject of chloroform.[6]

As soon as his lordship had taken his seat upon the bench, Mr. Lockwood rose and made application that the prisoners should be tried separately, a request with which Mr. Clarke expressed his complete concurrence. All discussion of the matter was, however, rendered unnecessary by the intervention of the Attorney-

---

[2] Russell, Charles, Baron Russell of Killowen (1832-1900); Attorney General, 1885 and 1892; raised to peerage, 1894, and appointed Lord Chief Justice.

[3] Wright, Robert Samuel (1839-1904); judge of High Court and knighted, 1891.

[4] Lockwood, Francis (1847-1897); Solicitor-General, 1894; caricaturist and contributor to *Punch;* knighted, 1894.

[5] Mathews, Charles Willie (1850-1920); called to the bar, 1872; senior prosecuting counsel to the Treasury, 1888; knighted, 1907; Director of Public Prosecutions, 1908.

[6] Sir Edward Clarke, "The Story of My Life," p. 249.

Adelaide Bartlett.

General. To the surprise of the general public, he declared that he and his learned friends had decided that there was no case to be submitted to the jury upon which they could ask them to convict Mr. Dyson. Both prisoners were then arraigned, and both having pleaded " not guilty," the Attorney-General announced that he proposed to offer no evidence against Mr. Dyson. His lordship thereupon directed the jury to find him " not guilty," and when that formality had been complied with he declared that he was discharged from custody. While Mr. Dyson left the dock the Attorney-General began to address the jury.

After pointing out that the decision not to proceed against Mr. Dyson was a distinct advantage to the prisoner, inasmuch as it would enable her counsel to cross-examine that gentleman upon his statements, Mr. Attorney proceeded to describe in some detail the married life of the Bartletts, down to the time when Mr. Dyson crossed their path. Their acquaintance with him grew apace and developed into a close intimacy. And that brought them to an important date, 3rd September, 1885. On that day the deceased made a will leaving everything to his wife and appointing Mr. Dyson one of his executors. Both the prisoner and Mr. Dyson were aware of the contents of this will. At the lodgings in Claverton Street, to which the Bartletts moved in October, Mr. Dyson continued to visit them as regularly as ever. It was only fair to say, however, that nothing occurred to suggest the existence of any quarrel between husband and wife. " So far as ordinary observers could see and judge, they seem to have lived together on fairly good terms." But, on the other hand, there could be no doubt that the prisoner's relations with her father-in-law were " a little strained." The illness from which the deceased began to suffer, about 10th December, was not a serious complaint, but it was complicated by nervous depression, sleeplessness, and the bad condition of the teeth. Nevertheless, on 28th December, when he went out for a drive, he was almost well and was talking about going to the seaside for change of air. The next point to be considered, and it was a highly important one, was the purchase of the chloroform. Seeing that Mr. Dyson had been declared guiltless, it was impossible for Mr. Attorney to allude to his proceedings as suspicious. He spoke of him therefore " as yielding meekly to the prisoner's request," while drawing attention to the many false statements by which she had sought to explain her desire to possess the drug. There were no grounds, said Mr. Attorney, for suggesting that her husband suffered from any internal ailment, and it was untrue that Annie

26

Introduction.

Walker had ever supplied her with chloroform or that she was in America. It was equally untrue that Dr. Nichols had ever said that the deceased would not live another twelve months. Mr. Attorney then passed on to the events of 31st December—the visit to the dentist, the meals of which the deceased partook so heartily, and the conversation about chloroform between the prisoner and Mrs. Doggett.

Having carried the story down to the death of Mr. Bartlett, the Attorney-General related how, in the early hours of the morning, on 1st January, Mrs. Bartlett aroused the house. He recounted how Mr. Doggett, on entering the chamber of death, noticed a smell of chloric ether, and how he discovered that the same smell pervaded a tumbler of brandy standing upon the mantelpiece close to the bed. Mr. Doggett also observed that the fire was burning brightly and appeared to have been attended to recently. Dr. Leach was quite unable to explain his patient's sudden death. He saw no bottle of chloroform, but he did find a small bottle which had contained chlorodyne. So perplexed was he that he asked the prisoner whether it were possible that the deceased could have obtained poison, but she replied that " he had no poison, and could not have got it, or had it, without her knowledge." With regard to the post-mortem examination, the doctors, said Mr. Attorney, found nothing in the vital organs— the heart, the lungs, or the liver—to account for death. What did strike them, directly they opened the stomach, was the over-powering smell of chloroform which issued from it. After the post-mortem several interviews took place between the prisoner, Mr. Dyson, the Matthews, and Dr. Leach, at which some very curious statements were made, but he would say nothing about them at present, preferring that the jury should hear what oc-curred from the witnesses themselves. One exception, however, he must make. He could not pass over in silence the interview between the prisoner and Dr. Leach on 26th January, and he proceeded to place before them in an abbreviated form the strange story which on that day she confided to the doctor. The practical result of that statement, Mr. Attorney pointed out, was an ad-mission that at the time of her husband's death she had in her possession a large quantity of chloroform. The prisoner, con-tinued Mr. Attorney, was present at the inquest, but did not come forward to give evidence or to offer any explanation. The jury, however, would not, he hoped, draw an unfavourable in-ference from her abstention.

After giving this short outline of the case the Attorney-

27

Adelaide Bartlett.

General concluded by propounding the theory of the prosecution. When they had heard the evidence he did not suppose that they would find any difficulty in arriving at the conclusion that the deceased died from chloroform which found its way into his stomach. The question they had to decide was, "How did it get there?" There were three possibilities to be considered. The deceased might have taken it himself with suicidal intent, but after they had heard the facts they would "find nothing in the circumstances of the case to support or even lend an air of plausibility to that suggestion." Alternatively, he might have swallowed it by accident. But chloroform was a drug which no man could take inadvertently. Even should he not find out his mistake before he raised the glass to his lips, he must inevitably discover it as soon as the liquid entered his mouth. The sensation of burning which must inevitably ensue would be so intense that, however great his self-control might be, he would be unable to repress cries or groans of anguish which could not fail to be heard. There remained, therefore, only the third possibility, that it was administered by another person. But the same objection would hold good. Swallowing it under these conditions would cause the same pain and be followed by the same outcry. In the opinion of the medical men, there was one way, and one way only, in which the difficulty could be overcome. The internal administration must be preceded by an external application producing stupor or semi-stupor. Inasmuch as no one that night heard any unusual sounds, the operation of conveying chloroform into the stomach of the deceased must have been performed when he was either wholly or partially unconscious.

As soon as Dr. Broadbent had been called to prove that Dr. Green was seriously ill and in no condition to attend the Court, old Mr. Bartlett entered the witness-box. Replying to Mr. Poland, he related the circumstances of the deceased's marriage, and gave some details about the life at Herne Hill, Lordship Lane, and Merton. His son's business was in a most flourishing condition. He understood that the prisoner suffered greatly in her confinement. So far as the witness knew, she resumed, on her recovery, ordinary marital relations with her husband. His son always enjoyed excellent health, and worked hard. When he fell ill in Claverton Street the witness went to the house on six or seven occasions, but was only allowed to see him three times. He was told that he was suffering from verdigris poisoning. He was not informed of the name of the doctor attending him, only that he was "a doctor up the street." At this stage eight

28

Introduction.

letters were put in which the prisoner had written to the witness during her husband's illness. Some began " Dear Mr. Bartlett," and others " Dear Father." Most of them were to the effect that her husband was too ill to see anybody, but the last one, dated " Sunday night," had reference to a visit which the witness proposed to pay to his son on Monday, 28th December. It ran as follows :—

Dear Mr. Bartlett,—I hear that you are a little disturbed because Edwin has been too ill to see you. I wish, if possible, to be friends with you, but you must place yourself on the same footing as other persons— that is to say, you are welcome here when I invite you, and at no other time. You seem to forget that I have not been in bed for thirteen days, and consequently am too tired to speak to visitors. I am sorry to speak so plainly, but I wish you to understand that I have neither forgotten nor forgiven the past. Edwin will be pleased to see you Monday evening any time after six.

Witness went to Claverton Street on Monday, 28th December, and sat with the deceased for over two hours. It was the last occasion on which he saw him alive. The deceased appeared to be in better spirits, and talked of returning to business. Something was also said about his going to Poole or Bournemouth to re-cuperate. Some time previous to that, the witness had suggested to the prisoner the advisability of calling in another doctor. She said, " We cannot afford it," and he replied, " Nonsense, Adelaide." But in the course of his visit, on 28th December, she told him that another doctor, whose name she did not mention, had seen her husband. The reference in her letter to a past which she could not forgive was an allusion to an unpleasantness in which one of his other sons had been concerned. When he went to Claverton Street, after hearing of his son's death, he sniffed at his lips, thinking that he might have died from prussic acid, but he could detect no smell of that kind. The witness then went on to describe the conversation with Dr. Leach about the holding of the post-mortem, and repeated the account which the prisoner gave of the circumstances in which she found that her husband was dead. After describing what had happened, she remarked that " he was a very kind and generous man." On 2nd January the witness only entered the house to learn the result of the post-mortem, when he saw Dr. Green come out. The doctors said that they had been unable to discover the cause of death. They would not allow the prisoner to remain in the house. The witness said " Good-bye " to her and kissed her. At this stage a clerk from the Probate Office produced a document pur-

Adelaide Bartlett.

porting to be the deceased's will, and Mr. Poland inquired of the witness whether the signature was that of his son. " To the best of my belief it is not," he replied. In answer to the learned judge, however, he presently admitted that it was his son's habit constantly to change his handwriting. But, in the meantime, Herbert Eustace and Arthur Brook, grocer's assistants in the employment of Baxter & Bartlett, deposed to witnessing the deceased's signature to the document, which was read by the clerk of the Court :—

Herne Hill,
September 3rd, 1885.

I, Edwin Bartlett, will and bequeath all my property and everything I am possessed of to my wife, Adelaide, for her sole use, and appoint George Dyson, B.A., Wesleyan minister, and Edward Wood, Esq., of 66 Gresham Street, to be my executors.

(Signed)   EDWIN BARTLETT.

Witnesses to my signature—
Herbert Eustace and Arthur Brook.

Under cross-examination by Mr. Clarke the witness said that he did not " much approve " of his son's marriage, but he did " not disapprove of it." He was not asked to the marriage, " because they knew I was busy." He believed that he enjoyed the complete confidence both of his son and of his daughter-in-law. He signed " an apology for things he had said about her," but he " knew it to be false." What he said at the time was true. Mr. Clarke thereupon produced a paper and read as follows :—

December 31, 1878.

Having made statements reflecting on the character of Mrs. Adelaide Bartlett, the wife of my son, Edwin Bartlett, junior, which statements I have discovered to be unfounded and untrue, I hereby withdraw all such statements and express my regret for having made them. I also apologise to the said Mrs. Adelaide Bartlett and Mr. Edwin Bartlett, junior, and acknowledge that all such statements are unfounded and untrue. I authorise Mr. Edwin Bartlett, junior, to make what use he pleases of this apology.

That was the apology, said the witness, which he signed, " knowing it to be false." He signed it simply to make peace with his son. After the witness ceased to live with him, his son did not make him an allowance, but he intended to begin making him one on 1st January. Witness had always had from him what money he wanted. " He was the kindest of sons." He had examined his son's will at Somerset House, and had entered a caveat against it. He never knew his son to have " any solid ideas " about married life differing from those of other people.

30

Introduction.

His son was in the habit of chaffing and joking about such matters; he was always a " very merry man." He used to say " one ought to have two wives, one to take out and one to do the work." The witness had never heard of Dr. Nichols, nor had he seen his book. His son never spoke to him about mesmerism. " He was nothing but business, always in business." When he first saw his son, after he was taken ill in Claverton Street, he seemed as " though he were under a narcotic." He gave the witness throughout the impression that he was " dull and dazed." He complained much of sleeplessness, and said the doctor was injecting morphia into him. All through his illness he appeared to be in low spirits. Witness had seen him crying. On Saturday, 2nd January, as witness was going upstairs to hear the result of the post-mortem, the prisoner placed her arm round his neck and said, " Dear father, do not fret, it shall make no odds to you. I will see you never want. It shall be just the same as if Edwin were alive." Later on, when the doctors objected to the prisoner taking away her bag and cloak, the witness said that he would be answerable for the cloak. At the inquest he did not say that he gave her the cloak " after feeling in the pockets," but he might have said " after feeling for the pockets." In his re-examination witness was asked to explain the nature of the charge for the making of which he had had to apologise. " It was something very bad," he replied, and on Mr. Poland explaining that he must be more explicit, he said, " Well, Adelaide ran away, and was away for some week or more, and Edwin and me thought she had gone along—we almost knew she had gone—with Fred Bartlett, the brother, and we were after her." Fred, the witness went on to say, fled to America directly " it was found out."

Mr. Edwards Baxter, who was examined by Mr. Moloney, deposed that he had been in partnership with the deceased for thirteen years, during all of which time he had only been away from business, on account of ill-health, for one fortnight. So far as the witness knew, the deceased and the prisoner lived together as man and wife in the ordinary way. When the deceased was taken ill at Claverton Street, the witness went to see him on Sunday, 13th December. He appeared to be very ill. He also called and saw him on Sunday, 20th December, and Sunday, 27th December. The last occasion on which he saw him was on Wednesday, 30th December. He seemed quite cheerful —very much better. " He talked of going to the seaside, and hoped to be back at business in a fortnight." In reply to Mr.

31

Adelaide Bartlett.

Clarke, the witness stated that during the deceased's illness he received, almost every morning, a note from the prisoner about his state of health. The deceased, when he saw him, complained of sleeplessness, and the witness was aware that the doctor had given him sleeping draughts. The deceased never said anything to him about mesmerism, nor had the witness any reason to suppose that he held peculiar views about matrimony.

Replying to Mr. Poland, Mr. Doggett related how he had let the first-floor rooms of his house to the deceased, and how, to the best of his belief, he and the prisoner lived in them as man and wife. The witness was then taken through the events of 1st January. On entering the room in which the deceased lay dead he noticed at once a strong smell of chloric ether. He sniffed at a tumbler on the mantelpiece, the contents of which were " evidently brandy with some other drug in it; it smelt like ether or paregoric." The witness was present when Dr. Leach examined the body, and heard him declare, before the prisoner, that he could find nothing to account for the death. He assisted the doctor to search the room. He did not notice how the prisoner was dressed. " The fire," said the witness, " had been tended within a short time of my going into the room." As an experiment he had once lain upon his back upon the deceased's bed, and found that he could just reach the mantelpiece with his hand. " Anybody leaning upon the bed could easily reach it. It would be rather more difficult sitting up."

Mrs. Doggett, who followed her husband into the witness-box, spoke to the arrangements made with the Bartletts when they arrived at Claverton Street. The deceased informed her that a gentleman would dine with them once a week, but as a fact there was seldom a week in which Mr. Dyson did not dine with them more frequently. That gentleman came at all hours, and sometimes stayed all day. The deceased usually left the house soon after eight in the morning, and he and the prisoner generally dined about six. Mr. Dyson often had luncheon with the prisoner. An old serge jacket and slippers were kept for his use. The witness then went on to describe the meals which had been served up to the deceased on the last day of his life, and to repeat the conversation which, that evening, she had with the prisoner about chloroform. The next morning, when the house was aroused by the news that Mr. Bartlett was dead, she asked the prisoner whether she had given him any of the drops about which she had spoken overnight, but she answered, " I have given him nothing." The fire, said the witness, was burning brightly. Later on in the morning, the prisoner remarked to her, " How strange it was that Mr. Bartlett had not long ago made his will." In cross-examination she explained that the prisoner told her that all her own money was in the business, and that she would have lost it had her husband not made a will. But it was in vain that Mr. Clarke put it to her that if the fire had been " packed " at night and stirred up with a poker in the morning it might have presented the bright appearance which had arrested her attention. She persisted in saying that it had been attended to during the night; " it had not burnt hollow at all." Nor would she agree to the learned counsel's suggestion that the talk about the chloroform originated in some remark the deceased made about the gas which had been administered to him two hours earlier. Not a word, the witness was positive, was said about gas. The deceased talked about his tooth, but never said that " he had taken anything." On former occasions he mentioned that his gums had been frozen, but that evening he said nothing about the conditions under which his tooth had been extracted.

Alice Fulcher, the Doggetts' servant, the first witness to be called on the second day, deposed to waiting upon the Bartletts during the whole time that they were in Claverton Street. She confirmed her mistress's account of the length and frequency of Mr. Dyson's visits, and made mention of the old coat and slippers which were kept for his convenience. In addition, she described the two incidents which have been alluded to on a former page—how she found the window curtains pinned together and how she saw Mrs. Bartlett sitting on the floor with her head on Mr. Dyson's knees. With regard to that, she stated that they neither moved nor said anything when she entered the room. Never on any occasion had she found the door locked. Passing on to the events of 31st December, she spoke of the oysters, the jugged hare, and the other delicacies of which the deceased partook, and described the relish with which he ordered a large haddock for his breakfast. About twenty-five minutes to eleven the witness went up to the Bartletts' room for the last time to take in the coals. The prisoner told her not to disturb them again, and to leave the basin for her husband's beef tea on the table on the landing outside. Throughout the deceased's illness it had been the witness's practice " to take in the basin the last thing." When the prisoner aroused her at four o'clock in the morning to tell her that her husband was dead, the witness noticed that she was not wearing the dress which she had on overnight. Replying to Mr. Clarke, she said that while the deceased was ill the prisoner

D

Adelaide Bartlett.

always slept upon a sofa or a chair in the front room. But she often went at a late hour into the back room to wash, presumably before settling for the night. She could not recollect whether the basin in the bedroom was thus used on the night of 31st December. The deceased was in bed when the witness took in the coals, and the prisoner, seeing that she had not brought up a basin for the beef tea, told her to put it on the landing outside. It was not " a sort of loose jacket " which the prisoner was wearing when she awakened the witness at four in the morning and asked her to go for the doctor; it was an ordinary light walking dress, only differing in colour from the one she was wearing the night before.

Ann Boulter, a charwoman, employed by the undertakers to lay out the deceased's body, gave some particulars of a conversation which she had with the prisoner while engaged on that duty. To the witness's inquiry as to whether her husband had died in a fit, she replied, " No, poor dear, he suffered very much with his head, also his teeth for some time." The prisoner further remarked that it was " funny " or " curious " that he should have made his will only a day or two before his death. The witness agreed that it was " odd," and asked whether " it was in her favour." To that her reply was " Yes." In cross-examination, the witness adhered to her statement that the words which the prisoner used were " a day or two previous to his death," not, as Mr. Clarke suggested, " two or three months."

After Dr. W. Clapton, medical officer to the British Equitable Insurance Company, had deposed to examining the deceased on 15th November, 1880, and passing him as a first-class life, Mr. Dyson was called. Under examination by Mr. Poland, the witness recounted how he made the acquaintance of the Bartletts at Merton, how Mr. Bartlett invited him to superintend his wife's studies, and how he soon became their intimate friend. He told the story of his visits to Dover, and related how the deceased insisted upon paying his railway fare. So far as he knew, the Bartletts all that time were living together on the ordinary terms of husband and wife. During the deceased's stay at Dover, the witness received this letter from him :—

Dover, Monday.

Dear George,—Permit me to say that I feel great pleasure in thus addressing you for the first time. To me it is a privilege to think that I am allowed to feel towards you as a brother, and I hope our friendship may ripen as time goes on without anything to mar its future brightness. Would that I could find words to express my thankfulness to you for the very loving letter you sent Adelaide to-day. It would have done anybody good

34

Introduction.

to see her overflowing with joy as she read it whilst walking along the street and, afterwards, as she read it to me. I felt my heart going out to you. I long to tell you how proud I feel at the thought I should soon be able to clasp the hand of the man who from his heart could pen such noble thoughts. Who can help loving you? I felt that I must say two words, "Thank you," and my desire to do so is my excuse for troubling you with this. Looking towards the future with joyfulness,

I am, yours affectionately,

EDWIN.

To that the witness replied as follows :—

18 Parkfields,
Putney, September 23rd, 1885.

My dear Edwin,—Thank you very much for the brotherly letter you sent me yesterday. I am sure I respond from my heart to your wish that our friendship may ripen with the lapse of time, and I do so with confidence, for I feel that our friendship is founded on a firm, abiding basis—trust and esteem. I have from a boy been ever longing for the confidence and trust of others. I have never been so perfectly happy as when in possession of this. It is in this respect, among many others, that you have shown yourself a true friend. You have thanked me, and now I thank you, yet I ought to confess that I read your warm and generous letter with a kind of half-fear—a fear lest you should ever be disappointed in me and find me a far more prosy, matter-of-fact creature than you expect. Thank you, moreover, for the telegram, it was very considerate to send it. I am looking forward with much pleasure to next week. Thus far I have been able to stave off any work, and trust to be able to keep it clear. Dear old Dover, it will ever possess a pleasant memory for me in my mind and a warm place in my heart. With very kind regards, believe me,

Yours affectionately,

GEORGE.

When the Bartletts moved to Claverton Street the deceased presented the witness with a season ticket from Putney to Waterloo. He constantly went to see them. On one of his first visits he remarked to the prisoner that it was strange that her husband should wish to throw them so much together. She told him that the deceased did not expect to live long, and that his friends were not kindly disposed towards her. He had great confidence in, and affection for, the witness, and wished him to be her guardian. Either on that occasion or a little later the witness inquired the nature of the ailment which was shortening the deceased's life. The prisoner replied that it was an "internal complaint," from which he had suffered for about six years. "He was very sensitive about this affliction," and on that account "had no regular doctor to attend him." She told him subsequently that this complaint caused him great pain, and that to soothe him she was in the habit of administering chloroform.

Adelaide Bartlett.

She had on the deceased's behalf sought the advice of Dr. Nichols, of Fopstone Road. The nurse, Annie Walker, attended him, and brought him whatever medicine he required. She also supplied the prisoner with chloroform. The witness was interested in Dr. Nichols, and asked the prisoner some questions about him. He could not recollect what she said, but he did remember that she told him that Dr. Nichols had expressed the opinion that her husband "might die within twelve months." As far as the witness could judge, the deceased appeared to be in good health. He, nevertheless, noticed that he sometimes placed his hand to his side "convulsively." The deceased once said to the witness that he suffered severely from dyspepsia.

The circumstances in which the witness came to buy the chloroform formed the next subject of inquiry. The prisoner talked of her husband's internal complaint to explain her desire to obtain some. Annie Walker, who always procured it for her, was, she said, in America. The witness then proceeded to describe how, in order to supply himself with the amount which he required, he went to three different chemists' shops. Having thus bought four small bottles of the drug, he poured the whole quantity into a 6-ounce medicine bottle, and on the following day, Tuesday, 29th December, gave it to the prisoner as they were walking together by the river. On that day and on the two following days he saw the deceased, who appeared decidedly better, although he still complained of sleeplessness. The last time the witness saw him alive was on Thursday, the 31st. He was preparing to go to the dentist, and the prisoner said in his presence that the doctor had told her that necrosis of the jaw was setting in. The next day he received a letter from her apprising him of her husband's death, and asking him to come to see her " in the middle of the morning " of the following day.

The witness arrived at Claverton Street about half-past eleven on Saturday morning, 2nd January, and stayed to hear the result of the post-mortem. When he first saw the prisoner she inquired whether he did not think " it was sudden," and he replied, " very sudden." She told him how she had been awakened in the night by a pain in her arm and found her husband dead. The doctor, she said, was of opinion that he must have ruptured a small blood-vessel near the heart. The witness then related how, after the post-mortem, when he was accompanying the prisoner to the Matthews' house at Dulwich, he asked her about the chloroform, and how she assured him that the bottle was intact, and intimated that she " must not be worried about it." On Monday,

Introduction.

4th January, he called on Dr. Leach, and in consequence of what he told him went down to Dulwich and saw the prisoner. When he mentioned the chloroform she became very angry, and, stamping upon the floor, exclaimed, " Oh, damn the chloroform." By Mrs. Matthews' advice he soon after left the house, but he went back in the evening and told the prisoner that he should " make a clean breast of it " at the inquest. She sought to dissuade him from carrying out his intention. In the course of their talk he returned to her her husband's gold watch which she had given him at Claverton Street on the previous Saturday. She told the witness on that occasion that it was her husband's wish that " I should have that watch in memory of him when he was gone." Witness at the same time gave her four pounds, the balance of a cheque which he had cashed for her some three weeks earlier. Mr. Dyson's examination-in-chief concluded with his account of the strange words used by the prisoner in the confectioner's shop on 7th January, and of his subsequent interview with her on 9th January when, after asking indignantly why he did not charge her outright with murdering her husband, she proceeded to relate how she had poured the chloroform out of the window of the railway carriage. It was on Sunday, 3rd January, that he threw away the chloroform bottles on Wandsworth Common. He afterwards pointed out to the police the spot at which he had disposed of them. He had been under the impression that the rules of his body debarred him from marrying for two years after his entry into the ministry; but he was mistaken. One year was the prescribed time, and it was therefore open to him to marry " next October or thereabouts."

Mr. Clarke, as may be supposed, had given the most careful consideration to the difficult and delicate task which now confronted him. Were he to drive Mr. Dyson too hard, it was to be feared that he would seek to extricate himself from an awkward position by saying something very damaging to the defence. On the other hand, it was out of the question to accept his story as true and allow his statements to pass unchallenged. The learned counsel, therefore, decided to treat him in a friendly spirit and associate his actions as far as possible with those of his client. Under these conditions the witness would have no excuse for further incriminating the prisoner, and, at the same time, the natural reluctance of the jury to consign her to her doom while he passed away to freedom would be greatly strengthened.[7] With

---

[7] Sir E. Clarke, " The Story of My Life," p. 250; *Cornhill Magazine*, December, 1920, " Leaves from a Lawyer's Case Book," p. 16.

Adelaide Bartlett.

this in his mind Mr. Clarke opened his cross-examination. The first suggestion, the witness admitted, that she had administered chloroform to her husband came from the prisoner herself. At his last interview with her, at the Matthews' house, on the evening of 9th January, she inquired indignantly why he did not " charge her outright " with giving it to him. There was no secret understanding between the prisoner and himself about their future marriage. No impropriety of conduct took place between them, but he had kissed her both in and out of her husband's presence. All through the deceased's illness at Claverton Street the witness and the prisoner " were anxious for his welfare and tried to serve him." Until he was examined before the coroner he was under the impression that by the rules of his body he could not marry before October, 1887. It was very probable, therefore, that, at some time or another, he did tell the prisoner that he could not marry for two years. He had on occasions discussed marriage in general with the deceased. The deceased inquired of him whether the teaching of the Bible was distinctly in favour of a man having only one wife. The suggestion which he made was that there might be " a wife for companionship and one for service." The witness told him that he would find no sanction for any arrangement of that kind in the Bible. In reply to the learned judge, the witness said that he was not certain " whether the deceased meant that both were to be his bedfellows." But he rather gathered that both were to be his wives in " a full and complete sense." The witness regarded it as a remarkable suggestion. He did not ascribe it to moral obliquity, rather to " oddity." " Was it not an unwholesome sort of talk? " asked Mr. Justice Wills. " Not coming from him, my lord," replied the witness; " he was a man who had some strange ideas." " Was this said seriously," inquired the learned judge, " or was the man speaking in jest? " " It was said," stated the witness, " tentatively, half-playfully the first time, but I have a recollection of his speaking more seriously of it on some later occasion."

While at Dover the deceased told the witness that " he was no longer the strong man he once was." He ascribed his failing health to overwork. The witness could not swear that the prisoner did not say in the deceased's presence at Dover that his life would not be a long one. He rather thought, however, that the incident took place in Claverton Street. The witness and the deceased were on the closest terms of intimacy. They were " as brother to brother." The deceased often talked to the witness about books, but he never mentioned " Esoteric Anthropology; or the

38

Introduction.

Mysteries of Man." Nor had he ever heard him speak of Dr. Nichols. The deceased, said the witness, spoke in a manner which left no doubt that "he contemplated Mrs. Bartlett and myself being ultimately married." At this point Mr. Justice Wills intervened with the request that he would be "a little more definite." He doubted whether there was a man in Court who had ever had experience of so remarkable a statement. "On one occasion," answered the witness, "when the deceased was finding fault with his wife for some trifling fault, I said, 'If ever she comes under my care, I shall have to teach her differently.' The deceased smiled and said something to the effect that he had no doubt that I should take good care of her." Both his lordship and Mr. Clarke, however, insisted that language of that kind could hardly have been used unless there had been a previous understanding between them. There was the letter, said the witness, which the deceased wrote him from Dover, and that he admitted was the outcome of a conversation at Putney which he showed great reluctance to repeat. But on his lordship exclaiming "we have long ago overstepped the bounds of delicacy," he told the following story. While the deceased was staying at Dover he called upon the witness at Putney and informed him that he had made a will leaving everything to his wife and appointing him an executor. In return for this proof of confidence in him, the witness said that he was growing very attached to Mrs. Bartlett, that it was disturbing him in his work, and that he thought it would be well for him to discontinue his friendship with her. The deceased replied, "Why should you discontinue it?" He assured the witness that he had been "a great benefit" to her. She liked his preaching, and, showing him one of her letters, a very devotional letter, which she had written from her convent, said "he should like me to endeavour to lead her back more closely to that frame of mind or disposition of heart. He said he had confidence in me, and that he should be pleased if I would continue as friendly as I had been with them." Not on that occasion, but soon afterwards at Claverton Street, the deceased said to him in relation to his wife, "if anything happens to me, you two may come together."

On his oath, Mrs. Bartlett never told him that Annie Walker had nursed her in her confinement. What she did say was that Annie Walker attended her husband. The name of Dr. Nichols was never mentioned in the presence of the deceased. The prisoner warned him not to speak to her husband about him, because of his sensitiveness about his internal affliction. The

Adelaide Bartlett.

witness understood that, without actually seeing the deceased, Dr. Nichols was in the habit of prescribing for him. When the deceased was taken ill at Claverton Street, the witness saw Dr. Leach. He was then on terms of " honest and true friendship " with the deceased, but he never said to Dr. Leach that it " would be as well for him to see Dr. Nichols." He should have considered a suggestion of that kind as " an impertinence." He really meant that. All through his illness at Claverton Street the deceased complained of pain and sleeplessness. He was often very depressed, and the witness had seen him cry. On the Sunday before his death he asked the witness " whether any one could be lower than he was without passing away altogether." At Merton the witness had some conversation with the deceased about mesmerism. The deceased never told him that on the night of 28th December " he got up and stood for two hours waving his hands over his sleeping wife." The witness never said to the prisoner that he would marry her on her husband's death. There was no more than an understanding that, at some time or another, he and she might " come together." When the witness bought the chloroform he had not the faintest idea that it would be used for an improper purpose. He had seen the prisoner with Squire's " Companion to the British Pharmacopœia " in her hands. He understood that the chloroform was to be sprinkled upon a handkerchief. He believed that it could be used without danger in that way. He knew very little about chloroform, and had never seen it administered. He did not say anything to the deceased about the matter, because he had been told that the disease for which the chloroform was required was never to be mentioned to him. When he arrived at Claverton Street with the chloroform the Bartletts had a visitor. Had they been alone it is possible that he might have given the prisoner the bottle in her husband's presence. He was not prepared to say for certain what he might have done. The Bartletts always called him " George," and he addressed Mrs. Bartlett as " Adelaide." When he saw the prisoner on Monday, 4th January, at the Matthews', he did not tell her that, on the previous day, he had thrown away the chloroform bottles on Wandsworth Common. It did not occur to him to tell her. He was at that time in " great anxiety and distress." He threw the bottles away in a panic; the sight of them was hateful. His motive was not self-protection. He exclaimed " he was a ruined man because of what might have happened." He would be a ruined man " if my fears were true." At this interview, although it did not occur to him to tell the prisoner that he had

Introduction.

thrown away the empty chloroform bottles, it did occur to him to ask her for a piece of poetry which he had addressed to her a few weeks earlier. So far as he could remember, she gave it back to him, torn in pieces, on the following Saturday, 9th January.

Incidentally it may be mentioned that this poem which the witness was so anxious to retrieve was never produced in Court. The following verse which Mr. Clarke had committed to memory, in case he should need to quote it, may be taken as a fair measure of its literary quality as a whole :—

> Who is it that hath burst the door,
> Unclosed the heart that shut before,
> And set her queen-like on its throne,
> And made its homage all her own—
> My Birdie.

Mrs. Bartlett, said the witness, was not the only person who had counselled him to say nothing about the chloroform. Mr. Matthews suggested that he should await the result of the analysis, and he took his advice. In his re-examination of the witness, Mr. Poland, referring to the interview at Putney, invited him to describe in greater detail the effect which the deceased suggested his preaching had had upon his wife. " He did not describe the particular way," replied the witness, " but thought it had benefited her, since you ask the question, in a spiritual way." In answer to his lordship, the witness said that he went to three different shops to buy the chloroform, because he did not expect to obtain all he required at one. He did not say to the first man, " I want four or five times that amount," because he did not wish " to enter into a long explanation." The shopman " would not understand that Mrs. Bartlett was skilled in the use of medicines." It was also to avoid explanations that he led the chemists to suppose that the chloroform was to be used for the removal of grease spots.

At the opening of the proceedings on the third day the three chemists, John Hamble, Thomas Penrose, and Joseph Mellin, were called to prove Mr. Dyson's purchase of chloroform on 28th December, and, when their evidence was concluded, Mrs. Matthews went into the witness-box. She had known the Bartletts intimately for three and a half years. In July, 1885, she and her husband stayed for a week with them at The Cottage, Merton. The Bartletts appeared to live together on very affectionate terms. Mr. Bartlett's health was, so far as the witness knew, very good. On the morning of 1st January she went to Claverton Street in consequence of a telegram which she had received from the prisoner.

41

Adelaide Bartlett.

She saw the body in the front room. The prisoner told her how she had found her husband dead in the early morning. Witness inquired what he died of. She said, " We do not know; there must be a post-mortem." On the evening of the following day the prisoner came to stay with her. The rooms in Claverton Street were, she explained, to be sealed up, because the doctors were not agreed as to the cause of death. The witness then described the angry scene between the prisoner and Mr. Dyson on 4th January, which terminated in his leaving the house exclaiming that he was " a ruined man." After that she related how on the following Wednesday, 6th January, she went up to London with the prisoner and Mr. Dyson, with whom she had a private conversation in Dr. Leach's waiting room. The witness then went on to tell the story of the interview of 9th January, in the course of which the prisoner indignantly repudiated Mr. Dyson's suspicions, and stated that she had poured the chloroform out of the railway carriage window on 6th January. Peckham Rye pond, into which the prisoner said that she had thrown the bottle, was, to the best of the witness's belief, frozen over on 6th January. Some boys were certainly sliding at one end of it. Either on 9th January, or on the following Monday, 11th January, the witness had a talk with the prisoner about the conversation which she had had with Mr. Dyson at Dr. Leach's. She asked the prisoner why she had told Mr. Dyson so many lies. She said that " he bothered so. He did not believe her when she spoke the truth." The truth was that her husband did not expect to live long. It was a fact, the prisoner assured her, " that Edwin did think latterly that he was going to die." After the prisoner went to live in Weymouth Street she several times came to see the witness. On one of these occasions, on 20th January, she told the witness and her husband that " she had asked Dr. Leach about giving Edwin chloroform, and that he had told her that she could not possibly have given him chloroform, because it would have shown in his brain, if she had given it to him by inhalation, and that, if she had given it to him to drink, it would have burnt his throat all down, and his screams would have alarmed the house."

Mr. Matthews, who followed his wife into the witness-box, stated that, up to his last illness, Mr. Bartlett's health had been good. He had never heard him express any peculiar ideas. So far as he could judge, the Bartletts lived together as man and wife. The witness visited the deceased once during his illness on 15th December. " He seemed very prostrated." The prisoner said that he was suffering from " slight mercurial poisoning,

Introduction.

also from verdigris." She suggested that he might " have got it from moving things in the warehouse; he had been hunting rats." On Sunday, 3rd January, while the prisoner was his guest at Dulwich, the witness discussed with her the circumstances of her husband's death. He inquired whether it were possible that the deceased might have " taken poison himself." She replied that " she did not think that there were any poisons in the house." The doctors, she said, perceived a small bottle of chlorodyne at the post-mortem which could, in Dr. Leach's opinion, " be accounted for by her husband having used chlorodyne." The witness told her that he had heard that they had also noticed a smell of garlic. Did she think that " he could have got any arsenic "? Her reply was " No." On returning from business, on the evening of 6th January, the witness had a long conversation with Mr. Dyson in the road between Peckham Rye Station and his house. The witness then gave the same account as his wife of the interview between Mr. Dyson and the prisoner on 9th January, and of the visit which the prisoner paid them on 20th January, when she told them that she could by no possibility have given chloroform to her husband. The deceased, the witness stated in cross-examination, never talked to him about medical matters or mesmerism, nor had he ever communicated to him any strange ideas about matrimony. The prisoner some two years ago showed him Dr. Nichols' book. He did not read it—" It was scarcely in my line of business." When re-examined he said that he knew nothing of Dr. Nichols, and " had never seen Mr. Bartlett with his book."

Annie Walker described how, in 1881, she was recommended by Mrs. Nichols and went to nurse the prisoner in her confinement. She related how the deceased was reluctant that a doctor should be called in, and how the child was born dead. During one of her subsequent visits, the prisoner said " that she never meant to have any more children." The witness then recounted the conversations in which the prisoner spoke of her husband's lack of appreciation of her work, and complained that he had stipulated in his will that she must not re-marry. The witness did not know Dr. Nichols, but she had seen his book lying about at the Bartletts'. She had never talked to the prisoner about chloroform, and had never bought any for her. She had never been in America, and had never attended Mr. Bartlett. In reply to Mr. Clarke, she said that no chloroform was used at the prisoner's confinement. The prisoner was always most attentive to her husband. " She would get up very early and see that he had his breakfast before he started out." There was nothing unusual in a woman

43

Adelaide Bartlett.

saying that " she hopes never to have another child." In her re-examination she stated that, so far as she knew, the Bartletts always occupied the same room and slept in the same bed. That was the state of affairs when she stayed with them at The Cottage in October, 1884.

Dr. Thomas Low Nichols, the author of " Esoteric Anthropology," stated that he was not entitled to practise in England. He had never seen the prisoner until he saw her at Westminster Police Court. He knew nobody of the name of Bartlett in this country. He had never said that anybody " of the name of Bartlett would die within twelve months." In cross-examination Mr. Clarke elicited that he kept no record of any patients who visited him in England.

Mr. Thomas Roberts, a dentist, deposed that in December, 1885, he was called in to attend to the deceased. He visited him on three occasions, and removed some seventeen loose stumps. On 31st December the deceased came to the witness's house with Dr. Leach. The doctor administered gas, and the witness extracted a tooth. The witness noticed the bad condition of the deceased's lower jaw, and, pointing it out to Dr. Leach, said, " This looks very like necrosis setting in." The disease was not deep seated. " It was only commencing." Replying to Mr. Clarke, the witness said that three or four minutes elapsed before the gas took complete effect. Two minutes were generally sufficient. His remark about the necrosis was made in the hearing of the deceased.

The deposition of Dr. Green at the Westminster Police Court and his subsequent cross-examination by Mr. Beal and Mr. Lickfold were now put in and read. Very briefly they amounted to this. The post-mortem on the deceased was carried out under the witness's direction on 2nd January, 1886. The stomach was removed and placed with its contents in large glass jars. They emitted a strong smell of chloroform and garlic. The whole of the stomach was slightly inflamed. The vital organs—the heart, the lungs, and the liver—were in a healthy condition. The brain, the larnyx, the trachea, and the kidneys were examined, and no trace of disease was found in them. The fluidity of the blood was abnormal. In the jaw traces of slight necrosis were apparent. The conclusion which the witness formed was that death was probably due to the contents of the stomach. He got a notion of chloroform directly the stomach was opened. Before that no one had suggested to him the presence of chloroform. The smell of chlorodyne is not as pungent as the smell which issued from the

Introduction.

deceased's stomach. It was as strong as that of "a freshly opened bottle of chloroform."

Dr. Leach, who proved a tiresome witness, was then called. His self-consciousness, which was very pronounced, led him to qualify his answers and enter unasked into explanations of his statements. The Attorney-General, who conducted his examination, began by inquiring into the medical history of the deceased's illness in Claverton Street. In reply to his questions, the witness related how from 10th December until the day of his death he was in constant attendance upon him. He described the opinion which he formed of his condition, and the treatment which he prescribed in consequence. He explained the circumstances in which Dr. Dudley was called in, and narrated how the prisoner told him that "unless her husband were soon to get better his friends would say that she was poisoning him." This remark, said the witness, "extraordinary as it was, made little effect on me. I hear many strange things, and I thought it referred to the mercurialism I had found on my first visit." The last time he saw the deceased alive was on 31st December, outside the dentist's house in Charlwood Street. By that time he had almost recovered from his indisposition, and there was no longer any reason for the witness to continue to visit him professionally. Soon after four o'clock, the next morning, the Doggetts' servant came round with the news that he was dead. The witness went at once to Claverton Street. On entering the room he perceived "that naturally close odour of a sleeping room, the odour of supper and of condiments, and of brandy and of gas." The deceased was lying upon his back. His mouth was open. There was no smell about it, nor was there any froth upon the lips. The witness was totally at a loss to account for his death, and he proceeded to relate how he searched the room and how he questioned the prisoner about the possibility of his having obtained poison. At the time he attached importance to the discovery of a bottle of chlorodyne, but he had now entirely given up the theory that it might have been the cause of death, "because the analysis proved the absence of the other ingredients of chlorodyne. I am sorry," he added, "that I ever entertained it." He was not aware on 1st January that the prisoner had in her possession a large quantity of chloroform. He only learnt that twenty-six days later.

The post-mortem examination, on 2nd January, was performed by Dr. Green, Dr. Murray, Dr. Dudley, and Dr. Cheyne. The witness himself took notes, which he was now requested to

Adelaide Bartlett.

read. These showed that all the vital organs were in a healthy state, and that the only " abnormalisms " were the appearance of the stomach and the fluidity of the blood. Subsequently, at the request of his colleagues, he communicated the result of their investigations to the family and friends of the deceased. When inviting them to come upstairs to meet the doctors, he disclosed certain facts to the prisoner. He told her that the contents of the stomach emitted " a pungent ethereal odour," and, not improbably, added, " Dr. Green suggests chloroform." His own opinion, said the witness, and he communicated it to the prisoner, was that the smell was caused by chlorodyne. The prisoner made no observation when the word chloroform was mentioned. He had a long talk with her in his consulting room on 6th January, the day before the inquest. He asked her to write out an account of everything which happened between the time of the deceased's return from the dentist and the witness's own arrival, at half-past four, on the morning of the following day. He advised her to keep her notes, as he supposed that she would give evidence. No reference, to the best of the witness's recollection, was made " to the impossibility of his swallowing chloroform." Chlorodyne was mentioned, for, unfortunately, explained the witness, " I continued to harp upon that subject." Mrs. Bartlett visited him on 6th, 14th, 18th, and 26th January. On this last occasion he congratulated her warmly, directly he saw her, on the analyst's report. It was good news, indeed, that Dr. Stevenson should ascribe the cause of death to chloroform. Had he attributed it to some secret poison, which " could be administered without the patient knowing it," she would have fallen under grave suspicion. But to his surprise, far from displaying satisfaction, she expressed extreme regret that chloroform had been discovered, and, in answer to his questions, she confided to him the story of her strange compact with her husband and her relations with Mr. Dyson. She narrated how, after making her over to Mr. Dyson, her husband had sought to assert those marital rights which he had never exercised during all the years in which they had been married. " It was a duty to her womanhood and to the man to whom she was practically affianced " to resist his advances, and she, in consequence, obtained some chloroform with the idea of sprinkling it upon a handkerchief and waving it in his face. But she never carried out her intention. The thought of the chloroform in her drawer troubled her. She had never had a secret from " Edwin," and, on the night of 31st December, when he was in bed, she handed over to him her whole supply, after explaining the reason which had led her to procure it. He showed no displeasure, but took the bottle and placed it upon the mantelpiece, close to his bedside. There it remained until " about breakfast time " on 1st January, when she removed it and put it away in a drawer in the back room. But that could not be, declared the witness. There was no chloroform bottle in the room when he searched it between four and five o'clock that morning.

Under cross-examination by Mr. Clarke, the witness stated that between 10th and 31st December he had constantly seen the Bartletts together. Mrs. Bartlett always appeared to be tending her husband with the most " anxious affection." " Emphatically " he could not wish for a better nurse. The witness asked her to go to bed, but she always refused. On one occasion, in the third week of his attendance, she said, " What is the use of my going to bed, doctor? He will walk about the room like a ghost. He will not sleep unless I sit and hold his toe." At this stage the learned counsel took the witness through the various phases of the deceased's illness. About 21st December the prisoner told him that her husband " still talked about dying." She said so in the deceased's presence. In the witness's opinion, " he was practically a hysterical patient at that time, and his wife petted him too much." The deceased told the witness an extraordinary tale on 26th December. In answer to an inquiry as to how he had slept, he said, " I could not sleep. I was nervous and restless. I saw my wife asleep in the easy chair, so I went and stood over her for two hours holding up my hands like this, and felt the vital force being drawn from her to me. I felt it going through my finger tips. After that I lay down and slept." The prisoner observed, " That is a nice story. Imagine him standing for two hours and doing anything." Prior to that the deceased had told the witness some " rigmarole " about the possibility of being under somebody's influence from a distance. He said that " he and his wife had both been mesmerised by a friend."

When the proceedings opened on the fourth day, Dr. Leach was recalled and was further cross-examined. The deceased was distressed when the witness told him that he should not visit him again. Mrs. Bartlett said, " You had better come, doctor; he will be anxious." The witness had never seen the deceased cry, but he had been told that he had fits of crying, and had spoken to him about them. The prisoner observed that he said that he cried " because he was so happy." The witness ascribed that to " male hysteria." He would not call " the jaw symptoms," which manifested themselves on 29th December, really " alarming."

Adelaide Bartlett.

It was "a necrosis due to local causes, and he had no great fear as to its ultimate result." The prisoner always " tried to cheer him (the deceased) up in every way." This statement was made in reference to her remark in the cab on the way to the dentist that " only this morning Edwin and I were saying that we wished we were unmarried that we might have the pleasure of marrying over again." On the morning of 1st January, when the witness was called in to Claverton Street, the prisoner appeared greatly distressed. She cried bitterly when he told her that her husband was dead. It would be asking him to judge of things beyond his ken to say whether her conduct was perfectly natural. He could only " give an opinion for what it was worth." The impression which he formed, and it might be that " after-events had biased " his mind, was that " she seemed not only grieved, but very much alarmed, very much scared. Of course, I did not think it then, but I do now." The prisoner was very anxious that the post-mortem should take place as soon as possible. Her words were, " Spare no expense ; get any assistance you want. We are all interested in knowing the cause of death."

The witness regarded the story which the prisoner told him on 26th January as an absolutely confidential communication. When he attended the Coroner's Court, on 4th February, he did not expect to be called upon to reveal it. The prisoner in her statement of the 26th said that " her first real suspicions as to the cause of death were aroused when she heard it stated that the contents of the stomach smelled of chloroform, but, hearing that that smell might be due to the deceased having swallowed some chlorodyne, she refrained from making any suggestions that would necessarily throw grave suspicion upon herself." In the account of the interview of 26th January which he drew up for the coroner, the witness made use of these words in reference to the platonic relations alleged to have existed between the prisoner and her husband. " I was personally cognisant of these facts up to this point. They had been partly told me, partly implied, partly gathered from observation." Pressed to say what he meant to convey by that statement, the witness explained that Mrs. Bartlett had consulted him two or three times since her husband's death, and " I had become aware of facts that somewhat paved the way to my accepting what she told me on the 26th." On its being represented to him that he must be more definite, the witness said, " Mr. Bartlett was a man of very strange ideas. That goes with-out saying." This remark caused him to be reminded by his lord-ship that " he might take it as an axiom that nothing goes without

Introduction.

saying here." At the same time he invited him to explain the nature of these ideas. They had nothing to do with matrimony, replied the witness, but had reference to mesmerism and vital force and other matters which collectively " conveyed to my mind the impression that my patient was one of the most extraordinary men I ever had to deal with—though a very pleasant and nice man." In answer to a further question by the learned judge, the witness said, " With regard to the matter about two wives—one for use and one for companionship—that did not come from him. I never heard him allude to it. That came from her." When the deceased was recovering, and when the prisoner was suffering from the strain of nursing him, the witness suggested that they should both go to bed in the back room. He could not remember what the deceased said, but he certainly did not act upon his advice. That incident and the fact that the deceased slept in a camp bed tended, in the witness's opinion, to confirm the truth of the prisoner's story about their relations. In his attendance upon the deceased the witness perceived " great signs of affection and kindness both on his part and on that of his wife, but, looking back, he could recollect nothing which was inconsistent with their alleged compact that they should be no more than loving friends." He was prepared to believe the prisoner's story that six years ago this agreement was broken on one occasion, in order that she should become a mother. He had heard in her husband's lifetime that she was fond of children and dogs. He had no comment to make upon her statement that after the child was born dead " she grew disheartened, and the two lived together, but their relations were not those of matrimony." The prisoner's allegation that her husband " liked to surround her with male acquaintances " explained a good deal that had puzzled " the witness about Mr. Dyson. He had heard the deceased speak of that gentleman in terms of the greatest admiration." Both he and the prisoner were " proud of Mr. Dyson."

" By rising on the left arm " it was quite easy to reach the mantelpiece from the deceased's bed. The witness had never heard of a case of poisoning with liquid chloroform. Vomiting usually occurs when chloroform is inhaled. It would be still more likely to happen if the administration took place after a recent meal. An indigestible substance, such as mango-chutney, would increase the probability of vomiting. The witness had never given chloroform to a sleeping person, and knew of no authentic case in which it had been successfully administered under those conditions. In cases of death from an excessive amount of chloroform, the witness

E

49

Adelaide Bartlett.

would expect to find at the post-mortem fluidity of the blood and a smell of chloroform in the brain and in the lungs. If death were caused by asphyxia through an overdose by inhalation, he would be prepared to see the right side of the heart and the lungs engorged with blood.

Mr. Poland, on whom, in the absence of the Attorney-General, devolved the task of re-examining Dr. Leach, returned to the question of the alleged platonic compact. When she consulted him as a patient, stated the witness, the prisoner said nothing about her relations with her husband. Nor had the deceased himself ever suggested anything to lead the witness to suppose that " his married life was other than the ordinary state." Nevertheless, from " the general bearing of the parties," the witness was now prepared to believe that their relations were " asexual." He could not describe it. " I might as well," he pleaded, " try to describe the general expression of their countenances. I am sure his lordship sees it." But his lordship would not admit that he was endowed with the " delicate discrimination " which the witness wished to ascribe to him. On the contrary, he was " a plain man," and it seemed to him that, if he were to come to any such conclusion about people he knew, he would be able to give some reason for it. He had not, the witness admitted, seen other persons about whom " he fancied the same thing." He could not say that he had had actual experience of a man sleeping year after year in the same bed with his wife and all the time maintaining platonic relations with her, but he had " heard of things very much like it." From first to last, in all his conversations with the prisoner at Claverton Street, he had never encouraged the idea that her husband would not recover. " He always told her that was nonsense." He had heard the Bartletts in talking together speak of some individual as " *Georgius Rex.*" He knew now—in fact, he knew before the deceased died—that Mr. Dyson was the person to whom they alluded. The witness on the morning of 1st January took particular notice of the state of the fire. He looked at it for the purpose of estimating the temperature in which the corpse had been lying. It was not sufficiently large to have influenced the temperature of the room to any perceptible extent.

Dr. Dudley deposed to visiting the deceased in Claverton Street on 19th December. He appeared to be depressed and lacking in energy, and complained of overwork and sleeplessness. The witness examined him, in conjunction with Dr. Leach, and found that all his organs were healthy. He told him that he was a

Introduction.

sound man, and advised him to sit up and go out every day for a walk or a drive. The prisoner was present throughout the interview. The witness heard of Mr. Bartlett's death on 1st January, and on the following day attended the post-mortem. In the stomach " there was an erosion, a patch, where the mucous membrane was destroyed in the most dependent part," by which the witness meant the portion near the spinal cord, which would be the lowest when a person was lying down. Such a patch would be caused by an irritant poison. Liquid chloroform would account for it. The blood was very fluid. That was a symptom of poisoning by chloroform. The stomach exhaled a smell of chloroform and garlic. Replying to Mr. Clarke, the witness said that when he went to see the deceased, on 19th December, the prisoner appeared to be " very attentive to," and " very anxious about," him.

Dr. Montague Murray stated that at the post-mortem on 2nd January he performed " the operative part." With the exception of the conditions of the stomach, there was nothing to account for death. The lower part of the gullet, that is the lower three inches, had the same inflammatory blush as the lining membrane of the stomach. In cross-examination the witness explained that the state of the gullet showed that " the poison was taken down the throat." The situation of the red patch in the stomach indicated that, for the greater part of the time during which life lasted, after the poison was taken, the body of the deceased was in a recumbent position. The witness had never heard of a case in which liquid chloroform had been poured down the throat of an insensible person. If the insensibility were profound, the operation should not present any insuperable difficulties. It would be necessary, however, to use a tube. If no mechanical means were employed, some of the liquid would remain in the mouth and some would trickle down the gullet. Insensibility would prevent the action of swallowing. There might be " an insensibility so profound that the person operated upon might swallow without resistance, and yet so little profound that the muscular action would not be paralysed." A medical man would judge by the reflexes in other parts whether the particular stage had been reached at which the reflex action of the muscles of the throat would continue and yet the insensibility be sufficient to deaden the pain of the burning. He would test it by touching the eye. If there were a closure of the eyelids, that would indicate the presence of reflexes which would render the act of swallowing instinctive. He would judge of the insensibility to pain by the relaxation of the muscles. Cases do occur in which it is not desirable to produce complete anæsthesia,

51

only sufficient to deaden pain. In those cases the physician has to judge "whether the moment has come in which there is sufficient insensibility to produce anæsthesia, yet not sufficient to produce the complete abolition of the reflex action." In reply to Mr. Justice Wills, the witness said that in operations under chloroform it was sometimes necessary to give the patient brandy. It was difficult, however, to administer it through the mouth, and the general practice was to inject it.

Tom Ralph, a metropolitan police constable, who acted as coroner's officer in the case, deposed to searching the first-floor rooms at 85 Claverton Street with Inspector Marshall on 11th January. In one of the boxes which he examined he found Mr. Dyson's letter, beginning "Dear Edwin," and signed "George," and on one of the tables a copy of Squire's "Companion." In the front room was a box containing a man's clothes. In the right-hand trousers pocket of one of the suits were several of those articles which, as their name suggests, are popularly supposed to be a French invention.

Dr. Thomas Stevenson, professor of medical jurisprudence at Guy's Hospital and senior scientific analyst to the Home Office, succeeded the policeman in the witness-box. In answer to the Attorney-General, he related how, on 12th January, he began to analyse certain portions of the deceased's body which had been submitted to him. The characteristic smell of the contents of the stomach was that of chloroform. There was also about them a slight odour of garlic, due to the mango-chutney. He was able to establish the presence in the stomach of $11\frac{1}{4}$ grains of chloroform, equivalent to between 8 and 9 minims. This amount represented 5 per cent. of the weight of the whole quantity analysed. The witness also tested for all the poisons which suggested themselves to him, but could find no other traces of any alkaloids. He devoted several days to his experiments. He could discover no traces of chlorodyne. Speaking of the appearance of the stomach, the witness stated that the patch of inflammation was "about the part to which the liquid would flow when a person was lying on his back. It was the usual spot at which we find it after the swallowing of an irritant poison." It was at the point to which "by gravitation the liquid would find its way." The conclusion which the witness formed was that the deceased must have swallowed a large dose of chloroform, "such a quantity as would be sufficient to cause death." A person swallowing chloroform would certainly perceive the peculiar character of the liquid which he had absorbed. It had a hot, fiery taste, and would cause pain. It

Introduction.

was hardly possible that any one could take it under the impression that it was some innocuous article of food or drink. If the chloroform were contained in an ordinary medicine bottle, there was "no insuperable difficulty" in the way of pouring it down the throat of a person in a condition of insensibility. Witness himself with a teaspoon had put liquid down the throat of a person while he had been "chloroforming" him. It would not be a difficult operation, if a man were lying on his back with his mouth open. Up to a certain point of insensibility the presence of a liquid at the back of the throat would occasion the act of swallowing. But, once the reflexes had disappeared, there could be no swallowing. He had given a rabbit a quarter of an ounce of chloroform, and found that its blood, when analysed, contained traces of chloroform. He had seen one person suffering from the effects of swallowing chloroform. He had not taken a fatal dose. It produced copious vomiting and pain, and the patient was greatly alarmed. He should regard vomiting as a frequent, but not an invariable, symptom of poisoning by chloroform. It was possible with chloroform to render insensible a sleeping person. Witness had never himself performed the operation, but he knew of instances in which it had been performed successfully. Were drops of chloroform to fall upon the chin or the breast they would leave no lasting mark. They would produce no more than a temporary redness.

Under cross-examination the witness stated that he could refer to no recorded case of murder by the administration of liquid chloroform. The majority of deaths from chloroform were accidental. About 30 per cent. of the cases known to the witness of swallowing chloroform proved fatal. He did not regard an odour of chloroform in the ventricles of the brain as an invariable symptom in cases in which the drug had been inhaled shortly before death, but it was one for which he would certainly look. If the patient were brought to the verge of asphyxia—a state of insensibility from the administration of chloroform—and death were to supervene from any cause whatever, he would expect to find an engorgement of the right side of the heart. He did not agree with either of the passages, quoted by the learned counsel from Guy and Ferrier's "Forensic Medicine," that in cases of inhalation there was always an intense inflammation of the air passages, or that the vapour of chloroform, when inhaled, acted more powerfully than when swallowed in a liquid form. He admitted the authority, but he did not admit the statement. The witness had never given chloroform to a patient while asleep. He

53

Adelaide Bartlett.

did not consider that an adult person would " almost invariably " wake up, if it were attempted. He was aware that in Dolbeau's " Annales d'Hygiène " it was stated that great skill would be required to perform the operation successfully, and that in 75 per cent. of the cases the individuals awoke directly they were exposed to the vapour. He knew of the experiments carried out by the American doctor, Quimby, and others which are mentioned in Wharton and Stillé's " Medical Jurisprudence." In that work it was said that, out of six persons on whom the attempt was made, all resisted more or less, and two woke up immediately. The only English authorities on the subject to which the witness could refer were the *Medical Times and Gazette* and Woodman and Tidy's " Forensic Medicine." The first contained a letter from Dr. Hussey, who witnessed the successful administration of chloroform to a young man of seventeen in the Oxford Infirmary, as far back as the year 1850, and the other spoke of the practice in the Bristol General Hospital of chloroforming children, who were to be operated upon for hip disease, while they were asleep. The witness agreed that there were four stages in the administration of the vapour. " In the first the patient becomes excited; in the second he talks incoherently and sensibility is diminished; in the third he is unconscious, but the muscles are rigid; and in the fourth they are completely relaxed and the patient is perfectly insensible." If liquid chloroform were to be placed in the mouth in the first, or even in the second, stage it would cause pain. In the third the jaw becomes rigid, and force would have to be exerted to open the mouth. The moment at which the patient would cease to be able to swallow is altogether a question of degree. After being completely anæsthetised he would still continue to swallow his own saliva for some time. Without doubt, there is a point in the process of chloroforming when he would be able to swallow, but yet would suffer no pain. The practical test to determine whether the condition has been reached, in which the patient would be insensible to pain, is to ascertain whether the reflex of the eye has been abolished. Having elicited that, the learned counsel put to the witness this proposition— " Suppose you had to deal with a sleeping man, and it was your object to get down his throat, without his knowing it, a liquid the administration of which to the lips or throat would cause great pain, do you not agree that it would be a very difficult and delicate operation? " " I think," replied the witness, " that it would be an operation which would often fail and might often succeed. I should look upon it as a delicate operation, because I

54

Introduction.

should be afraid of pouring it down the windpipe.'' If insensibility or partial insensibility had been produced, the rejection of the liquid by the windpipe would probably be less active than if the patient were awake. If chloroform went down the windpipe it would probably burn it and leave traces which would be apparent for some hours after death. If the post-mortem had been performed on the very day on which the death took place the chances of determining the cause of death would have been increased. On this Mr. Clarke concluded his cross-examination, and the Court adjourned.

On the following day, Friday, 16th April, the fifth day of the trial, the proceedings began with the recall of Dr. Stevenson, who was re-examined by the Attorney-General. If chloroform had been swallowed, the witness would not necessarily expect to find a smell about the mouth. If the mouth were open he would be prepared to find that the smell had disappeared in as short a time as half an hour. If chloroform were taken into the stomach it would probably act with greater effect if the person had, before that, been rendered insensible, or partially insensible, by inhalation. The period of rigidity in the third stage of the administration of chloroform would last only a few seconds or a minute at the most. Referring, in answer to a question by the learned judge, to the difficulty said to have been experienced in bringing the deceased under the influence of nitrous oxide gas at the dentist's, the witness could only say that, '' if a person were insensible to one anæsthetic, he would probably be less sensible to another.''

Dr. Tidy, an official analyst to the Home Office and one of the authors of Woodman and Tidy's '' Forensic Medicine,'' deposed that of his own knowledge he only knew of one death from swallowing liquid chloroform. He believed that the amount absorbed on that occasion was an ounce and a half, but it was a case of suicide, and it was in consequence unnecessary to determine the quantity. If a fatal dose of chloroform were swallowed, he would not be surprised to learn that no smell of it was perceptible about the mouth two or three hours afterwards, but at the post-mortem he should expect to find fluidity of the blood. Chloroform dropped upon the skin leaves only a slight redness, which would probably pass away in a quarter of an hour. Rigidity of the jaw was not an invariable concomitant of the administration of chloroform. Partial insensibility could be produced by the inhalation of chloroform during sleep. If an individual were thus rendered unconscious, liquid might be poured down his throat. But as regards administering chloroform to persons while they

55

were asleep, it was only fair to say that he himself had tried it in three cases. In one, the case of a boy between fifteen and sixteen, he had been successful, and in the other two he had failed. In cross-examination the witness stated that he had had a very long experience of chloroform. Rigidity of the jaw might last for a few seconds, or it might go on for a considerably longer period. He would not be prepared to say that it might not last for five minutes. The symptoms of the inhalation of chloroform are very variable. One person might go off in two minutes, while another might take much longer. The quantity required to produce the necessary effect varies also. Great judgment and experience are needed in its administration. There is considerable uncertainty about the action of swallowing chloroform. Much depends upon whether the person does, or does not, vomit. " A great deal less is known about swallowing chloroform than about chloroform inhaled." In reply to a juryman, the witness said that, supposing drops of chloroform were to fall upon the delicate parts of the mouth, the marks would be more likely to remain than if dropped upon the skin of the hand.

Mary Anne Furlong, a married woman, living at Merton, stated that from 6th January until 1st September, 1885, she acted as daily servant to the Bartletts at The Cottage, Merton. She generally began her work at eight o'clock. Mr. and Mrs. Bartlett occupied the same bed. Mrs. Bartlett sometimes helped her to make it. Towards the latter part of her service Mr. Dyson came frequently to the house. The witness went home usually about eleven o'clock in the morning, but if Mrs. Bartlett had company she would stay and cook the dinner. Mr. and Mrs. Matthews and Mr. Dyson were the only visitors. Mr. and Mrs. Bartlett appeared to be on very affectionate terms and to live together as man and wife.

Inspector Marshall, of the Metropolitan Police, deposed that he searched the railway line from Victoria to Peckham Rye, but could not find the bottle which he expected to find. He was present at Claverton Street on 11th January when the house was searched. On 15th February the witness went with Mr. Dyson to Wandsworth Common, and at a spot which the last-named pointed out he found a bottle labelled " Poison. Not to be taken." He had twice since that time searched the Common, but had been unable to find the other bottles.

Mrs. Doggett, who was recalled and examined by the Attorney-General, said that during the first week of the Bartlett's stay in Claverton Street they occupied one bed. After that they slept

Introduction.

in different beds in the same room—the back room. When Mr. Bartlett was taken ill, his bed was carried into the drawing-room. During Mr. Bartlett's illness the sofa in the front room was moved into a position in front of the folding doors, but this did not prevent any one from using them. To pass from one room to another it was not necessary to go outside on to the landing. The witness saw nothing unusual in the relations of Mr. and Mrs. Bartlett. In cross-examination the witness stated that, when the Bartletts first came, they asked for two beds in the bedroom. The witness did not possess a bed small enough, and it was some days before she could find time '' to run out '' and order one at the stores, and another few days elapsed before it was delivered. Alice Fulcher, who was also recalled, concurred with her mistress that the Bartletts only slept in the same bed during their first week in Claverton Street, and that when Mr. Bartlett was taken ill his bed was moved into the front room. After that Mrs. Bartlett slept upon the sofa in the same room. She had, said the witness in reply to the learned judge, waited upon the Bartletts when Mr. Dyson was dining with them. She had heard the prisoner address him both as '' George '' and as '' Mr. Dyson.'' She had heard her call him '' George '' before Mr. Bartlett. On the occasion of Mr. Dyson's visits the witness had seen books lying about, but whether they were open or shut she was not prepared to say. She never at the time heard it said that Mr. Dyson was giving the prisoner lessons. When opening the door to him she had never noticed that he brought any books to the house.

This concluded the case for the Crown, and Mr. Clarke, who called no witnesses, proceeded at once to address the jury. His speech, which will always be remembered as a brilliant example of forensic eloquence and of skilful advocacy, should be read in full in the report of the trial, for in this narrative it is only possible to present a short summary of the principal arguments upon which he founded his plea for his client's acquittal.

They were asked to believe, said the learned counsel, that this woman, who had lived on the most affectionate terms with her husband, who, when he fell ill, sent for doctors and nursed him with tender devotion, was on this New Year's night '' suddenly transformed into a murderess.'' Nor was that all. If she were guilty she must have committed a crime '' absolutely unknown in the history of medical jurisprudence.'' Never before has it been suggested that liquid chloroform has been employed to per-petrate a murder. And the reason is obvious. Not only is it

Adelaide Bartlett.

very variable in its effect, but it cannot be secretly administered because of the intense pain which must follow its absorption. The prosecution, however, has sought to overcome this last difficulty by suggesting that the drug was poured down the deceased's throat after he had been reduced to a state of insensibility by inhalation. But before proceeding to consider all which that involves, this question may fairly be asked—if the prisoner had succeeded in producing insensibility, why did she not go on and effect her purpose by inhalation? Why should she "interrupt the process of anæsthesia, which, if continued, must result in death," in order to attempt another operation which might "destroy the anæsthetic influence" and arouse in the deceased "the capacity of sensation and resistance"?

That Mr. Bartlett's death was caused by the swallowing of liquid chloroform was not open to dispute. What counsel hoped to make clear was that the theory of the prosecution with regard to the manner in which it was given to him was inconsistent with reasonable probabilities. It was suggested that while he was asleep he was rendered unconscious by the inhalation of the vapour. Much evidence had been heard with respect to the possibility of administering chloroform under these conditions. While none of the authorities denied the feasibility of the operation, all of them spoke of it as difficult and delicate, if attempted upon a full-grown man. The Frenchman, Dolbeau, laid it down that the experiment failed in 75 per cent. of the cases in which it was tried. Dr. Tidy, a chloroformist of vast experience, stated in the witness-box that he contrived to produce insensibility in a boy while he was asleep, but that he met with no success when he sought to bring about the same result with two adult persons. And, supposing that the sleep of the deceased, a man upon whom anæsthetics did not readily take effect, had been converted into insensibility, how great were the difficulties which still had to be surmounted. It was impossible to pour a liquid down the throat of an unconscious person in whom the power of swallowing no longer existed. Nevertheless, as Dr. Stevenson had explained, "there was, or there might be, a time the duration of which no man could measure, the existence and the condition of which the most careful doctor could not predict," in which the patient might be so far insensible as not to feel the pain and yet sufficiently sensible to be able to swallow. Is it believable that this woman, alone that night with her husband, performed upon him an operation which Dr. Stevenson with all his skill and knowledge would, on his own admission, have found great difficulty in bringing to a successful issue?

Introduction.

So much for the scientific side of the case. In his opening address, continued the learned counsel, the Attorney-General referred to certain circumstances as throwing suspicion upon the prisoner. Some of them were of a very trivial character, and any unfavourable construction which could be placed upon them had, he ventured to think, disappeared in the course of his cross-examination. There was the conversation about the chloroform with Mrs. Doggett on the evening of 31st December. But was it a matter for surprise that there should be some talk about anæsthetics when, only an hour or two before, Mr. Bartlett had been under gas at the dentist's? Was it to be regarded as suspicious that the prisoner should tell the servant to place the basin for the beef tea on the table on the landing? It now appeared that, on that particular night, when the woman came upstairs she brought the coals, but forgot the basin. What more natural in the circumstances than that the prisoner should give her those instructions, seeing that her husband had gone to bed and would not wish to be disturbed a second time? The prosecution attached importance to the statement of the Doggetts that, on the fatal morning, the fire appeared to have been attended to recently. Was it not probable, however, that it had been banked up overnight, and, if that were so, the prisoner, after arousing the house, had only to touch it with the poker to make it burn up brightly? Lastly, there was the matter of the untrue statements about Annie Walker and Dr. Nichols in connection with the purchase of the chloroform. With regard to that the learned counsel must observe that what the prisoner actually said rested wholly upon the unsupported word of Mr. Dyson. He had certainly no wish " to impeach the innocence " of Mr. Dyson, but, if the making of false statements were to be taken as evidence of guilt, it was strange that he should be in the witness-box and not in the dock beside the prisoner. No one could say whether the deceased did, or did not, see Dr. Nichols. The doctor himself had stated that he knew no one of the name of Bartlett. But he was not qualified to practise in this country, and it is not unlikely that the deceased may have presented himself to him under an assumed name. There can be no doubt that the prisoner did consult Mrs. Nichols, because it was on her recommendation that she engaged Annie Walker. It was also perfectly clear that at the time of her confinement she possessed a copy of Dr. Nichols' book. Counsel, however, was not prepared to deny that she gave Mr. Dyson a false reason for desiring to obtain the chloroform. But, if her account of her relations with her husband were true, she

59

Adelaide Bartlett.

could not, unless she were lost to all sense of delicacy, acknowledge to this man the purpose for which she required it.

The story of the platonic compact was so extraordinary that no reasonable person would believe in its existence, except upon the most conclusive evidence. Mr. Dyson was not the only witness who had spoken to the deceased's strange views on the matrimonial state. Old Mr. Bartlett had very reluctantly admitted that he had heard his son say that every man should have two wives. Mr. Dyson's account of his conversations on that subject and of the interview at Putney, when he confessed to the deceased that he was becoming too interested in his wife, would be unbelievable were it not corroborated to a great extent by written documents. There was the new will of 3rd September, 1885, which the deceased, be it noted, executed at his place of business, when neither his wife nor Mr. Dyson was present, and there was the correspondence exchanged between the two men at the time of the Dover visit. Mr. Bartlett's letter of 21st September was " the key to the whole case." Why should he express thankfulness that another man had written " a very loving letter to Adelaide "? That letter, counsel contended, went a long way towards confirming the statement which had been made about his matrimonial relations. When they took up their abode in Claverton Street the Bartletts stipulated with the landlady for two beds. No great significance should perhaps be attached to that; nevertheless, as far as it went, it supported the prisoner's story. In the course of his professional visits to Claverton Street Dr. Leach had many opportunities of observing the deceased and his wife together. He has been examined and cross-examined at length about the impression which they made upon him. He has said that on 26th January, when the prisoner confided to him the terms upon which she lived with her husband, he did not treat her statement as either " extraordinary " or " unbelievable." As he thought the matter over, he remembered their demeanour and the general " tone of their companionship," and came to the conclusion that what she told him might not improbably be true. " That is the whole of the evidence. It is amazing that there should be so much."

It was no part of his duty, continued counsel, to explain how this man met his death, but probabilities in a case of this kind had to be considered. During nearly the whole of the last three weeks of his life the deceased was ill and confined to his room, if not to his bed. His physical condition was not perhaps very serious, but it was complicated by severe toothache and by hypochondria

60

Introduction.

and sleeplessness brought on by overwork. The history of the case was one of frequent relapses, which must have tried him sorely. Drugs to which he did not readily respond were administered, and only served to increase his depression. Then in the last days of December, when he seemed to be regaining his health, the trouble in the jaw set in, and at the dentist's the ugly word necrosis was mentioned in his hearing. Who can doubt that his spirits were greatly affected by this fresh misfortune? And that same night, when he was in bed, his wife gave him the chloroform, and, having explained why she had procured it, told him that there could be no going back upon the sanction which he had given to her relations with Mr. Dyson. "No longer was he to enjoy the rights that a husband can exercise." What happened after that can " be sketched in imagination." It was the prisoner's habit to go into the back room to wash and make other preparations before settling down for the night. There are no grounds for supposing that she departed from her usual practice on this particular evening. If she acted thus, the deceased would be left alone, and the poison would be within his reach. His spirit had been weakened by suffering and ill-health, and he had just been told that he must look upon " the effectual marriage tie between his wife and himself " as severed. May he not have seized the chloroform bottle, and, pouring out a glass—half a wine-glassful would suffice—have put an end to all his troubles? If something of this kind did occur, he may have passed into a state of coma before the prisoner returned to the room. According to her statement, she noticed nothing during the night except that he snored in a somewhat peculiar fashion. Stertorous breathing is a well-known symptom of chloroform poisoning, and, if she were guilty, it is difficult to believe that she would have mentioned the circumstance to Dr. Leach. Taking everything into consideration, it is surely more probable that in a fit of despair he took the fatal draught than that, alone and unassisted, " the grocer's widow " worked a " scientific miracle."

From the moment that she discovered that her husband was dead the prisoner behaved like the loving and devoted wife which she had shown herself to be throughout his illness. She sent for the doctor, she aroused the house, and, when she was told that a post-mortem examination would be necessary, the only wish which she expressed was that it should take place as soon as possible. When the doctor spoke of chlorodyne as the possible cause of death she combated the notion. Yet it was a suggestion which a guilty woman would have adopted eagerly. When she quitted Claverton

61

Adelaide Bartlett.

Street she made no attempt to remove the chloroform bottle, but left it behind in one of the drawers. Eventually, it is true, she threw it away, but she did not thus dispose of it until three days after Mr. Dyson had cast away his bottles amidst the gorse bushes on Wandsworth Common. Without doubt at the Matthews' she was very angry that Mr. Dyson should bother her about his wretched verses. A few days later, on 9th January, she gave them back to him, and when he said something about the chloroform, she turned upon him indignantly and told him " not to mince matters " but to say " I gave it to him." The first challenge to the world to bring this charge came from her lips. The learned counsel concluded by drawing a moving picture of the lonely and unprotected woman whose fate was in the hands of the jury. One friend she still had, the spirit of justice. That spirit would be present at their deliberations, and would speak with no uncertain voice when they brought in their verdict that Adelaide Bartlett was not guilty.

When Mr. Clarke sat down, amidst a burst of applause such as is seldom heard in an English Court, he had been speaking for six hours. His lordship, accordingly, adjourned the further proceedings to the morrow, when he announced that he would sit at nine o'clock. On Saturday, 17th April, the sixth and the last day of the trial, the greater part of the morning was taken up with the Attorney-General's reply. They had been told, said Mr. Attorney, that " this was the first case of suggested death by the use of chloroform." But might not Palmer's counsel have said the same of strychnine and Lamson's of aconitine? The question they had to decide was whether chloroform had been applied with criminal intent, and, if so, was the prisoner the person who used it? The learned counsel for the defence had confined himself to suggesting difficulties in the way of administering it to another person, and had " marshalled his facts and arguments in support of one suggestion only—suicide, deliberate suicide on the part of the deceased." It must always be borne in mind that in cases of this kind " proof to demonstration of the crime " was never obtainable. The clue to the truth must, so to speak, be groped for in the dark. Now it was very necessary to consider the antecedent history of these people, and with regard to that the autumn of 1881 was of especial importance. It was the date of the prisoner's confinement. According to her own account, she was so anxious to become a mother that she submitted to one, only one, act of sexual intercourse, in order to realise her wish. She has alleged that in all the previous years of her married life she had had no sexual relations with her husband. Is that a story which any man of

62

Introduction.

common sense can accept? " How did she know, how could she know, that one act would enable her to count with certainty or probability on the fruition of her hopes? " The birth of the still-born child appears to have been a source of " great physical anguish to her," and her longing to be a mother seems quickly to have disappeared. But for all that her words to Annie Walker are " consistent only with the desire to avoid child-bearing." They do not necessarily imply a cessation of marital intercourse, and with regard to that the articles which the police found among the clothes at Claverton Street were highly significant.

There was not a scintilla of evidence to support the idea that these two people did not live on the ordinary terms of husband and wife. In 1885 they made the acquaintance of Mr. Dyson. It was impossible to speak with certainty about the nature of the relations between the prisoner at the bar and George Dyson. It was, however, " quite clear that George Dyson was received on terms of dangerous intimacy by Mrs. Bartlett and by Mrs. Bartlett's husband." His learned friend's description of the situation was, unless he had misunderstood him, something to this effect. The deceased perceived that there was a growing affection between his wife and Mr. Dyson. This he recognised would, in the event of his death, " culminate in a closer and nearer relation—the relation of man and wife." Nor was that all. He, a man only a few years older than either of them, so far contemplated the possibility that he would predecease them that he actually " made over in reversion his living wife to the man whose friendship he was cultivating." And what happened after that? This compliant husband, when his wife said to him, " You have made me over to George Dyson, it is unfair that you should exercise your rights as a husband," turns over on his pillow and does an act " which removes the only obstacle to their immediate union." It has been urged that the correspondence which has been produced in Court and the deceased's will confirm the existence of this extraordinary compact. But it was Mr. Attorney's submission that the letters which passed between the deceased and Mr. Dyson suggested nothing more than that the two men entertained for one another feelings of respect and admiration. The words which the deceased is said to have used at Putney, when Mr. Dyson told him that he was growing too interested in his wife, only showed that he had confidence in his friend and, apparently, in his wife, and the same might be said about the will of 3rd September.

It would be incorrect to speak of the illness from which the deceased began to suffer on 10th December as serious or dangerous.

Adelaide Bartlett.

It was true that it was attended by tiresome complications, and that the patient was troubled with his teeth. There was no suggestion that during this time the prisoner ever failed in her attention to him. But in regard to that, Mr. Attorney felt bound to observe that if she had a guilty purpose in her mind, when she requested Mr. Dyson to procure the chloroform, she had to be very careful to avoid raising a suspicion that she was wanting in affection to the person against whom her criminal intentions were directed. The jury would doubtless remember her sentimental talk in the cab on the way to the dentist's—a situation hardly calculated to arouse romantic feelings. The question which he would now invite them to ask themselves was, why did she want the chloroform? Was it probable, was it even possible, that her statements about Dr. Nichols and Annie Walker and the mysterious internal complaint were figments of Mr. Dyson's imagination? It was plain that she must have given him some reason to explain her desire to possess the chloroform. Her own account of the matter was that, with the exception of the one act which was to gratify her longing to be a mother, her relations with her husband were always platonic. Nevertheless, about 16th December, when he was still an invalid, his passion, which had lain dormant for ten years, began to manifest itself. It was in order to be able to wave a handkerchief soaked in chloroform in his face and thus resist his advances that she commissioned Mr. Dyson to purchase the drug for her. " Gentlemen," said the Attorney-General, " if you can accept that statement or that explanation, by all means accept it."

There were but two ways in which the poison could have been criminally administered. Either the prisoner, for no other person could have done it, must have given it to the deceased, while he was lying upon his back, with his mouth open in a state of partial or total insensibility, or she must have handed him a glass containing the fatal draught, " as if for an ordinary purpose." These last words called forth a strong protest from Mr. Clarke against the introduction of a fresh theory at this stage of the case. This was the first, he contended, that they had heard of this new suggestion. He had founded his comments and his cross-examination upon the passage in the Attorney-General's address in which he said that, if the chloroform had been criminally administered to the deceased, he must have been " lulled into a state of stupor." Seeing that his learned friend had " erected " the theory of suicide, he was bound, replied Mr. Attorney, to submit any theory which " pointed in a more prob-

Mrs. Adelaide Bartlett.

Introduction.

able direction." He did not pretend for a moment that the suggestion that the deceased took the poison from the hands of the prisoner and " gulped it down in confidence " was free from difficulties. It would cause pain and would presumably be followed by " violent exclamations." Nevertheless, it was an infinitely more acceptable theory than that of suicide. Adverting to the first theory and the medical evidence in regard to it, Mr. Attorney did not deny that the experts had described the process of administering chloroform to a sleeping person as difficult. But was it not possible that the attempt to render the deceased insensible had been begun before he fell asleep? The doctors also spoke of the introduction of a liquid into the gullet of an insensible man as " a delicate operation." But it must be borne in mind that they were talking from a purely medical point of view. If chloroform were given to this man with criminal intent, no considerations of surgical delicacy would arise. It would simply be a question of pouring it down his throat effectively.

The behaviour of the deceased on that last day, the oysters and the delicacies of which he partook so generously, the relish with which he ordered his next day's breakfast, his pleasurable anticipation of a visit to the seaside, were suggestive only of a man who felt the enjoyment of life, and not of one who meditated suicide. The theory propounded by his learned friend was that, that night, after his strange conversation with his wife, he was left alone, and took a fatal dose from the bottle which stood upon the mantelpiece within reach of his bed. The question of what became of that bottle was of the very highest importance. Dr. Leach swore that he searched the room carefully about half-past four that morning and could not find it. " You must ask yourselves gravely," by whom and for what reason that bottle was removed? The prisoner was questioned by Dr. Leach as to whether the deceased could have obtained any poison. Her reply was that it was impossible, and to that she adhered until 26th January, when she told him that amazing story of how she came to procure the chloroform. On the day following her husband's death she presented Mr. Dyson with his gold watch, saying that " Edwin told her to give it to him." When did he say that? Is there a shred of evidence that he contemplated anything but a life of ordinary duration? They must consider whether all these circumstances were " reasonably consistent with the innocence " of the prisoner, who, if the poison were criminally administered, was the only person who could have administered it.

It was fair to suggest that this woman not improbably saw in

F

Adelaide Bartlett.

Mr. Dyson a man with whom her husband compared unfavourably. She knew that the restrictions of which she had formerly complained were no longer present in the will which was executed on 3rd September. On 10th December, when the deceased fell ill, he was attended by a doctor who was certainly not a strong-headed man, and was in addition a stranger. May she not have taken this opportunity of ridding herself of a husband who had become distasteful to her, in order " to clear the way to a union with a man for whom of late she had conceived admiration and apparently affection? " Motive is important, and the absence of motive is important; but if the logic of facts drove them to one conclusion, they could not escape from giving effect to it by their verdict, because " they were unable to satisfy themselves about the strength or the character of the motive. . . . "

When the Attorney-General sat down, Mr. Clarke begged his lordship to recall Annie Walker and put to her one question with regard to anything which she knew about " the single act "—his lordship would understand what he meant. Annie Walker was, accordingly, invited " to step up," and Mr. Clarke, by his lordship's direction, asked her whether, while she was attending the prisoner in her confinement, anything was said to lead her to suppose that it was the result of a single act. Her reply was a simple affirmative, with which Mr. Clarke was well content, but, unfortunately for him, his lordship would not allow the matter to rest at that. Two or three questions from the bench were sufficient to elicit from the witness that what she meant by " a single act " was a single act without a resort to preventive measures. Both husband and wife had told her that, except on one solitary occasion, they always took precautions.

At the conclusion of this incident, which must have caused Mr. Clarke to regret very bitterly that he had asked for the witness's recall, Mr. Justice Wills began his charge to the jury. The decision of the Crown, he told them, not to proceed against Mr. Dyson, far from being a disadvantage, was on the contrary " an immense gain," to the prisoner at the bar. Not only did it enable her counsel to cross-examine him, but it prevented the calling of evidence as to " circumstances of uncommon suspicion " which could not fail to have " told with more or less fatal effect against her, as well as against him." His lordship then adverted to the principal events in the early history of the Bartletts. It was unnecessary to inquire into the merits of the dispute of 1878— " very little, indeed, depended upon the evidence of the senior Bartlett." But one remark he must make : from the moment

Introduction.

that he appeared upon the scene after his son's death, the prisoner may fairly be said to have " lived under the observation of keen and suspicious eyes." Passing on to the prisoner's confinement, the learned judge denounced in scathing terms works such as " Esoteric Anthropology." " The women of the present day were used to strange things, and it was such reading as that which helped to unsex them." The articles discovered in Claverton Street, and what they had just now heard from Annie Walker in the witness-box, were " the natural and expected consequences of indulgence in literature of that kind." Nevertheless, despite these " vulgar facts," these people were, " after their fashion," living happily and contentedly together, when they had the misfortune to make the acquaintance of the Rev. George Dyson. They had been told how a close intimacy grew up between them, and how a Christian minister took advantage of the husband's weakness to spend long hours with the wife, under the pretence of giving her lessons. He admitted that he kissed her, and they had heard how she had been seen reclining at his feet with her head upon his knees. And, unfortunately, it was impossible to doubt, because they " had it on the statement of the wife as well as on the statement of the Rev. George Dyson," that a degree of intimacy was reached in which " the death of the husband and the possibility of Dyson succeeding him " were discussed.

With regard to the Rev. George Dyson, his lordship had this advice to offer. They should only place " a very slender faith " in anything he said. They must remember that he had to make the story which he told them agree with what he had already said at the inquest. Now, when he deposed in the Coroner's Court, he was in fear of his life, and could any one doubt, who had watched him during these proceedings, that he gave his evidence on that occasion with the full determination that, whatever might happen, the Rev. George Dyson should suffer as little harm as possible? There was his account of the interview at Putney when, if he can be believed, he informed the deceased that he was growing too interested in his wife, and the deceased replied by pressing him to continue the intimacy. That story rested upon his own word, and, in his lordship's opinion, presented features of " almost revolting improbability." On the other hand, he was disposed to believe what Dyson said about the letter which the deceased sent him from Dover. It was probably true that it referred to the prisoner's spiritual state and to the effect which Mr. Dyson's preaching had upon her. In any event, neither in the husband's letter nor in Dyson's reply could his lordship discover anything

Adelaide Bartlett.

to support Mr. Clarke's contention that those documents "stamped a new phase of life" in which this woman was "consecrated" as the object of Mr. Dyson's "special personal interest." Dyson has said that at Claverton Street the prisoner spoke of her husband's death as likely to occur in the near future. According to his story, he was incredulous and asked her to explain, and it was then that she told him about the internal complaint. Other conversations on this subject followed, culminating in the mention of chloroform—"chloroform which was to be used when he was violent or in a paroxysm." If all this be true, it is a serious matter, for, said his lordship, this tale about the internal complaint is "all moonshine." As he had already observed, they must receive everything which this man said with "becoming caution," but in this instance his story was confirmed by another witness. Mrs. Matthews has stated that the prisoner assured her, when she asked her why she "told those lies to Mr. Dyson," that "Edwin did think that he was going to die." Mr. Dyson, however, disbelieved her, and to convince him she told him lies. In the face of that, it is hardly open to doubt that some conversation, such as Mr. Dyson described, did in effect take place.

All the available evidence as to the prisoner's conduct during her husband's illness pointed to the care with which she watched over him. Throughout that trying time she scarcely took off her clothes, and nursed him with unremitting attention. In all the years of her married life she was never anything but "perfectly devoted, perfectly affectionate." That was greatly in her favour. It should never be lost sight of, and should "stand her in the fullest stead." The learned judge then went on to discuss the circumstances attending the death of the deceased. In view of the conditions under which it took place, he could see nothing suspicious in the conversation about chloroform with Mrs. Doggett, and the same might be said about the trivial directions for the night given to the maidservant. According to the prisoner's statement, she woke up at four o'clock in the morning and found that her husband was dead. There could be no doubt that he died from swallowing liquid chloroform. And at this stage he must warn them to disregard every supposition which has been put forward except the original theory of the prosecution. "In the name of justice," he must ask them completely to ignore the further suggestions which "the Attorney-General let fall this morning." They had heard a great deal about the possibility of producing partial insensibility and of the ability of a person in that condition to swallow. It all amounted to this: the operation would

Introduction.

be so fraught with difficulties that a skilled person would hardly
venture to attempt it.   They were not dealing, however, with the
possible action of an individual possessed of technical knowledge,
and, in connection with that, he must remind them of Pope's
line—" Fools rush in where angels fear to tread."   Nevertheless,
it appeared to be established that, up to the present time, there
was no recorded instance in this country of the successful administration of chloroform to a grown up man in his sleep.   Moreover,
supposing this first difficulty were to be overcome, there would still
remain " the second difficulty of selecting the right moment for
the rest of the operation."   It was plain that only by a singularly
lucky concatenation of circumstances could this double operation
be successfully performed.   That was one of the great objections
—and " a very formidable one "—to the theory of murder. Now,
if the difficulties attending the administration of chloroform to
this man be considered apart from surrounding circumstances,
they will be found to be so great that most people would say that
it could never have taken place.   But Bartlett did swallow
chloroform which must have been given him " either criminally or
not criminally."   One of two seemingly impossible theories must
therefore be right.   They had to choose between them.   If they
could not decide the question, then the Crown had failed to make
out a case.

They had now to consider " the history of the chloroform
bottle."   It was " the most material element in the case," and
one which " pressed more strongly against the prisoner than almost
any other."   But before going into the matter he would ask them
to assume that, for some innocent reason, a bottle of chloroform
was, on the fatal night, within the reach of the deceased.   He had
been suffering terribly from insomnia.   Only those who have had
a similar experience can realise the intense craving which a man,
so afflicted, would feel for that which would give him sleep.   Was
it not conceivable that he might have sought to obtain relief from
that bottle, and in the dark have poured out a larger amount than
he intended?   It was only a conjecture, but it offered a better
explanation of the man's death than that of suicide which the
learned counsel for the defence had been instructed to suggest.   If
the chloroform were administered to Bartlett non-criminally (and
under that denomination his lordship included " every variety of
suicide and accident "), some of the contents of that bottle must
have found their way into the glass which Doggett described as
having a smell of ether or paregoric about it.   It was a strong
fact in the prisoner's favour that no attempt was made to clean it.

Adelaide Bartlett.

It could not be that she purposely left it with the smell lingering about it in order to create the impression that the deceased took the poison accidentally. If that had been her idea, she would have suggested something of the kind, and that she never did.

The glass remained upon the mantelpiece, but the bottle disappeared. The prisoner has said that, " about breakfast time," she placed it in a drawer in the back room. But what happened to it in the meantime? Soon after half-past four Dr. Leach searched the room, and, if there be one circumstance in this case about which he is clear, it is that " that bottle was not there." The learned counsel for the defence was yesterday unable to offer any satisfactory explanation of its disappearance. In the course of an anxious discussion with the prisoner about the cause of death Dr. Leach told her that he had found a bottle of chlorodyne. The smell of chlorodyne closely resembles that of chloroform. Nevertheless, she, who must at the time have had " a large bottle of the fatal stuff in her possession, said nothing about it." There is a complete answer to all this, provided that the story which she told Dr. Leach on 26th January be accepted. If it be true, there are " principles of modesty, reserve, and delicacy " which might well restrain any woman from disclosing the real facts. It would, moreover, explain why she made those false statements to Mr. Dyson when asking him to procure the chloroform. Much must, therefore, depend upon the light in which they regarded that story. But, before going into the matter, his lordship ran through the chief events which intervened between Mr. Bartlett's death and the prisoner's visit to Dr. Leach on 26th January. It was much in her favour that she appeared to have been genuinely anxious that the post-mortem should take place as soon as possible. No one can say whether, when she left the house after the post-mortem, she took the chloroform bottle with her. She says that she left it behind in a drawer in the back room. Unfortunately, the coroner's officer, " a grown-up policeman," who, on the following Monday, 4th January, removed some empty medicine bottles and the sealed-up jars from Claverton Street, omitted to search the bedroom. It was probably true that, while escorting her to Dulwich, Mr. Dyson did speak about the chloroform. That he was uneasy on that subject is shown by his action the following day, when " he sanctified the Sabbath " by throwing away on Wandsworth Common the four bottles which had originally contained the drug. With regard to the angry scene at the Matthews' house on 4th January, when Mr. Dyson bowed his head and exclaimed, " Oh, my God," his lordship was disposed to think that

70

Introduction.

" the key to it was missing. Probably it does not suit Mr. Dyson to give it to us." But, seeing that in the main it was corroborated by the Matthews, they would be justified in accepting Dyson's account of his subsequent interviews with the prisoner.

For the first time, on 26th January, the prisoner informed Dr. Leach that, when her husband died, she had chloroform in her possession. She explained the matter by that wonderful story of a platonic union, broken by one solitary act which led to her confinement and the birth of a still-born child. If that were true, it might also be true that she intended " to wave the chloroform in her husband's face and so produce a cessation of his urgency." Dr. Leach has said that his own observations strongly disposed him to believe her. But, when examined, he was unable to point to a single fact which would induce an ordinary person to suppose that the relations of these people were other than those which normally subsist between husband and wife. They had been told about the articles found in the deceased's trousers pocket, and they had heard what Annie Walker said in the witness-box that morning. Had she not by one sentence swept away the whole foundation of that morbid romance? And, if they rejected that story, this was the situation which they must face—" chloroform procured for an unexplained and inexplicable purpose, death by chloroform, the bottle disappearing, and by the statement of the woman herself emptied and thrown away by her. When at last an explanation is given it is a tissue of romance such as, if the evidence of Annie Walker be accepted, could deceive no one but the ecstatic person to whom it was originally detailed."

They were dealing, said his Lordship in conclusion, " with the case of a married woman who had fallen into a perilous friendship with a man who was not her husband." That husband in the latter part of his life was probably " no attractive object either mentally or physically, and the only explanation of the circumstances connected with his disappearance from this world would not stand in the presence of vulgar facts." That, however, was only his opinion. They were the jury, and they must decide. He had drawn their attention to certain very important points which told greatly in the prisoner's favour, and, with regard to the others, he would feel " no tinge of regret " should they come to the conclusion that he had " erred on the side of severity." But they must do their duty, and, with a few words of advice, he invited them to retire and consider their verdict.

Every day since the opening of the trial public interest in the case had increased, and it was in a densely crowded Court

71

Adelaide Bartlett.

that Mr. Justice Wills delivered his charge. " No one," says an anonymous contributor to the *Pall Mall Gazette*,[8] is likely ever to forget the lucid, the impressive, and the eloquent summing up of Judge Wills. He will remember the grave but kind voice which rose to vehemence and sank to a whisper. . . . As the afternoon grew older and the shadows deeper the tone of the judge seemed to increase in solemnity, until the faintest sound, the shutting of a door, the fall of a book, the scratching of a pen became an irritant, so tense had the occasion become." After about an hour the clatter of tongues, which broke out directly the jury retired and the judge quitted the bench, was hushed as the jurymen re-entered the box and as a fragile figure in black supported on either side by two female warders, the only woman in Court without a hat,[9] appeared in the front of the dock. It was not, however, to announce their verdict, but to inquire at what hour the Doggetts had gone to bed on the fatal night, that the jury had returned. Mr. Doggett was present in Court, and, having stated, in reply to the learned judge, that it was at half-past twelve, as near as he could tell, they again retired. More than another hour elapsed before they came back and " with solemn faces ascended to their pew-like seats." Once more the terrible silence was broken " by the click of the dock handle as it turned to give passage to the prisoner, whose face was now livid, her eyes closed, her lips glued together, and scarcely alive. Carried to the front of the dock, she was supported on each side by the faithful women, pale but composed. Two spruce doctors and the grave chaplain stood on her left, and behind her again was the sturdy policeman."[1] " Do you find Adelaide Bartlett guilty or not guilty?" asked the Clerk. " Although," replied the foreman, and then he paused, for from the street outside came the sound of a great crowd cheering, " although," he continued, " we think there is the gravest suspicion attaching to the prisoner, we do not think there is sufficient evidence to show how or by whom the chloroform was administered." " Then you say, gentlemen, that the prisoner is not guilty?" " Not guilty," replied the foreman, and at these words the spectators gave vent to their pent-up feelings in a loud burst of applause—a demonstration which the learned judge sternly repressed. Then, after the prisoner in a fainting condition had been assisted down the stairs

---

[8] *Pall Mall Gazette*, 19th April, 1886.
[9] *Daily Telegraph*, 19th April, 1886.
[1] *Pall Mall Gazette*, 19th April, 1886.

Introduction.

from the dock, he addressed a few courteous thanks to the jury. But, whether by accident or by design, when he thus dismissed them, he omitted to say that he concurred with their verdict.

Mr. Clarke was the hero of the hour. When his brougham emerged from the courtyard of the Old Bailey it was followed along the Strand by excited admirers,[2] and that evening, when he went to the Lyceum to see Irving in " Faust," the audience gave him an enthusiastic welcome. The newspapers throughout the kingdom joined in the general chorus of approval, but in a more subdued tone. " No other verdict," said the *Times*, " could be expected, but the Pimlico mystery was as much a mystery as ever. . . . Whether on the theory of guilt or innocence, the whole story was marvellous."[3] A few days later, the *Lancet*,[4] in a closely reasoned article, expressed the opinion that there was " not sufficient evidence to prove beyond all reasonable doubt that a murder had been committed." Nevertheless, " the purchase of the chloroform by Mr. Dyson, at Mrs. Bartlett's request, the certain death of Mr. Bartlett by swallowing the drug, and the disappearance of the bottle which contained it, formed a chain of events which required all the forensic talent of Mr. Clarke to loosen and unlink to the satisfaction of the jury." A month later the same paper, in two successive issues, published an article by Dr. Leach, in which he told the story of his attendance upon Mr. Bartlett in Claverton Street.[5] It was simply a very technical account of his illness, but it concluded with a suggestion as to how the patient came to swallow the chloroform. According to Dr. Leach, " he took it out of sheer mischief with the intention of alarming by his symptoms the wife who, an hour or two before, had talked about using it in an emergency."[6]

All attempts to solve the problem are fraught with difficulties, and, on the hypothesis of Mrs. Bartlett's innocence, Dr. Leach's conjecture is as good as any other. He accepts her explanation of why she procured the chloroform. That a bottle of chloroform was, for some innocent reason, in the room is a necessary corollary to any theory that Mr. Bartlett himself either deliberately or accidentally took the poison. Turning to the other side of the question, it is evident that, when the Attorney-General came into Court, his knowledge of the scientific side of the case was greatly

---

[2] Sir E. Clarke, "The Story of My Life," 253.
[3] The *Times*, 19th April, 1886.
[4] The *Lancet*, 24th April, 1886.
[5] The *Lancet*, 22nd and 29th May, 1886.
[6] The *Lancet*, 29th May, 1886.

Adelaide Bartlett.

inferior to that of Mr. Clarke. It was a time of considerable political excitement. Mr. Gladstone had just introduced his first Home Rule Bill, and Mr. Attorney, an ardent nationalist, threw himself heart and soul into the struggle. Had he been less occupied with other matters, it is possible that the case for the Crown might have been presented differently. As it was, the theory of the prosecution was so weakened by the cross-examination of the medical witnesses that Mr. Attorney tried to shift his ground, and, in his final address to the jury, made two new suggestions which Mr. Justice Wills ruled came too late and were inadmissible. The first of these was that the prisoner might have given the deceased the fatal dose in a glass of water which " he gulped down in confidence." But, as Mr. Attorney himself acknowledged, that was open to the grave objection that the pain of swallowing the drug must have caused the unfortunate man to break out into " violent exclamations." The second suggestion was of a different character, and, like the original theory, was based on the supposition that the poison was poured down his throat after he had been " lulled into a stupor " by the process of inhalation. There was this difference, however, that Mr. Attorney now intimated that the attempt to render him insensible might very probably have begun before, not after, he fell asleep. But, having put forward the idea, he did not follow it up and develop it. Yet it appears to be deserving of serious consideration.

It is interesting to wonder whether the trial might have had another termination had the Crown proceeded on the supposition that Mr. Bartlett allowed himself to be " chloroformed." The general circumstances are by no means inconsistent with that possibility. In the course of the day gas had been given him at the dentist's, and, not only did he suffer no inconvenient after-effects, but, according to Dr. Leach,[7] who administered it, he recovered from it with exceptional rapidity and went home in excellent spirits. He had been greatly troubled with insomnia, and the soporifics which the doctor prescribed afforded him little relief. He trusted his wife implicitly, and, if she told him that she could insure him a good night's rest through the instrumentality of chloroform, he may very well have allowed her to try the experiment. And in connection with that her inquiry as to whether chloroform was not pleasant to take, which she put to Mrs. Doggett in her husband's presence, acquires some significance. If the Crown had adopted this theory, the question of the

---

[7] The *Lancet*, 22nd May, 1886.

Introduction.

feasibility of administering chloroform during sleep would never have arisen. It would only have been necessary to show that the difficulty of pouring the liquid down the throat of an unconscious person was not insurmountable.

That, however, is mere speculation. What happened on that New Year's night in Claverton Street is never likely to be known, and most people who study the case will probably come to the conclusion that, in the circumstances, the jury returned the right verdict. But among those who hold that opinion there may be some who will say with Sir James Paget[8] that, once it was all over, she should have told us, in the interests of science, how she did it.

---

[8] Paget, Sir James (1814-1899); created Baronet, 1871; sergeant-surgeon to Queen Victoria, 1877; consulting surgeon to St. Bartholomew's Hospital.

Leading Dates in the Bartlett Trial.

1875.

April   9   Thomas Edwin Bartlett married Adelaide Blanche de la Tremoille, of which marriage there was a stillborn child.

1880.

November   15   Mr. Bartlett accepted by the British Equitable as a first-class life.

1885.

June   The Bartletts made the acquaintance of the Rev. George Dyson.

September   3   Mr. Bartlett made a will leaving everything to his wife, and nominating Dyson one of his executors.

              Dyson twice visited the Bartletts at Dover.

October   The Bartletts moved to Claverton Street, London, where Dyson visited them repeatedly.

December   8   Mr. Bartlett took ill, and Dr. Leach found systems o mercurial poisoning.

          15-21   Mr. Bartlett, troubled by his teeth, made visits to the dentist.

          19   Dr. Dudley called in to assist Dr. Leach.

          27   Dyson agreed to purchase chloroform for Mrs. Bartlett.

          28   Dyson bought 6 ounces of chloroform.

          31   Mr. Bartlett, apparently in excellent spirits, visited the dentist. Mrs. Bartlett had a discussion with Mrs. Doggett about chloroform.

1886.

January   1   Mr. Bartlett died in the early morning.

          2   Post-mortem examination; no natural cause of death found.

          3   Dyson threw away four bottles which had contained chloroform on Wandsworth Common.

          6   Mrs. Bartlett threw away a bottle of chloroform.

          7   Opening of Coroner's inquest.

          26   Government analyst reported chloroform to be the cause of death.

February   4   Inquest resumed.

          11   Mrs. Bartlett arrested.

          18   Coroner's jury returned verdict of "wilful murder" against Mrs. Bartlett, and found Dyson accessory before the fact. Dyson was then taken into custody.

March   20   Mrs. Bartlett and Dyson committed for trial.

April   12   Trial commenced, and Attorney-General withdrew the charge against Dyson.

          17   Mrs. Bartlett found "Not Guilty."

THE TRIAL

WITHIN THE

CENTRAL CRIMINAL COURT,
OLD BAILEY, LONDON,

MONDAY, 12TH APRIL, 1886.

———————

Judge—
THE HON. MR. JUSTICE WILLS.

Counsel for the Crown—
The ATTORNEY-GENERAL (Sir CHARLES RUSSELL, Q.C., M.P.),
Mr. HARRY B. POLAND,
Mr. R. S. WRIGHT, and
Mr. MOLONEY.

(Instructed by the Solicitor to the Treasury.)

Counsel for the Prisoner, Mrs. Bartlett—
Mr. EDWARD CLARKE, Q.C., M.P.,
Mr. MEAD, and
Mr. EDWARD BEAL.

(Instructed by Messrs. Lewis & Lewis.)

Counsel for Rev. G. Dyson—
Mr. LOCKWOOD, Q.C., M.P.,
Mr. CHARLES MATHEWS.

*Solicitor for Mrs. Bartlett—*Mr. E. N. Wood.

First Day—Monday, 12th April, 1886.

Application on behalf of Rev. G. Dyson.

Mr. LOCKWOOD—My lord, before the Court proceeds to arraign the prisoners, I appear before your lordship with my learned friend, Mr. Charles Mathews, on behalf of the prisoner Dyson, and, with reference to the course that is to be pursued in this Court, I do not propose to go at any length into the reason for making the application that I am about to make to your lordship, because that would be obviously an inconvenient course. Therefore, I do not think it necessary to do it, because I am sure your lordship is fully familiar from the depositions with the main facts of this case. Those main facts are also very familiar both to my learned friend and myself, and, having regard to those facts contained in those depositions, I make this application on behalf of my client, that the prisoners be tried separately.

Mr. JUSTICE WILLS—I quite understand and anticipate your reasons, Mr. Lockwood; they are patent to anybody who has read such depositions as these.

Mr. CLARKE—My Lord, the application that my learned friend has made on behalf of his client I know is made upon his own responsibility; but it is one that I most sincerely concur in, for reasons which your lordship may anticipate.

The ATTORNEY-GENERAL—It is unnecessary, my lord, to consider the application that has been made, because of the course which, after the anxious and careful consideration my learned friends and myself have given to this matter, we have resolved to take. We have come to the conclusion that there is no case to be submitted to the jury upon which we could properly ask them to convict George Dyson, and after his arraignment we propose to offer no evidence against him.

Mr. JUSTICE WILLS—All I have to say upon this subject is that it is in the competence of the Crown to take such course as they think fit to take, and no one can doubt that it is taken under a due sense of responsibility. With regard to matters, I think the more proper course, for every reason, is that I should express no opinion about it one way or the other; any expression of mine shall be reserved until the case has been investigated against the other prisoner.

A JUROR—I beg to inform your lordship, as to Mr. Dyson, that I am a personal friend of his.

Mr. JUSTICE WILLS—Well, that is no disqualification.

The ATTORNEY-GENERAL—If the Crown expresses no opinion upon the question, I may say that Mr. Dyson may certainly be

Application on behalf of Rev. G. Dyson.

called as a witness. There can be no desire that any personal friend of his should be on the jury. I will therefore, on behalf of the Crown, ask the gentleman to stand by.

[The juror retired, and another gentleman was substituted in his place.]

The prisoners pleaded not guilty.

The jury were then sworn, and both prisoners were given in charge on the indictment, and also on the coroner's inquisition.

The ATTORNEY-GENERAL—My lord, I offer no evidence on the part of the Crown against Mr. Dyson; and in taking that course we follow the course that was taken by the late Lord Chief Baron Pollock, and offer no evidence against him.

Mr. JUSTICE WILLS—Gentlemen, the Attorney-General, who appears for the Crown in this case, having thoroughly considered the matter, and having the best means of knowledge of anybody, and acting under a grave sense of responsibility, has decided that the proper course to be followed in this case is to offer no evidence on the part of the Crown against Mr. Dyson. Therefore your duty is to say at once that he is not guilty.

The FOREMAN—Not guilty, my lord.

Mr. LOCKWOOD—I do not know whether your lordship will take upon yourself formally to discharge him.

Mr. JUSTICE WILLS—Yes; he is entitled to his discharge; the grand jury are not sitting.

Opening Statement for the Crown.

The ATTORNEY-GENERAL—My lord, and gentlemen of the jury, it now becomes my duty to lay before you, as clearly as I can, the facts of this case in support of the very serious charge upon which the prisoner at the bar is arraigned. Before I enter upon these facts, I owe a word of explanation as to the course which has just been taken in reference to Mr. Dyson. There would have been great inconvenience in trying these prisoners together. As my learned friend Mr. Lockwood, however, has applied they should be tried separately, that removes any inconvenience, which possibly might result in injustice; but that is a question which need not at this moment be decided. There would be a still greater inconvenience, and even greater peril of injustice, if they had been tried together, because if they were tried together the statements which have been made by Mr. Dyson would have been admissible in evidence on the part of the prosecution as evidence against him, but which statements, except in so far as they were proved to have been made in the hearing and presence of the prisoner, would not have been any evidence whatever against her. You cannot fail to see that, although it would not be evidence against her, her case

Adeleide Bartlett.

might be prejudiced by statements so proved to have been made by the other prisoner, and it would have been obviously unjust to her that she should have been in any way affected by statements made by him, some of which were not made on oath, and as to none of which could her learned counsel have an opportunity before you of cross-examining the man who made them. But beyond this consideration, gentlemen, as I am sure you will believe, we, representing the interests of the Crown and the interests of the public, having carefully examined for ourselves whether there was a case which it would be proper to lay before you, and upon which it would have been proper for you to have been asked to give a decision, felt certain upon the best consideration that we could give to the case—in view not only of the evidence given at the previous inquiry, but as the result of later and of more extended inquiry and examination—we came to the conclusion that, after we had exhausted the evidence at our command, the learned judge who presides here would in all probability ask me to say, would certainly have felt called upon to ask the counsel for the prosecution whether in fact there was a case proper to be considered by the jury against Mr. Dyson, and we should have felt called upon to say, as we now say, that, although there are circumstances of some suspicion in the case against Mr. Dyson, yet that upon the whole there is no rule by which we should have been justified in asking it to be considered by you in the box upon the question of his guilt.

Now, gentlemen of the jury, the prisoner at the bar, Adelaide Bartlett, is charged with the murder of her husband, that murder having taken place—if it were a murder—either on the night of 31st December or early on the morning of 1st January in the present year. The deceased was a man named Thomas Edwin Bartlett. He was at the time of his death forty years of age. He had married the prisoner at the bar on 9th April, 1875, at the parish church of Croydon. She is now some thirty or thirty-one years of age, having been born in the month of December, 1855. Her maiden name—for she was a Frenchwoman—was Adelaide Blanche de la Tremoille. She was born at Orleans in the year and month I have stated. She appears to have met her husband for the first time in the beginning of 1875, while she was staying or lodging with one Charles Bartlett, a brother of the deceased. Thomas Edwin Bartlett started in business some thirteen years ago, in partnership with a Mr. Baxter, in the neighbourhood of Herne Hill and Dulwich. Their business, being that of grocers, apparently thrived and grew, until, at the time of his death, the deceased was owner, or part owner, and interested in altogether some six shops or places of business, which are about Brixton, Dulwich, and that neighbourhood. After the marriage, which occurred, as I have told you, in the month of April, 1875,

Sir Charles Russell, Q.C., M.P.

Opening Statement for the Crown.

this lady was sent to school—or went to school, perhaps I ought more correctly to say—at Stoke Newington, and during the vacation she cohabited with her husband. At a later period she went to a convent school in Belgium, where she remained for some eighteen months, and in the intervals of the vacation she was in the habit of rejoining her husband. In 1877 she came to live with her husband, and at that time they took up their residence at one of the shops of the deceased—namely, a shop in Station Road, Herne Hill—and they continued to live there from the year 1877 till 1883. In the Christmas of 1881 the prisoner gave birth to a stillborn child, and on that occasion the pain of labour seems to have been exceptionally great; and she seems to have formed the resolution, or at all events to have expressed a resolution, that she would have no more children.

In 1882 the deceased and his wife, the prisoner at the bar, moved to a place in Lordship Lane, also one of the deceased's shops. In 1883 they removed to The Cottage at Merton Abbey, not far from Wimbledon, and there they remained until the month of September, 1885.

Early in 1885 the deceased and the prisoner at the bar first made the acquaintance of George Dyson, who not long ago stood in that dock. He is a man, I think, of some twenty-seven or thirty years of age. He is a Wesleyan, and I believe is a Wesleyan minister. He graduated at Trinity College, Dublin, and he is the son of a Wesleyan minister at Poole, who, I believe, is well known and respected. Finally, Mr. George Dyson was placed in charge of some Wesleyan chapel, and the congregation belonging to it, in the neighbourhood of Putney. He seems very early to have become acquainted with the deceased and with the prisoner at the bar. Their acquaintance, I think, began by the prisoner and her husband attending at his place of worship. He seems to have been in the habit of visiting and dining and being on close terms of social intimacy with the deceased and with the prisoner at the bar; and there is no doubt that, so far as the evidence enables one to judge, his acquaintance and his friendship seems to have been greatly valued, if I may judge by some letters which are put before me, by the deceased himself.

I have given, gentlemen, the narration in the order in which you may probably find it most convenient, namely, in the order of time. In the month of September, 1885, the deceased made his will—on the 3rd of September; and by that will, which was witnessed by two of his own clerks in one of his places of business, he left all he possessed to the prisoner at the bar, and by that will he made Mr. Dyson and a solicitor, Mr. Wood, the executors. Whether that was the first will that the deceased made may be doubted. There seems to be some suggestion, in the statement of a witness who will be called before you, that he had made a

G

Adelaide Bartlett.

previous will, unquestionably benefiting his wife, but supposed to contain, according to her statement of it, some restriction upon the benefits which she was to receive under it—in this sense, that if she married again those benefits should cease, or should be lessened. There is no doubt, as regards the will of September, 1885, both Mr. Dyson and the prisoner knew the contents of that will.

Now, gentlemen, the next date is October, 1885. About that date the deceased and his wife moved to Claverton Street—No. 85, I think—where they had lodgings on the first or drawing-room floor, consisting of the drawing-room, which faced the street, and of a bedroom opening from and behind the drawing-room; and they continued to live there from the month of October, 1885, until the date of his death, on the night of 31st December, or the morning of 1st January in this year.

Mr. Dyson's intimacy was continued with the deceased and his wife down to the time of the husband's death; and, as I have mentioned, the will by which his wife, the prisoner at the bar, was benefited—in fact, the sole person benefited—had been made. And it is right to state that so far as the evidence which we have to offer to you on the part of the Crown (and, of course, we shall put before you all the evidence we have, whether it makes for or against the prisoner at the bar) does not point to the existence of any quarrel between the husband and wife. There is no evidence that points to any existing ill-will between the husband and wife. They seem to have lived, so far as ordinary observers could see and judge, upon fairly good terms.

In the month of December, 1885, while they were continuing to live at Claverton Street, the deceased, for I believe the first time in his life, became seriously ill. That illness began on 10th December. There was something which excited curiosity and some surprise on the part of the medical man who attended him in some of the symptoms which his condition disclosed. The state of his gums particularly suggested to the medical man who was called in, and who will be called before you, that his illness was certainly due to mercury having been in some fashion or other taken by him, or administered to him; but although he then suffered, and undoubtedly severely suffered, it was simply in the form of nervous depression, sleeplessness, and so forth; and Dr. Leach will tell you that from the illness he had on that day he had entirely recovered. He was also apparently troubled with his teeth, which seem to have been in a very bad state, and which required the assistance of a dentist on several occasions.

On 19th December—the ordinary medical attendant, being the gentleman whose name I have mentioned, Dr. Leach — a Dr. Dudley was also called in. I will not stop to explain why Dr. Dudley was called in. Dr. Leach attributes to the deceased a

Opening Statement for the Crown.

The Attorney-General

suggestion certainly of some very extraordinary kind, namely, that the deceased himself thought it was advisable that a second doctor should be called in, lest the friends of the deceased should suspect, if anything happened to him, that Mrs. Bartlett, his wife, was poisoning him—a very extraordinary suggestion certainly; but that is a suggestion, and is a statement that he had already made, which Dr. Leach attributes to the deceased man.

I ought, perhaps, in this connection, to say that, although there is no evidence of any feeling of ill-will existing between the husband and the wife, she did not seem to have got on very cordially with his relations, and notably with the father of her husband. She seems to have kept him at arm's length, and during the illness to which I am now adverting, in the month of December, she wrote a letter, which will be read, and which, while disclaiming any intention of being otherwise than desiring to be on friendly relations with her husband's father, she in effect stated to him—I do not stop to read it at this moment, it will be put in in the course of the case—she in effect stated to him that he must consider himself, in the matter of visits, simply like any other ordinary visitor; in other words, that he could not come and go as he liked, but as he was told he might come. The relation, therefore, between them seems to have been a little strained.

Now, gentlemen, by that 19th of December the symptoms that had excited the curiosity and surprise of Dr. Leach had passed away, and the deceased was upon a fair way of recovery. By 24th December he was practically convalescent, and it was arranged that he should upon an early day, for change of air, go to some seaside place, and I think Torquay was mentioned, and by that time—by the 24th or 26th of December—Dr. Leach will tell you that he was practically well, although he was still suffering from weakness, and so forth, from the illness from which he was recovering. On 28th December he went out for a drive, and came back, showing in the food which he was able to take, and the appetite which he displayed for it, every sign of returning to his ordinary health.

On 27th December one important thing took place : the prisoner at the bar applied to Mr. Dyson to procure for her a considerable quantity of chloroform; and he did procure it for her in the way and under the circumstances which I will detail to you. That she had the chloroform will not depend upon Dyson's statement only; for, indeed, it will be made clear that she had the chloroform apart wholly from Dyson's statement. She gave to him a reason that she had used it before with effect for her husband; that he was suffering from what she called an internal ailment, an affliction of long standing; that this internal affliction or ailment had upon previous occasions given him paroxysms. She expressed apparently some belief that he might die suddenly in one of those paroxysms.

Adelaide Bartlett.

The Attorney-General

She said that upon previous occasions she had obtained the chloroform, which she alleged she had used, through the instrumentality of one Annie Walker. She said that Annie Walker was not then within her knowledge as to her residence and so forth. Indeed, she suggested that she had gone to America, and she said that, on one of those occasions on which her husband had suffered from this internal ailment or affliction, a Dr. Nichols, of Fopstone Road, Earl's Court, had said to her that her husband, Mr. Bartlett, would die soon. Now, according to the evidence which will be laid before you, there was apparently no ground for suggesting that he was suffering from any internal ailment or affliction. I think she used on one occasion the word " growth." It is not true that she had, through the instrumentality of Annie Walker, on previous occasions obtained chloroform and applied it for external purposes; and it is not true that Dr. Nichols, of Fopstone Road, Earl's Court, had ever been called in in relation to this matter, or expressed any opinion as to the possible sudden death or dying soon which was attributed to him.

Gentlemen, I think you will—I will say you may—when you have heard the whole of this case, and especially when you hear some extraordinary statements made by the prisoner herself to Dr. Leach, come to the conclusion that she had somehow or other obtained considerable influence over Mr. Dyson. He meekly yielded to her request, and he proceeded to obtain for her the chloroform which she demanded. But it is proper to say at once that he did that by making application to three persons, to all of whom he would appear to have been known, and one of them had his shop or place of business within, I think, fifty paces of the Wesleyan chapel of which Mr. Dyson was the minister. He does certainly at once place—I am not sure whether it was that of the person who supplied the drug—make a statement. My friend Mr. Clarke reminds me that I ought, perhaps, not to dwell upon what took place then. It is enough to say that he got the chloroform at those places—first at the shop of a man called Humble, which was, I think, within a very short distance of the chapel. Another vendor was Mr. Penrose, at Wimbledon; and another a Mr. Mellin, also at Wimbledon. Portions, I think, of the chloroform so obtained were methylated, but it was all put into one bottle, and I think the entire quantity altogether—certainly a large, and I believe an unusual, quantity—was about, or exceeded 4 ounces. On 29th December the chloroform was given to the prisoner at the bar. On 30th December the deceased was so well that Dr. Leach, who was in attendance, declared that it was unnecessary for him to keep up his medical visits; and on 30th and 31st December the deceased appeared to have regained almost his usual health and usual spirits. And on 31st December, according to the statement which Dr. Leach attributes to Mrs. Bartlett, the prisoner at the

84

Opening Statement for the Crown.

bar was on particularly affectionate terms with her husband; in fact, she is stated to have declared that she wished they were unmarried in order that she might have the happiness of marrying him again.

On that 31st December the deceased takes his dinner with a healthy appetite. He takes his supper, and, indeed, makes arrangements for his breakfast the next morning, and directs what was to be prepared for his breakfast. I ought perhaps to have said that, living in lodgings, they had no regular servant; the persons in the house appear to have attended to them. My friend reminds me that on that 31st of December he had in fact been to see the dentist. On that night of 31st December, about half-past ten o'clock, Mrs. Bartlett told the servant that she need not come again; and, according to the landlady, Mrs. Doggett, who will be called before you, Mrs. Bartlett, in the course of conversation that day, appears to have made an inquiry as to whether she (Mrs. Doggett) had ever taken chloroform, or knew anything about the effects of chloroform. Mr. and Mrs. Doggett sat up to see the New Year in, and did not go to bed until after the midnight hour had passed. At four o'clock the next morning, 1st January, the house was aroused by Mrs. Bartlett, and it was discovered that her husband was dead in bed.

Gentlemen, I think I had better at this stage—although the account was not given until a considerably later period—tell you what the explanation was which this lady gave of the occurrence of the night of 31st December and the morning of 1st January. It appears that on this night—and that had been the course pursued during his recent illness—the deceased slept on the bed, not in the bedroom, but in the drawing-room, in a place near the window of that room, and that the prisoner at the bar rested on a couch which was in the same room. Her statement was, that when her husband went to bed she sat down at the foot of the bed; that her hand was resting upon his feet; that she dozed off in her chair; that she awoke with a sensation of cramp in her hand or her arm, and she was then horrified to find that her husband's feet were dead cold; that she tried to pour some brandy down his throat, and she found he was dead; that she then aroused the household, and I think the first person who came into the room was Mr. Doggett, the landlord. He was, as you may well suppose, shocked at the occurrence. He will tell you his observations that he made at the time of the condition of the room; and, notably, he will tell you that he observed no bottle on the mantelshelf. He noticed a smell, which suggested to his mind chloric ether; and he noticed that the fire in the room was well made up, as if it had been well attended to.

So far, gentlemen, as to the events of that morning. Dr. Leach was promptly sent for. He finds, so far as external examina-

Adelaide Bartlett.

tion could enable him to judge, nothing to account for death. He saw no bottle of chloroform, but he does see a small bottle with a very insignificant portion—a little more than two drops—of chlorodyne in it, which he says was either on the mantelpiece or somewhere else. Mr. Doggett, the landlord, is registrar of births and deaths, and he promptly and, as I have no doubt you will believe, most properly declined to register the death until there was a post-mortem examination. You will find that, so perplexed was Dr. Leach as to the cause of death, he asked the prisoner at the bar, and pressed her, as to whether it was possible that the deceased could have got hold of any poison, and she said that she could not suppose he could have got hold of any poison; that he had no poison, and could not have got it, or had it, without her knowledge.

On 2nd January the post-mortem examination took place, and at that examination the persons who took part in it (the medical men) were five—Drs. Green, Murray, Dudley, Cheyne, and Leach. I ought to say that one of the doctors—Dr. Green—who has been examined before the magistrate, and whose evidence was taken down in the presence of the prisoner with great minuteness and detail before the magistrate, and in the presence of her counsel, who had then the opportunity of cross-examining—I regret to say that Dr. Green is so seriously ill as to render it impossible that he should attend in person here at this Court. Of course, before his deposition can be read, before his examination-in-chief, and his cross-examination can be read, it will be necessary to satisfy my lord that the facts are as I have stated, namely, that Dr. Green is in such a condition as to render it impossible, from ill-health, that he should be able to attend at this Court. One other of the doctors, Dr. Cheyne, is now, as I understand, in Berlin; but you will have before you the fully taken and carefully taken cross-examination of Dr. Green, and the *vivâ voce* evidence given before you in this Court of Dr. Murray and Dr. Dudley, and also the evidence of Dr. Leach, whose part, I think, on this occasion was noting down the symptoms which were observed in the course of the post-mortem examination. The first thing that attracted their attention was the overpowering smell of chloroform in the stomach, described by some of them—I think by Dr. Green— as almost as strong as a freshly opened bottle of chloroform; showing that the chloroform had somehow or other got into the stomach of the deceased at a comparatively recent time. Their examination was next directed—indeed, it was all along directed—to see whether or not there was in the condition of the deceased, in the condition of his heart, or lungs, or liver, or any vital organ, anything in any way to account for, or to suggest the cause of, death; and they came to the conclusion that there was nothing in the most remote degree to account for the death in the condition of the heart, the lungs, the liver, in fact, anything in the physical

Opening Statement for the Crown.

The Attorney-General

condition of the man; and I think in this inquiry, probably, when you have heard the evidence, you will have little difficulty in coming to this conclusion, that the deceased's death was caused by the chloroform, the evidence of the existence of which was disclosed at the post-mortem examination, and that the serious and real question in this case will be, how came the chloroform there?

Several interviews occurred between Mr. Dyson and the prisoner and other persons, notably Mrs. Matthews and Dr. Leach, to which I do not desire at this stage to refer in any detail. They contained some very curious statements, but so curious that I prefer that in the main, and certainly in detail, with one exception, you should hear them from the witnesses as they are called before you. That one exception is the statement which the prisoner at the bar made as to the chloroform itself, as to the point of whether she had in any way, and how, used it for the purpose for which she alleged to Dr. Leach that she had obtained it. That I cannot except, but must trouble you with now. The first statement she made to Dr. Leach, or the first conversation in reference to the chloroform, was on 6th January. He appears to have had on that day a long interview with her. He appears, indeed, to have gone the length of reading over to her the post-mortem notes which he had taken, and she asked—if Dr. Leach is to be relied upon—on that occasion, " Can he have died from chloroform?" and Dr. Leach, on that occasion, appears to have suggested chlorodyne as the cause of death, and not chloroform. She had a conversation on the same day, or about the same time, with Mrs. and with Mr. Matthews.

Gentlemen, on 7th January, the coroner's jury met, and adjourned from 7th January to 4th February; for you will observe that, although there was this post-mortem examination on the 2nd, to which I had adverted, there had not been at this time, nor up to this time, any examination in the nature of an analytical one of the stomach, or the contents of the stomach. Between 7th January, when the coroner's jury first met, and 26th January, the prisoner at the bar had several interviews with several people; and on 11th January the contents of the stomach of the deceased were taken to the analyst, Dr. Stevenson, who again discovers, and will tell you then discovers, or notices, a smell of chloroform, and ascertained the fact of the marked presence of chloroform in the stomach. At that date also was brought to him a bottle, and I ought to notice the fact without dwelling upon it with significance, if it has any significance, at this moment. I also introduce the fact that, in the examination in Claverton Street, some French letters were discovered in the clothes at Claverton Street—in the clothes, you will understand, of the deceased, the husband. Meanwhile, gentlemen, on 26th January, the prisoner again sees Dr. Leach, and it is on that occasion that she makes the statement that I told you I must

Adelaide Bartlett.

trouble you with in some little detail—a statement of a very extraordinary kind, following upon the announcement of the fact that chloroform had been discovered in the stomach, and that that was pointed to as a probable—nay, the almost certain—cause of death. The police had meanwhile been making inquiries, and had probably begun to get upon the track of those who supplied the chloroform in question. On 26th January, the prisoner at the bar was told by Dr. Leach that chloroform was assigned as the cause of death; that it was lucky for her it was not prussic acid, or secret poison, as she might be suspected if it had been poison of that nature. She answered that she wished it were anything else than chloroform; and then, after some further conversation, she made a statement, the substance of which I am about to tell you, but which resulted practically as to one point in an admission that she had had in her possession—I will tell you her motive and object, as she then explained them—that she had in her possession chloroform upon the occasion in question; and, indeed, a similar statement, so far as that point is concerned, she made with perhaps more circumstantiality to Mrs. Matthews, to the effect that she had, after this tragedy, on the morning of 6th January, emptied the contents and thrown the bottle itself away. But her story was this. She said that her relations with her husband had not been pleasant relations; that there had been no sexual intercourse between them for a considerable period of time; that he had himself, in conversation, spoken to her as if contemplating his own death, and in that case making her over to Dyson; that when after his illness, to which I have adverted, he was returning to health, with returning health he seemed to have manifested some desire to renew sexual intercourse with her; that she did not desire this; that she desired to prevent it; and that she considered that she had been made over in the future to Dyson, and she did not desire to allow her husband to have any intercourse with her; but that, when he was manifesting, with returning health, a desire to renew that intercourse, she desired to have the chloroform for the purpose of waving it before his face, lulling him into a kind of stupor, and so prevent him giving effect to his sexual passion. That is the story she tells.

Gentlemen, she did not appear before the coroner at the coroner's inquiry. She was there, but she did not tender herself to give evidence or any explanation; but I would not, of course, have you at all to understand from that fact that any inference is, or ought to be, drawn against her. I only wish that you should understand exactly how the matter was.

Mr. Dyson did come before the coroner's jury, and did make a lengthened statement. If he were on his trial with the prisoner at the bar that statement, of course, could be read before you, and would be evidence in the case against him. As it is, that

Opening Statement for the Crown.

The Attorney-General

statement, so far as it has any bearing on the serious question you will hereafter have to determine, will be made by him in the witness-box on his oath, face to face with the prisoner, before you and my lord, and under conditions that will insure, by the cross-examination of my learned friend, every test which my friend's experience and ingenuity can suggest as to its truth. It is not my duty to say anything here, or in this connection, in relief of Mr. Dyson so far as concerns the question of indiscretion and of culpability. When you have heard the witness you will be able to judge whether indiscretion and culpability of that meaning and kind can be or not properly attributed to him.

Now, gentlemen, in the result the coroner's jury found a verdict of wilful murder. Since that, it has, of course, been the duty of those who represent the Crown, desiring to see nothing done but justice, to inquire into the facts and circumstances of the case, with the result that they have felt bound to take the course that they have announced as necessary to take at the beginning of this trial.

I now come to the question which you probably will find is the real question in this case. For the reasons which I have already given, you will probably have no difficulty in coming to the conclusion that the deceased died from the effects of chloroform, which chloroform found its way somehow or other to his stomach. How did it get there? So far as I know, there are only three ways in which it could have got there. The first of those ways is that the deceased himself should have intentionally taken it with the view of destroying his life. I submit, when you have heard the facts, that you will find nothing in the circumstances of the case to support, or even to lend an air of plausibility to, that suggestion. He was in returning health, in improved spirits, and, as I have told you, he had gone to his bed on that night having made arrangements as to what he should desire for breakfast next morning.

As to the second possible suggestion—that he took it accidentally—that is to say, that he had no intention of taking the thing to injure himself, but that he took it accidentally, you will be told by those—your own common experience may perhaps enable you to judge that—but you will be told by those who know the qualities of this particular thing—the chloroform—that it is in the highest degree improbable that a man, if he accidentally poured out into a glass or tumbler this liquid, would not at once perceive the mistake he had made even before it was raised to his lips, but that the moment it touched, he must become—he could not fail to become (provided always that it reaches his lips when he was in the act of consciousness)—he could not have failed to notice that it was something which he ought not to take. But, further, gentlemen, it will be shown to you by evidence (as to the reliability

Adelaide Bartlett.

of it you must judge) that if it was taken with the intention of committing suicide or if taken accidentally, then the effect of the thing itself taken by the throat into the stomach, the pain it causes is so acute that no amount of self-control which any one could suppose to exist could restrain the paroxysms that would follow of pain, followed by contortion and by outcry and by exclamation, which could not have failed to attract attention. That the great probability is that if taken accidentally—and probably, not to put it higher than that—if taken intentionally, the person who administered it to himself could not restrain the strong expression by voice and by moan of the pain and agony which the administration of it had caused.

There remains in the opinions of the medical men only one other mode. You will say, of course, that if it was administered by any third person the physical effect would be the same; that there would be the same outcry, the same acute pain, and so forth; and you would be quite right, provided that the administration into the stomach was not preceded by some external application of chloroform which might lull into a stupor or a semi-stupor; and in that condition it might be possible—and in that condition of things alone, as the medical men think, probable—that it could be conveyed to the stomach without it being followed by circumstances and occurrences which must have attracted attention.

I need not warn you—I think I need not warn you—of two things. First, to dismiss from your minds anything that you have heard of this case before you came into Court, and I ask you to apply your minds—as I am sure you are anxious to do—to the candid consideration, the thorough consideration, of the evidence to be presented to you here. The next thing that I would ask you to do is to bear in mind that it is for the Crown to make out the case of guilt; that suspicion will not do; that probability of itself will not do; that you ought not to find the prisoner guilty unless the result of the evidence against her, dispassionately weighed, dispassionately considered, brings home to your minds the conviction of guilt beyond any reasonable doubt which would influence your minds in any of the ordinary affairs of life.

Gentlemen, I think I have now discharged my task so far as it is to be discharged at this stage of the inquiry, and I would ask you now to bring to the consideration of the evidence which my learned friends will assist me in placing before you, a fair and careful attention.

Mr. POLAND—My lord, it would be a great convenience if you would allow me to prove the illness of Dr. Green, as the medical man who is to prove it is anxious to get away.

Mr. JUSTICE WILLS—Certainly.

Evidence for Prosecution.

Evidence for the Prosecution.

WILLIAM HENRY BROADBENT, examined by Mr. POLAND—I am a physician, and reside at 34 Seymour Street, Portman Square. I know Thomas Henry Green, physician, of Charing Cross Hospital. He resides at 74 Wimpole Street. On the 6th of this month he was taken seriously ill, and I saw him on the 7th. I have been attending him ever since. I saw him yesterday. He was confined to his bed, and it would be quite impossible for him to attend. He is quite unfit to travel or come into Court, and I think he will be unfit for at least a month. I know his signature. (Shown deposition of Thomas Henry Green)—The signature to that deposition is, I believe, Dr. Green's signature.

EDWIN BARTLETT, examined by Mr. POLAND—Thomas Edwin Bartlett, the deceased, was my son. I am a carpenter and builder, living at 44 Chancellor Road, Herne Hill. My son was forty years of age on 8th October last. He was a grocer and provision dealer, and carried on business in partnership with Mr. Baxter. At the time of his death he and his partner had six shops altogether. There were two in Herne Hill, one " The Exchange," at Lordship Lane, Dulwich; then there was the Group Mart in Lordship Lane, and at 33 Milkwood Road, Loughborough Junction, and the corner of Chaucer Road, the West Hill Park Supply Stores. As far as I could judge, he was in a prosperous way of business. The prisoner was his wife. In his marriage certificate he is described as Thomas Edwin Bartlett, and the prisoner as Adelaide de la Tremoille. My son was a bachelor when he married the prisoner. The prisoner is described in the certificate as a spinster, aged nineteen.

I first knew the prisoner just before she was married; she came to my house with my son. I knew she had been living at Richmond. Afterwards I knew she had been living at one of my son's, Charles, at Kingston, for a short time. My son, Thomas Edwin, the deceased, first became acquainted with her there. When she was first introduced to me she was called Blanche. I was not present at the wedding, but I know that after the wedding she went to a school, Miss Dodd's, at Stoke Newington, and resided there. During the holidays she lived in furnished apartments with my son, her husband. Afterwards I believe she went abroad to a convent school in Belgium. My son used to go from time to time to see her. About the middle of 1877 she returned, and resided with her husband at 2 Station Road, Herne Hill. At that time that was one of my son's shops. On the death of my wife I went to live with them there. I lived with them for about five or six years. He offered me a home for life on the death of my wife. During all that time they lived together as man and wife, occupying the same room and the same bed.

91

Adelaide Bartlett.

Edwin Bartlett

I remember the birth of a child, but I really do not remember the date; I think it was about two years after they were married— about two years after she came to reside, I should say. I really cannot fix the date any nearer than that. It was a stillborn child, I understood. The witness Annie Walker attended to her at that time. There was also a Mrs. Purse; she came down once.

There was no doctor, I think. Dr. Woodward was called in at last. My son told me that he resided in Dulwich Road. I believe the prisoner suffered a great deal at the birth. After she got over it she continued to live in the ordinary way with my son. After that they changed their residence and went to live at The Exchange, Lordship Lane. They were there about twelve months, and I believe they lived in the same way there. I visited them once or twice. There was no room for me in that house, so I went elsewhere. From Lordship Lane they went to The Cottage, Merton Abbey, about two miles from Wimbledon. They resided there about a year and nine months, I think. I visited them frequently. They were living together then in the ordinary way as man and wife. From there they went on 1st September last for a month to Dover, my son taking a season ticket. They returned from Dover on the last day of September, and I believe they then went for a few days to a hotel in the Strand. My son told me they were staying at a hotel. Afterwards, in October, they went to live at 85 Claverton Street, in St. George's district. I believe they also lived there as man and wife in the usual way. Up to that period they had lived together as man and wife on affectionate terms, as far as I know; I know nothing to the contrary.

Up to that time my son had always enjoyed very strong health. He was regularly attending to his business, and was a very hard-working man. About thirteen years ago my son had a doctor attending him. He had had a slight bilious attack, and Dr. Barraclough was called in. My son was not laid up at that time; I believe he had insured his life in 1880 or 1881. I know what the policy was worth, but I do not know all the particulars. Besides that bilious attack, on one other occasion my son overworked himself, and he went a voyage on the sea. It was in connection with his business and a little carpenter work that he was doing (he laid a floor in the house) that he overworked himself. On that occasion when he went to sea he was away for a week or a fortnight.

I used to visit at 85 Claverton Street. Up to the time of their going to Claverton Street I did not know anything of the Rev. Mr. Dyson. I had never seen him. It was in the beginning of December last that I first heard of my son's illness. About the first day after he was taken ill he complained to me of mercurial poison in his mouth, and then after that I went to see him. The prisoner was present when he spoke about mercurial poisoning; he said the doctor had told him he was suffering from mercurial

Evidence for Prosecution.

Edwin Bartlett

poisoning. He was in the front drawing-room when he told me that. The bedroom was at the back. He was lying on a sort of chair bed at the time, and was partially undressed. He appeared to me as if he was labouring under a narcotic.

By Mr. JUSTICE WILLS—He appeared rather dazed; he did not appear so fresh and sharp as he used to be.

Examination continued—I called to see him perhaps six or seven times during his illness, and I saw him on three occasions. I really cannot give the date of my second visit; I think it was on the Saturday; I was then refused to see him. The second occasion on which I did see him was a Saturday, and the first occasion, I think, was on the Wednesday of his first illness. The third time I saw my son was when I was invited; the letter is in Court. I saw the prisoner on two occasions, but I cannot remember the dates. The first time I saw her would be about eight or nine days after my first visit. I saw her in the house, in the downstairs room—the back room or smoking-room. She then told me that my son was too ill to see me. We then spoke about mercurial poisoning, and there was something said about verdigris poisoning. I do not remember what that was exactly, only I understood her to say that the doctor had said there were symptoms of verdigris poisoning. She did not tell me who the doctor was that was attending him, only that it was a doctor up the street. I asked particularly who the doctor was, but I was not told. During this illness the prisoner wrote to me from time to time informing me how my son was. (Shown letters)—These are the letters I received; they are signed by the prisoner. The first letter is addressed from 85 Claverton Street and reads as follows:—" Dear Father,—The doctor was very angry that I had permitted Edwin to see visitors last night, as it caused his head to be so bad; and he says no one is to be admitted unless he gives permission. Edwin is slightly better this morning. I will write to you every day and let you see and know how Edwin is. I can see myself how necessary it is that he should be kept calm. With love, Yours, Adelaide." Addressed to " Mr. Bartlett, 1 Saint David's Mews, Oxford Street." Postmark, " 12th December, 1885."

The second letter is without date and reads—" Dear Mr. Bartlett,—Edwin is up; he seems to have stood his tooth-drawing very well. Please do not trouble to come all this distance; it is not right to have visitors in a sickroom, and I don't feel it right to leave Edwin so long alone while I was downstairs talking to you. When he wishes to see you I will write and let you know.— Yours, Adelaide."

The third one reads—" Dear Father,—I fancy Edwin is slightly better this morning; the dysentery has left him, and he is certainly stronger. The doctor said last night there was a slight improvement in him.—Yours sincerely, Adelaide."

The fourth one, which is also in the prisoner's handwriting,

93

Adelaide Bartlett.

reads—" Dear Mr. Bartlett,—Edwin is slightly better, and is sleeping tolerably well.—Yours, Adelaide."

The fifth one is in her handwriting also, also the envelope, and reads—" Dear Father,—Edwin seems slightly better, and has passed a restful night. I am expecting another doctor, so you must excuse this note.—Yours sincerely, Adelaide." That is dated " 21st December, 1885."

The sixth one reads—" Dear Mr. Bartlett,—Edwin is not so well, he has passed a bad night.—Yours, Adelaide Bartlett. A merry Christmas." This was undated.

Mr. CLARKE—I think it would be very desirable if your lordship would note the dates of the week at this time, the 21st is the last postmark given, and that is Monday.

Mr. JUSTICE WILLS—And the 1st would be Saturday?

Mr. CLARKE—Yes.

Examination continued—The seventh letter is also in the prisoner's handwriting, and it reads—" 85 Claverton Street, Sunday night. Dear Mr. Bartlett,—Edwin will be very pleased to see you on Monday evening from six to eight. He is still very weak, and cannot bear visitors for long at a time. — Yours, Adelaide."

The eighth is also in her handwriting — " Sunday night. Dear Mr. Bartlett,—I hear that you are a little disturbed because Edwin has been too ill to see you. I wish, if possible, to be friends with you, but you must place yourself on the same footing as other persons—that is to say, you are welcome here when I invite you, and at no other time. You seem to forget that I have not been in bed for thirteen days, and consequently am too tired to speak to visitors. I am sorry to speak so plainly, but I wish you to understand that I have neither forgotten nor forgiven the past. Edwin will be pleased to see you on Monday evening any time after six." The postmark looks like the 28th. After getting that letter I went on the Monday, the 28th. That was the Monday before my son's death. I went about half-past six in the evening. I saw the prisoner there. My son was in the front drawing-room lying on a couch when I first saw him—on the same little iron bed. He was in a dressing gown. I was with him for two hours and a half. The prisoner said that he was better, and he also said he was better, and he hoped soon to be in business again and enjoy the evenings we had had before. I had been in the habit of seeing him at his place of business every evening, with few exceptions. I used to come down to the station, and I always called in before I went home. My son seemed to be better, a good deal stronger, on that occasion. He got up and walked about the room. I think he said something about having worms on that occasion. I believe the prisoner also said so too. He said they were crawling all up him, and Mrs. Bartlett said, " We call them

94

Evidence for Prosecution.

Edwin Bartlett

snakes." I believe that was the time that conversation took place. I said it was strange, and my son said, " A good job she has doctored the dogs to clear away the worms, because she knew I had worms." There was something said about taking croton oil at one time, but whether that was the time the conversation took place or not I cannot say. At one visit I remember their saying they had called in a physician, because I had wanted to send them a physician from London. I had spoken to the prisoner about it some time previous; I said that we had better have a physician, as Edwin did not seem to get any better. I said I would send one down from London, and she said, " No, we cannot afford it." I said, " Nonsense, Adelaide; not afford it, indeed ! " " Well," she said, " we cannot." I said, " You had better." " No," she said, " we cannot afford it, and he is going on very well." I did not say anything more to her on that subject then. On the Monday she told me she had had a physician, but she did not say who he was. She said my son had had some teeth drawn ; he also spoke of that himself, and said he had had some stumps out. That is all I recollect that he said. It would be somewhere about half-past eight when I left the house that Monday night— or it might be nearer nine. He seemed much better in his spirits that night. He spoke then about going down to Poole or Bournemouth, or somewhere down in Dorsetshire. I think he spoke about going on the following Tuesday. I then went away, and that was the last time I saw him alive. I said good-night to him and the prisoner, as I always had done. I parted with the prisoner on the best of terms. I kissed her and shook hands with her and wished her good-night.

There is one allusion in this letter, I do not know what it means exactly. " I am sorry to speak so plainly, but I have not forgotten or forgiven the past " ?—Is it necessary for me to say that there had been an unpleasantness? Some six years ago my youngest son had to go to America.

That is sufficient, I think it related to an old matter. I think you next received a telegram informing you of your son's death ?— Yes. (Shown telegram)—I knew he was dying before I received that. The telegram reads—" To Mr. Bartlett,—Edwin is dead, come at once.—Bartlett." The postmark is " 1st January, 1886. Handed in at 9.36 in the morning." I took that telegram out of the letter-box after Mr. Baxter had called on me to say that he was dead. I went down to 85 Claverton Street. I think it was something like half-past twelve when I got there, but I cannot remember exactly, for I was dreadfully cut up at the time. I saw the prisoner in the drawing-room. My son was lying dead there. I hardly remember what she said when I went in. She said Edwin was dead. Mr. Baxter was in the room, and he and

Adelaide Bartlett.

Edwin Bartlett

I went up together. I do not think I saw anything of Mrs. Matthews at that time.

Now, what passed between you and the prisoner about your son's death when you first saw her?—I saw him lying on the couch, and I went and kissed him and smelt his mouth. I thought he might have been poisoned with prussic acid, and I smelt to find it, but I did not detect any smell of the kind. I then turned to the mantelpiece. I believe Dr. Leach was there as well. I said, "We must have a post-mortem examination; this cannot pass." I did not smell anything when I kissed him. I did not kiss his mouth; I kissed his forehead. I believe I was admitted into the room at once when I went. I do not think I saw anybody else but Dr. Leach. He was in the room; I fancy he came in after me. Dr. Leach first mentioned Dr. Green and another doctor, and Dr. Dudley and himself for the post-mortem, and I said there must be one. Dr. Leach said that he could not give a certificate without a post-mortem. I suggested another doctor, but I did not mention any particular name. I said, "I want another," and Dr. Leach said, "I will get you one." I said, "No, I will get you one, not one that was in the case or the neighbourhood." I afterwards went down with Dr. Leach and selected Dr. Cheyne in Mandeville Place. He was suggested to attend the post-mortem on my behalf. I went up again in the evening, and my son was put in the coffin. I said to the prisoner, "You won't have him put in the coffin." She said, "Dr. Leach has to see to that; it has nothing to do with me or you." When I saw him in the coffin I said the undertaker had no business to put him in the coffin; the post-mortem would have to be held first. Nothing further passed about my son's death, except that she said what a generous man he was.

What did she say more about it? How came she to say that?—She said what a kind-hearted man he was. She was speaking about how he died, and said, "He died with my arm round his foot; he always liked to have my hand on his foot," and she showed me how she sat at the foot of the bed when he died.

Just describe how it was?—She said she was sitting with her arm round his foot, and she supposed she had been asleep, for she awoke with cramp in her arm, and she then went and called Mr. Doggett. That was all; she said very little about it. She described how she was sitting. (Shown model produced)—The little iron bedstead was near the window, with the side wall of the house at the head of the bed.

The post-mortem was held the following day, the 2nd. I went there a little after two, and I waited outside on the pavement till I saw Dr. Green coming out of the house. I then went into the house, and I saw the prisoner. There was very little said by

Evidence for Prosecution.

her, or in her presence, about the post-mortem. I saw her in the back smoking-room on the ground floor. She was speaking there to Mrs. Matthews, I believe. There was very little conversation with me. I did not hear anything; I do not recollect any conversation. I had not heard the result of the post-mortem by then. We went upstairs and heard the result. The prisoner was with me. We went into the front room. Dr. Dudley and Dr. Leach were present. I think Mr. Baxter also went up with me. I think it was said by one of the doctors that they found no cause of death in him. Dr. Dudley put his hand on my shoulder and said, " He has no business lying there, a strong man like that." I do not know that I gave that in my evidence before. The prisoner was in the room at that time. She did not have her hat on. Her dressing bag was lying on the table. I left the house after the prisoner. I wished her good-bye, when she was told to go out of the house, and kissed her. Some of the doctors had said she could not remain there. She did not take her bag away with her; it was left on the table. She took her cloak only. Mr. Wood, the solicitor, was in the room at the time. I had known Mr. Wood before, and my son had known him also for years before. It was suggested that I should take charge of the room, and I said, " No; Mr. Wood, he is a solicitor, he will be the best man to take charge of it." I left in that way. I think Dr. Leach was left in the room.

(At this stage William Montgomery Waterton, a clerk in the Probate Registry of Somerset House, produced what purported to be a will made by the deceased, Thomas Edwin Bartlett. The witness was then shown the document.)—I cannot swear whether that is my son's writing. The signature is something like this.

To the best of your belief, is that his signature; have you any real doubt?—It is so very different to what I have seen him write. I cannot swear it is his signature. The signature is very strange for his signature.

To the best of your belief, is that his signature?—It is not, to the best of my belief. I have seen that document before at Somerset House. The signatures of the two persons who witnessed it are H. Eustace and A. Brook. I do not know their handwriting. I know that these two persons were in my son's employment at Herne Hill. They were the first and second hands there. The document is written on paper and is stamped.

Mr. POLAND—It is on printed paper, half of a letter, and it has on it the address " The Cottage, Phipps Bridge, Merton Abbey, S.W."

Mr. JUSTICE WILLS—I suppose there will be no difficulty in proving this?

Mr. POLAND—Oh, no, my lord; I shall call the witnesses.

Examination continued—I have got some of my son's ordinary

Adelaide Bartlett.

handwriting with his ordinary signature. (Shown letter)—That is his ordinary signature, and the body of the letter is in his handwriting.

(Shown will)—What is your belief about the body of that will? —It does not look like his writing to me. I cannot swear it.

Mr. POLAND—Before reading the will I should like to call the two witnesses.

HERBERT EUSTACE, examined by Mr. POLAND—I was in the employment of the firm of Baxter & Bartlett, of Herne Hill. I know Arthur Brook, who was also employed in the same business. I remember one afternoon Mr. Bartlett, the deceased, calling me into his office at Herne Hill. I cannot give the exact date, but it was about the beginning of September. It was in the afternoon. Brook and I were called in together. We signed a document. (Shown will)—That is the document we signed. When we signed it I did not know what it was. I saw Mr. Bartlett sign it. He said, " I want you to witness my signature." I signed first. Mr. Bartlett signed it in the corner of the paper. We were all three together at the time. I did not know what it was. It was folded up at the time. (Witness indicated how the document was folded). Mr. Bartlett was staying at Dover at the time, and used to come up day by day. Mr. Brook signed it after me in my presence.

ARTHUR BROOK, examined by Mr. POLAND—I was in the service of Baxter & Bartlett, Herne Hill. (Shown will)—That is my signature. I remember signing that document. I saw Mr. Bartlett signing it first. I witnessed his signature. I did not know what it was when I signed it. The writing was turned away from me so that I could not see it.

(At this stage the will was read by the Clerk of Court as follows :—" Herne Hill, S.E., September 3, 1885. I, Edwin Bartlett, will and bequeath all my property and everything I am possessed of to my wife Adelaide, for her sole use, and appoint George Dyson, B.A., Wesleyan Minister, and Edward Wood, Esq., of 66 Gresham Street, to be my executors. (Signed) Edwin Bartlett. Witnesses to my signature, Herbert Eustace and Arthur Brook.")

Mr. JUSTICE WILLS—If I look at the document I cannot say that the handwriting of the body of it is even like that of the signature. It is unlike it, because it seems to have been written inclined backwards instead of forwards.

The FOREMAN—Will you ask, my lord, whether Mr. Bartlett wrote in that way?

Mr. JUSTICE WILLS (to the Witness)—Did you ever see him write in that sort of upright writing?—I have seen him often

Evidence for Prosecution.

write in several different hands. You could never depend on his writing to be the same a second time.

(The Court adjourned for a short time.)

Mr. BARTLETT, recalled, cross-examined by Mr. E. CLARKE— Mr. Bartlett, I believe you were not present at your son's marriage with the defendant?—I was not.

Did you disapprove of that marriage?—No, I did not; I was not asked.

Not asked to the marriage, or not asked whether you approved?—I was not asked whether I thought she was suitable or not.

As a matter of fact, did you disapprove of the marriage?— Well, no, not particularly disapproved of it. I certainly did not much approve of it, but I did not disapprove of it. I said nothing to my son about it.

Were you asked to the marriage?—I was not, because they knew I was busy.

At the time of the marriage and afterwards, where did your son reside?—At Herne Hill, after the prisoner came back from Belgium.

Will you observe that is not the question I ask you? At the time of the marriage, I ask you, where did your son reside?— At Herne Hill.

At the time of the marriage?—Yes.

After the marriage, did she go to a school in London?—She did.

For how long?—Something nearly a twelvemonth, I believe.

And did you say that during the holidays she would come to live with your son?—She did, ultimately.

When you say ultimately, will you tell me at what interval after the marriage itself you are able to say that she first came to live with your son?—Something between two and three years.

We have got the date of the marriage as being in 1875. What year was it you went to live with your son yourself?—I really do not know. It was 1877 or 1878, I fancy. It was the year my wife died, but I am sure I cannot say to a year—it was 1877 or 1878.

I can help you to fix the date, I think, by a question to which you can answer yes or no. Did you go to live with him before or after you wrote an apology?—Some time before that.

Do you undertake to say that the defendant never lived with your son before the beginning of the year 1878?—I would not. I have not booked it down. I know the month I went was something like June, but which year I cannot say.

It may have been June, 1878?—Yes.

Will you undertake to say that the defendant ever lived with

99

Adelaide Bartlett.

your son before 1878?—What, at his house, sir? I will not. It was either in 1877 or 1878; I will not say which year.

I think you have said that your son promised to give you a home for life?—Yes, he did. That was his words on the death of my wife. He said, "Where I have a home you shall have one."

When did your wife die?—She died on the 28th of May—either 1877 or 1878. I am not prepared to say. One of those years. I think it was 1877.

Do you say you cannot remember?—I do not remember the date of the year.

You do not remember the year?—I do not. I have not refreshed my memory, or else I might have answered.

Now, do you tell the jury that you enjoyed the complete confidence of your son and his wife after that time?—We lived on most friendly terms together.

Do you say you enjoyed the complete confidence of your son and his wife?—I believe so.

In the year 1878, very soon after Mrs. Bartlett came to live with your son, did you have to write an apology for things you had said about her?—I did. I signed an apology, but I knew it to be false. I knew it to be the truth what I said at the time.

What, sir?—When I signed it, it was to make peace with my son. He begged me to sign it, because it would make peace with him and his wife if I did.

You say now you signed the apology, knowing it to be false, because it would make peace with your son?—Yes; and Mr. Wood knew it to be false when I signed it in his office.

Was 38 Berkeley Square the place where you were carrying on business?—No, I do not work there. Why he should put 38 I do not know.

You were working at 38 Berkeley Square in December, 1878? —Yes.

Let me read this to you—you remember it well—" 38 Berkeley Square, W., December 31, 1878. Having made statements reflecting on the character of Mrs. Adelaide Bartlett, the wife of my son, Mr. Edwin Bartlett, junior, which statements I have discovered to be unfounded and untrue, I hereby withdraw all such statements, and express my regret for having made them. I also apologise to the said Mrs. Adelaide Bartlett and Mr. Edwin Bartlett, junior, and acknowledge that all such statements are altogether unfounded and untrue. I authorise Mr. Edwin Bartlett, junior, to make what use he pleases of this apology.—(Signed) EDWIN BARTLETT, Senr." Was that the apology you signed?—That was the apology I signed, knowing it to be false. I signed it to make peace with my son. That was all.

Do you know your son did make use of that apology, and had it printed?—Yes, I do, at her suggestion.

I should think so!—Yes; and Mr. Wood asked me to, because,

Evidence for Prosecution.

Edwin Bartlett

my son being in America, he asked me whether I thought she had had letters from my son.

Do you mean to say that the suggestion you had made against Mrs. Bartlett was also a suggestion against your son?—Against my son Fred. If witnesses are wanted to prove it, they can be had even now.

How long were you living under the same roof with your son and his wife?—Somewhere about five or six years.

Do you say your son promised to give you a home for the rest of his life?—He did.

He did not keep that promise, did he?—Because they removed to Lordship Lane, and there was not room for me there.

Has he made you any allowance in lieu of giving you a home? —He was going to on the 1st of this year.

Has he ever made you any allowance in lieu of giving you a home?—No, he has not; but I have had from him what money I wanted. He was the kindest of sons.

You were asked a question about his having insured his life? —Yes.

And you answered that in a way which makes me ask—did you know during his lifetime that he had insured his life?—I knew he had insured it during his lifetime.

But did you know during his lifetime?—I did.

How soon after insuring his life did you know it?—Well, I have heard the prisoner and him talk about it in my presence. I should think I had known it all two years, if not more.

By hearing conversations between them?—Yes, and me, of course—altogether as we were.

And you joined in those conversations?—Yes, certainly.

When that will was put before you just now, you said to the best of your belief it was not your son's signature?—I said that I could not swear that it was.

You said, to the best of your belief, it was not his signature? —To the best of my belief, I had not seen him write in that hand before.

You had examined it before at Somerset House?—Yes.

With whom did you go to Somerset House to examine it?—Mr. Hooper, of Clifford's Inn.

What is he?—A lawyer, I believe.

You have entered a caveat against that will, I believe?—I have.

You told the Attorney-General your son was always very strong?—He was from a child.

Never had any illness?—Never that I know of.

Some years ago he had a considerable number of teeth sawn off at some time?—Yes, because he wanted a false set; and I was in the house at the time he had them done.

Where was it they were done?—I believe they were done at

Adelaide Bartlett.

Edwin Bartlett

Herne Hill, but I would not say; Mr. Bellin, a dentist, sawed them off for him.

You do not know if they were sound teeth, and he had them off preferring artificial ones?—Mr. Bellin said they were all stuck together, and he could not put the others in.

Had no doctor attended him up to that time?—To my knowledge I do not know they had; I am not sure.

That was about the year 1878 or 1879, I believe?—I believe it was.

Now about the year 1881 he broke down through overwork, did he not?—Just through laying a floor he exerted himself too much.

He exerted himself, you say, through laying a floor, but it involved a nervous breakdown necessitating his going a sea voyage? —Yes, the doctors recommended a sea voyage, and he came back wholly restored.

Having been away a week or a fortnight?—Yes, something like that.

He went to Scotland?—Yes, he went to Balmoral—went because he simply had a holiday, that was all.

Who was attending him then?—I do not know. He went to a physician in London; I do not know who it was.

You know he went to a physician?—He told me he went to a physician.

Can you tell me the date that Dr. Barraclough attended him? —Some twelve years ago he attended him, once for a bilious attack, somewhere between twelve and thirteen years ago. At least he did not attend him; he simply came and saw him once, and gave him a bottle of medicine.

Did you know of your son's having any exceptional ideas on this subject of married life?—No; he used to chaff and joke about such things—that was all. I never knew him to have any solid ideas about anything different to other people.

What used he to say?—He said one ought to have two wives, one to take out and one to do the work.

When used he to say that?—When I was living with him I heard him make the remark.

Was that the first time you heard him make the remark?— Yes, I think so, as I heard a man say last night he should like to have forty wives just in the same way.

Keep your mind on the subject we are inquiring into. It was when you were living with him you heard him make that remark?—Yes; other remarks as well.

Other remarks of the same kind?—I do not know.

With reference to the same subject?—I do not know; he may have done so.

In conversation?—He may have.

Did he?—Only once—only once I heard him make that remark

Evidence for Prosecution.

Edwin Bartlett

—whether that was at Herne Hill or somewhere else, I do not know. He used to joke about it.

He used to chaff and joke, you said?—Yes; he was a very merry man.

When you said "chaff and joke," did you mean he only said it once?—He only once said it—them words.

With regard to that subject, did he mention it more than once, and before his wife?—He did before his wife, but only that once I call to mind.

Then it caught your attention?—I just recollect.

Did you think it was a very curious observation?—Certainly not, only a passing observation.

And you attached no importance to it?—No, I did not write it down.

And you have remembered it ever since?—Certainly; as I remember a remark the prisoner made just in the same passing manner, I remember this.

Did you know of your son having any book on that subject? —Never to my knowledge.

Do you know the name of Dr. Nichols at all?—I never heard of it until I saw him in Court.

You never saw Dr. Nichols' book?—I never heard of him till I saw him in Court, and never heard his name.

I am asking about the book now; did you ever see a book of Dr. Nichols'?—I did not.

Now, was your son a believer in mesmerism?—Not to my knowledge.

Did he ever speak to you about mesmerism?—Never in his life.

You never heard from him of his being mesmerised?—Never.

Or his mesmerising anybody else?—No, never; he was nothing but business—always in business.

His aspect with you was always business—nothing but business?—Nothing but business; he was wrapped up in his business.

Now, you visited him at Putney in 1875, did you?—He never lived at Putney.

At Merton?—Yes. I constantly visited him at Merton.

Did you ever go to see him at Dover?—I went once or twice.

Twice I suggest to you?—Once or twice, and spent a very happy day there.

Did you on that occasion hear anything of Mr. Dyson?—I did not.

You did not happen to hear, then, your son had offered Mr. Dyson a season ticket to go to Dover?—I never heard Mr. Dyson's name mentioned.

Shall I take it you never heard anything of Mr. Dyson nor saw

103

Adelaide Bartlett.

Edwin Bartlett

him until after your son's death?—No, I would not say that. I think I heard of him during my son's illness.

From whom?—Whether from my son or from whom I cannot say. I believe I only heard his name once, and only once, till after the death.

How long was it before you heard from Mr. Baxter of your son's illness that you had seen him?—I saw him on Monday, I believe, and he complained of neuralgia in his mouth.

Of neuralgia in his mouth? Now, Monday would be 7th December. We know he went home ill from business on 8th December—then on Monday you went to see him?—Not on the Monday.

On the Wednesday, I mean?—Yes, on the Wednesday I went to see him.

The Wednesday was the 9th, Thursday the 10th; then between the 9th and the 28th of December, that was nineteen days, you had been six or seven times to Claverton Street?—Something about that.

Do you undertake to say these letters produced to-day are all the letters you received during that time?—I produced all the letters I received, I believe. I did not tear any up, and I had no reason to keep any back.

You have produced all in your possession?—Yes, all in my possession.

Do you say they are all you received during the illness?—They are all, I believe—they are all the letters—there might have been a postcard.

You say to-day, the first day you saw him he appeared suffering from some narcotic?—He did.

Did the impression that he was suffering from some narcotic continue during the whole of his illness?—He did not appear as bright as he had formerly been.

At any period of his illness?—At any period he did not appear bright.

On every occasion you saw him did he appear to be in what you call a cross state and not inclined for talking?—Not inclined for talking much. The last time I saw him he talked more than he did before, and he appeared stronger and better.

Now, on the first day that you went to see him, what time would it be in the day?—It was in the evening, I believe, to the best of my recollection.

Did he complain of his head on that day?—Not particularly; he appeared very averse to talking.

Did he complain of his head on that day?—Rather, I believe.

What did he say about it?—I really do not recollect all this time. I did not know it was coming to this, or I should have booked it down.

Evidence for Prosecution.

Edwin Bartlett

Tell me what you recollect he said about his head?—Some more about having mercurial poisoning; that is what he said.

What did he say about his head?—He said he had got a headache. He did not make any great comment about his head.

You say he complained of mercurial poisoning—you say the first occasion you went to see him he mentioned that to you?—He did.

You have said to-day, on another occasion Mrs. Bartlett also mentioned it to you?—She did, or it might be on that occasion she and Edwin both together mentioned it.

You were examined before the coroner first on 7th January, I think?—Yes.

When all these matters were very fresh in your recollection?—They were then.

You say you saw him on the 28th, which was the last time you saw him before his death?—I did.

And did you say, " He said he was getting very much better, and he thought that he would be at business again; he did not appear to be quite himself. I was there for two and a half hours; he then told me he had passed a quantity of worms. He told me he had been poisoned with mercury; the doctor had told him so. It was only in a slight degree, too slight to have been developed. I said to him, ' You could not get mercury in any way, could you? ' He said that if it was lead poisoning he might have got it in opening tea-chests "? Now, I ask you whether the first time poison by mercury or by lead was mentioned between you, was not it on that 28th of December, the last time you saw him?—No; it had been mentioned before, no doubt.

Did you say before the coroner that that was the time on which that conversation took place?—I may have done so.

You saw him on Wednesday and you saw him again on Saturday, I think?—I went to see him on Saturday. I will not say I saw him on Saturday.

You told my lord this morning you saw him on Saturday?—I went to see him on Saturday; I will not say I saw him. I really could not go into the date of every day when I saw him. I did not put it down.

I am aware of that. I want you to tell us when you saw him, giving us the conversations that happened at different interviews. The first occasion when you saw him was the Wednesday?—I think on Wednesday.

Did Mrs. Bartlett then tell you they had called in a doctor?—I believe she did, and she told me the doctor up the street.

Did you ask her his name?—I did not; she did not tell me, and I did not ask her his name; she seemed reluctant to say much about the doctor.

What did you say about it—tell me what you asked her?—

105

Adelaide Bartlett.

Edwin Bartlett

I did not ask her anything. I said, either then or some time after, I thought she had better have a physician from London.

We will come to that presently. Now, on the Saturday, the second time you saw him, did you have a conversation with him?—Yes; very little at that time, very little indeed.

Was he worse then?—He appeared worse.

Did you suggest to him having another doctor?—I do not know whether I suggested it to him or to the prisoner, but they were both in the room at the time.

So that he would hear the conversation about having the doctor?—Yes, he would hear, but he was very reluctant to speak apparently.

Was he lying on the bed?—Yes; half lying down on the iron bedstead.

With half-closed eyes?—Yes; he appeared to shut his eyes and open them again.

Dull and dazed?—Yes; he certainly appeared labouring under something.

Now, when you first saw him, was that about the mercury or verdigris, the only thing stated as being the matter with him?—The only thing that I recollect being mentioned by him.

What?—That was the only thing that I recollect that was stated by him at that time.

Are you positive about that?—No, I am not positive; in general conversation you do not remember every word.

I ask you about the conversation when you went to see your son when he was ill. What was mentioned about his being ill—about being the matter with him?—That the doctor said there was a slight mercurial poisoning.

When you came before the coroner did you say, " About a month ago I heard from Mr. Baxter—his partner—that my son was ill, and went to see him, and I found him queer, but I could not make out what was the matter with him. He said he was suffering from dysentery "? Did you say that?—I did.

Was it true?—He told me so, that he was suffering from dysentery.

Why did not you tell us so to-day?—I do not know; I was not asked particularly. I do not come here to keep anything back. I come here to speak the truth and nothing else.

Observe, Mr. Bartlett, I asked you just now whether, when you first saw him, anything was complained of except the poisoning with mercury or verdigris. You said distinctly, No. Now you tell me it is because you were not asked that you did not mention the dysentery. I ask you now who was it who told you anything about dysentery?—Either the prisoner or Edwin. They were talking about it in general conversation.

In his presence?—Yes.

Evidence for Prosecution.

Edwin Bartlett

Was that the matter that was mentioned as being wrong with him when you first saw him?—I do not know if dysentery was mentioned when I first saw him. I cannot say.

Try and remember. I have reminded you how long ago you gave your evidence before the coroner?—It is simply my memory, and I have had lots through my head since then.

Let me read this letter to you which you received from Mrs. Bartlett, and ask you to tell me if you can at what date that came—" Dear Father,—I fancy Edwin is slightly better this morning; the dysentery has left him, and he is certainly stronger. The doctor said last night there was a slight improvement." Do you remember how soon after you first saw him you had that letter?—Does it say " Dear Father "?

Yes?—Yes, that is shortly after I saw him on the Wednesday if it is " Dear Father," because it was " Dear Mr. Bartlett " afterwards.

What?—The address dropped off to " Dear Mr. Bartlett " afterwards.

You tell the jury the letters afterwards dropped off to " Dear Mr. Bartlett "?—Yes; there they are, you can see them.

Here is a letter on 21st December, according to the arrangement of the envelopes—" Dear Father,—Edwin seems slightly better, and has passed a restful night." Here is the third letter—" Dear Father,—The doctors are very angry that I permitted him ——."—Yes, that was shortly after I had seen him. The letters have very likely got into the wrong envelopes. I did not keep them in the right envelopes. I did not think anything of them, that I should have had to produce them here, or I would have kept them in their right envelopes.

This one about the dysentery having left him was shortly after you saw him the first time, was it?—It must have been soon after that.

Now, the next time you saw him was on a Sunday, was it not? I am not speaking of the last visit; you saw him again on the Sunday?—I went to see him on Sunday, and was refused admission to him. I question whether I saw him on Sunday. I know I went on Sunday. I came up from Croydon to see him, and was refused admission to him.

Will you undertake to say you did not see him?—I will not.

Now, then, here is a later letter, in which Mrs. Bartlett says, " I am expecting another doctor, so you must excuse this note "? —Yes.

Was that letter before or after you had suggested seeing a physician?—Well, I suppose after.

Do you remember?—I do not.

When you saw Mrs. Bartlett soon after that letter, did you ask if the doctor had been?—They told me he had been.

Adelaide Bartlett.

Edwin Bartlett

Did you ask his name?—I did not, and I am not sure whether Mrs. Bartlett told me or not.

It was Dr. Dudley, was it not?—Yes, Dr. Dudley. I would not undertake to say whether I was told.

You would not undertake to say whether she told you the name or not?—No, I will not.

You did not ask the name, you were refused?—No; I was refused generally. I thought I told you what doctors came and who they had.

It would have fixed itself on your mind if they had not?—Well, I do not know.

Now, I notice in these letters that Mrs. Bartlett says several times—she speaks of Edwin having passed a restful night; says he has passed a bad night; and in another letter speaks about his sleeping better, and so on. Did you know he suffered from sleeplessness?—He told me so.

Did he tell you he was taking anything for that?—Oh, yes; he told me they were injecting morphia into him for it.

Can you remember about when it was that he told you that?—I do not.

Now, you know that his teeth became very troublesome?—He told me they were troublesome.

And painful?—He told me so.

Here is another letter which contains another matter by which we shall be able to fix the date—" Edwin seems to have stood his teeth-drawing very well." Were you aware that he had had a number of teeth drawn?—Yes, they told me he had.

A number of stumps?—Yes, they told me so.

Did he tell you he had taken gas?—No, he did not.

Did he complain of pain?—Yes.

Was he subject to curious bursts—fits of low spirits?—Not before that time. He appeared in low spirits then, but previous to his illness he was not.

But he appeared in low spirits?—He appeared in low spirits.

Have you noticed him from time to time bursting out crying?—I have seen him then, and I was very much surprised.

How many times do you think you saw him?—I saw him crying once.

Only once; was that the last time you saw him, or earlier?—No, earlier; he was much better the last time I saw him—very much.

Did he tell you how often he had had morphia injected?—No, he did not; but from his conversation I thought he had had it before he told me.

What?—I thought he had had it injected once before the time he was speaking of then.

You thought he had had it injected once?—Once before the time he told me. He said " I have had morphia injected again."

Evidence for Prosecution.

Edwin Bartlett

Yes, you gathered that the day on which he spoke to you was the day on which he had had it injected for the second time?—I cannot say the second, but he said, " I have had morphia injected again."

Did he tell you that on two successive days he had had morphia injected, and that his condition was so bad that on the third day he had it injected twice in one day?—I do not recollect he told me so.

You do not remember hearing that?—I do not remember his telling me.

Did he tell you that he was taking sleeping draughts?—He did.

He told you, you say, he felt worms crawling up him, thus (showing him)—was that the action he used?—Yes, and the prisoner said, " We call them snakes." He said, " They are crawling all up here "; that was the feeling.

Did he tell you he had passed worms also?—No, he did not; the prisoner told me he had passed worms.

In his presence?—Yes, but he did not contradict her.

Did he ever tell you he thought he felt a worm crawling up his throat?—No, I do not remember.

Are you sure?—I would not be sure. When worms were talked about, he might have said so, but I do not recollect; he said he had worms in his throat.

He might have said, as far as you remember, that he had worms crawling up him, and that he had passed worms, and also that he felt a worm in his throat?—No, he never told me. The prisoner told me he had passed worms.

But in his presence?—Yes, in his presence.

Did you ever hear mention made by him or in his presence about his being likely to die?—Never—never mentioned—never the least idea of it.

You say that?—I do; he was not a dying man.

Did not he ever say to you he thought no man could be worse than he was and alive?—No, never.

Nothing of the kind?—Nothing of the kind.

Did any other members of the family, as far as you know, visit at that house?—Of my family?

Of your family?—Not that I know of.

By Mr. JUSTICE WILLS—Were there other members?—Yes.

Cross-examination continued—You say on the last occasion you saw him, the 28th, he mentioned about worms crawling up him?—Not that day; I do not think it was on the last day.

You told us to-day it was?—It might have been; I do not think it was the last day, because he was——

Take plenty of time; try and recollect. Do yourself justice. Try and recollect accurately. You have described to-day the inter-

Adelaide Bartlett.

Edwin Bartlett

view on 28th December, which was from half-past six or six in the evening till perhaps nearly nine?—Yes.

You have told us he said worms were crawling all up him—you have told us you think he mentioned croton oil, that he had had a physician, and spoke about his teeth?—Yes, but I did not mean it for that day, he might have some other day—that would pass in conversation during the time I had been with him.

To the best of your recollection and belief was it not on 28th December that was said?—It might have been; I think it was said before.

You have said it was. Do you believe it was?—Yes.

How came he to mention croton oil?—I do not know; I cannot tell you that; he certainly mentioned it, and I believe he said Dr. Leach was giving him croton oil for the worms.

Did he tell you Dr. Leach had been trying all he could to rouse his bowels to action, and that the croton oil was given for that purpose?—No, he did not.

Did he tell you that on the previous Saturday Dr. Leach had not only given him two purgative draughts, but he also gave him two globules of croton oil, and, that failing, he applied galvanism to the abdomen?—No, he never told us about galvanism; he only said about croton oil.

Did he tell you about the galvanism at all?—No, he did not.

He did not tell you, then, that previous Saturday, all those remedies had been tried and had all failed, and that Dr. Leach had given it up in despair?—He did not tell me so.

There is one thing you may be able to fix about the time at which it was said—you have told us to-day you wanted to send a physician, and said to Mrs. Bartlett, " You had better have a physician, as Edwin does not get better "?—I did.

Does that reason, you say you gave, help you to say how long after you saw him ill?—That was on my second visit, to the best of my belief.

Which would be on Saturday?—I do not know. I would not fix the Saturday; it was on my second visit; I was only allowed three times to see him. That was on the second visit.

Now, you had a telegram informing you of the death, but you did not take that out of your letter post-box until late in the day. What time was it you actually received the telegram yourself?—I actually received it myself about half-past twelve, after Mr. Baxter had called on me. I was at 38 Berkeley Square then, not at my shop.

You did not go to your place where the telegram was delivered till later?—Yes, that is how it came to be later.

Was it not about half-past four in the afternoon that you got to Claverton Street?—Before that; we took a hansom cab and

110

Evidence for Prosecution.

went down directly. It must have been between twelve and one, I think.

Did you not say before the coroner, "It was about four o'clock in the afternoon Mr. Baxter and I went home together; we went to 85 Claverton Street about 4 p.m."?—Yes; I must say I made a mistake about the two o'clock between Saturday and Friday in the dreadful sorrow of my son's death. It was on Saturday we went at four o'clock, not on Friday.

Friday was the 1st of January?—Yes.

You went with Mr. Baxter?—Yes.

You went in at once?—Yes.

You went up with him?—Yes, that is again a mistake I have made between those two days. I must ask the indulgence of the Court for that.

I only want to get the facts. You went in with Mr. Baxter and went up with him?—Yes.

Have you told us all that passed on that day?—All that I happen to recollect, I believe.

Did Mrs. Bartlett say anything of a kindly fashion to you on that day?—Yes, she told me on the Saturday when I was going upstairs after the post-mortem examination——

I am asking you about the Friday now?—I do not think she said anything on the Friday.

Mr. Baxter was not there on the Saturday, was he?—No, he was not.

Now, is this the case—" She placed her arm round my neck, and she said, ' My dear father, do not fret; it shall make no odds to you. I will see you never want. It shall be just the same as if Edwin were alive.' That was just at the bottom of the stairs; in fact, on the stairs. Mr. Baxter was following us up "?—There I made the mistake. It was Saturday that took place, not on Friday.

Then Mr. Baxter was not there?—No; there is where I am in error which was on the Saturday when they called us up to see the post-mortem.

I am referring you now to the evidence given by you on 19th February?—I know, and I corrected my mistake as soon as possible at the Treasury.

You were examined both before the coroner's jury and then before the magistrate in February?—Yes.

Did you say when you described that conversation, "That was just at the bottom of the stairs; in fact, on the stairs. Mr. Baxter was following us up "?—Yes, that was my error. Mr. Baxter was not.

He was not following you up?—No.

No, he was not there at all?—No; I made that mistake between Friday and Saturday.

111

Adelaide Bartlett.

Edwin Bartlett

Whether it was Friday or Saturday, why have you not told us that to-day?—I was not examined on it; I was not asked.

It was said?—I was not asked.

Was it said by Mrs. Bartlett to you?—It was not; it was on the Saturday it was said, not on the Friday.

Very well, then; we have got that fact quite clear. Now, Mr. Bartlett, when you went on Friday you went upstairs to the drawing-room, and there you saw Mrs. Bartlett?—Yes.

And then on the following day, the Saturday, you waited outside?—I did.

Until the post-mortem examination was over?—Yes, I did.

Then you went in?—Yes.

And then you saw Mrs. Bartlett in the smoking-room, did you? —Yes, in the smoking-room. We waited there something like twenty minutes, I should think, before I went upstairs.

You say " when we were summoned upstairs "; who summoned you upstairs?—One of the doctors told us we could go upstairs, and I, Mrs. Bartlett, and Mr. Dyson went up together. Mr. Dyson followed behind us, I believe, to the best of my recollection.

You have a clear recollection that the doctors were upstairs, and that one of the doctors summoned you upstairs?—I believe so.

Is that to the best of your recollection?—Yes, to the best of my recollection.

" Some one came," you said, " and summoned us upstairs," that summons being addressed to Mrs. Bartlett and to all those who were waiting?—Yes.

You went up directly you were summoned upstairs, and you saw that there was Mrs. Bartlett's bag there, did you?—I did.

In which room?—In the front room, on the table.

Did you say before that it was on the dressing-table?—I do not recollect. I said it was on the dressing-table—there was no dressing-table in the front room.

Just try and remember. You do not remember about the dressing-table? There was no dressing-table in the front room?— No; I do not remember a dressing-table being mentioned.

Did some one say Mrs. Bartlett must not take the bag away?— They did.

Who said that?—I do not know; one of the doctors.

Cannot you remember? — I cannot — whether it was Dr. Dudley I would not undertake to say. And then they said she must not have her cloak. I said, " Yes, Adelaide may take her cloak; there is nothing in it, no pockets in it." She said, " I do not want my cloak." I said, " Yes, you can have it; I will be answerable for it."

You would be answerable for it?—Yes.

Did you feel in the pockets?—No; I knew there were none.

112

Old Bailey Court—Mr. Bartlett being cross=examined by Mr. Edward Clarke, Q.C.

Evidence for Prosecution.

Edwin Bartlett

Before the coroner did you not say, " I will be answerable for the cloak, and I gave it to her after feeling in the pockets " ?— No, not in the pockets; there were no pockets. " After feeling for the pockets," I might have said.

Who told Mrs. Bartlett to go out of the house ?—I cannot say.

She was inclined to take nothing—she did not want the cloak even ?—Yes.

You said you would be answerable for it ?—Yes.

She said she would not take it ?—Yes.

She had the cloak ?—Yes.

And nothing else ?—Yes.

And left the house ?—Yes.

When you went in the first time on 1st January you went to smell the mouth for prussic acid ?—I did.

Did you suspect poison ?—I did.

Have you told the jury now substantially all you can remember of the conversations that took place during the illness ?—Yes, I have, I believe.

Is there anything else that you have not told us that took place in conversations in Mr. Bartlett's presence, in your son's presence, which suggested to you the idea of poison ?—No, nothing.

Re-examined by Mr. POLAND—My learned friend reminded you that the prisoner said to you, " My dear father, do not fret; it will make no odds to you. I will see you never want. It shall be just the same as if Edwin were alive." When do you say that was said ?—On the Saturday evening, going up the stairs, when going out of the drawing-room, and we were just at the foot of the stairs.

Was that on your visit on Saturday, or when your son was ill ?—No; on the day of the post-mortem examination.

It was on the Saturday after the death ?—Yes; and after the post-mortem examination.

Now, my friend Mr. Clarke has referred to your having to sign this apology on 31st December, 1878. What had the apology reference to which you signed ?—It was something very bad.

Having made something reflecting upon the character of Mrs. Bartlett ?—Must I state it?

I think you must state what it was you had to apologise for. What charge had you made ?—Well, Adelaide ran away, and was away for some week or more, and Edwin and me thought she had gone along—we almost knew she had gone with Fred Bartlett, the brother, and we were after her.

By Mr. CLARKE—Is Fred in England ?—He appeared in Claverton Street.

Is he here now ?—He was at Claverton Street three days after his brother's death, according to Mr. Doggett.

Does that witness pretend to have seen Fred Bartlett there ?—

I

Adelaide Bartlett.

No, the elder Doggett; and he announced himself as the brother of the deceased man.

By Mr. JUSTICE WILLS—You are speaking of something Doggett told you?—Yes.

Re-examination continued—How long was she away?—Something less than a week on this occasion.   She had been away on other occasions.

On this occasion?—About a week.

How long was that before this apology?—It must have been some months before that.

Then did she return?—Yes.

What was the date of that?—31st December, 1878.   Then Fred ran away to America in the June.

All I ask you is, do you mean the June previous to your signing this apology?—Yes; the June previous to my signing that apology.

Then how long before he went away was it that Adelaide was away with him?—Only a day or two, because Fred flew directly it was found out.

Your son Fred went to America, you know?—I have scores of letters from him.

So you know he went to America?—Yes.

How long was he away?—He has not been back, only I heard he turned up on the 5th.   I sent him something to come home, and his brother was going to give him a manager's place in one of the establishments.

Have you seen him since his return?—I have not.

But you sent him money to return?—I sent him £60 one year in order to come home.

When was that?—The year he went away—the following year.

Did you send him money recently to come back?—No, not recently.

This apology, you say you signed it in the office of Mr. Wood, the solicitor?—Yes, I did.

Is that the gentleman in Court?—Yes.

Whose solicitor was he?—He was then my son's solicitor.   I recommended him to my son some years ago.

Then it was this apology was drawn up and you signed it?—Yes.   Edwin begged of me to sign it to make peace.

Now, you have told my learned friend that your son spoke about having two wives, one to take out and one to do the work. You say the prisoner made some remark?—Yes.

What was that—on that subject?—No, not on that subject.   I was speaking of passing remarks made in conversation.

Can you remember the date when your son went to Scotland? He went by sea and came back by sea?—Yes; something like four years ago—over four years ago.

Was your son a temperate man?—Very, indeed.

Evidence for Prosecution.

My friend has spoken to you about the morphia having been injected; we are told what that was for?—No. I do not know, only, I take it, to produce sleep.

Who had injected it?—Dr. Leach, I understood, injected it.

EDWARDS BAXTER, examined by Mr. MOLONEY—I live at 34 Deronda Road, Herne Hill. I was a partner with the deceased Bartlett for thirteen years. I have known him for over twenty years. I never knew him to be laid up by illness before his last illness, with the exception of one occasion, when he went away for the benefit of his health. He was away for about a fortnight for the benefit of his health after he had been doing some hard work—carpentering—which was rather out of his way. On that occasion he did not have to keep his bed at all. I was not at his marriage. I recollect Mrs. Bartlett coming to live with the deceased at Station Road. They lived at Station Road for about five years. They lived at the Exchange for about twelve months. I had frequent opportunities of seeing them when they were living over the shop, and seeing the terms on which they lived. So far as I knew, they lived there as man and wife.

We had six shops at the time of Mr. Bartlett's death. Our business at the time of his death was a prosperous business; it was a business that had been made by my partner and myself. The one at Station Road had been in existence for about three years when I went there, but all the other shops were opened by my partner and myself.

I recollect the deceased going home ill from business in December. I think it was the 8th December. I received a letter from him on the 10th. (Shown letter)—That is the letter I received. I could not say what was the cause of his going away on that occasion. It was not overwork. In that letter the deceased says, " If you wish to see me, come here and we can arrange about Friday, Edwin." On the Sunday following I called to see him. I am not certain whether I called to see him during the week. When I saw him on the Sunday he appeared very ill indeed. He did not say what was the matter with him; he was scarcely able to speak. The deceased had been in the habit of mixing teas. I did not mix teas, but I tasted the teas along with him. I have never found any ill consequences from the tasting of the teas. I perhaps was not in the habit of tasting tea as much as the deceased was. I called on the deceased the Sunday after I received his letter, and I called again on the following Sunday. On that occasion he was better. When I saw him on the 20th he said he felt ill, and hoped he would very soon be better, that he was gradually improving. The prisoner was present on that occasion. I really forget whether anything was said about what he was suffering from. As I have already said, on the following Sunday, the 27th, he appeared very much better.

Adelaide Bartlett.

Edwards Baxter

I saw him again on the following Wednesday. On that occasion he seemed quite cheerful—very much better—getting on very nicely then. I stayed about two hours on the Wednesday night. The prisoner was present on that occasion. There was something said on that occasion about his going to the seaside, hoping that the change of air would prove beneficial, and that he would be able in the course of a week or two to resume business. Bournemouth or Torquay were the two places mentioned. I told the deceased that we were getting on very nicely in the business. There was nothing further said, except that he hoped to be back again in the course of a short time. I did not see the deceased again until after his death. (Shown note)—That note is in Mrs. Bartlett's handwriting; the date is my handwriting, the date when I received it, 30th December. It came by post, and it reads, " Dear sir,—With the other things will you please send a bottle of brandy called *Lord's Extra*, a bottle of Colonel Skinner's mangochutney, a bottle of walnuts, and a nice fruit cake? I know these things are not fit for Edwin to eat, but he fancies them. You can see Edwin on Wednesday. A very happy New Year." I took the things referred to in that letter to Claverton Street on the Wednesday night, the 30th. I never saw Mr. Dyson on any of the occasions I visited Claverton Street. On New Year's Day I received a telegram, and I went to Claverton Street. I subsequently saw Mr. Bartlett, senior, on that same morning, the 1st January.

By Mr. Justice Wills—I received the telegram about a quarter-past nine at Station Road, Herne Hill. I went to Claverton Street first, and I saw Mrs. Bartlett there.

Examination continued—I went up to the drawing-room on that occasion. The prisoner was in the drawing-room then.

Did she say anything to you?—Yes.

What did she say?—That I am unable to state. The sudden decease was so much that really——

By Mr. Justice Wills—You mean you have forgotten it?—Yes, my lord.

You have no distinct recollection?—No distinct recollection at all.

Examination continued—Did you see the father soon after?—I fetched the father, and he and I went upstairs.

By Mr. Justice Wills—What time did you see the father?—I should think about half-past eleven. I went from Claverton Street to Berkeley Square for Mr. Bartlett, senior, and then I went back with him at once.

Cross-examined by Mr. E. Clarke—Had Mr. Bartlett been working very hard indeed while staying at Dover?—Not particularly so.

What time did he get to Herne Hill in the morning?—The time varied; sometimes as early as six o'clock.

Evidence for Prosecution.

Edwards Baxter

What, from Dover?—Yes.

He would come up from Dover so early as to get to Herne Hill at six?—Yes, by the boat express.

Did he often do that?—Sometimes.

Do you mean several times a week?—Two or three times a week, perhaps.

On other days what time would he get there?—Come by a later train; I think between ten and eleven there is one.

Did he leave business very late?—Sometimes he would—are you alluding to the time he was staying at Dover?

Yes?—Sometimes he would leave at four o'clock, and sometimes, again, by the eight o'clock train.

He had some dogs he was proud of, had he not, at Herne Hill?—He had some dogs.

And on 8th December, I think, he washed those dogs, or one of them—it was going to a show next day?—Previous to the 8th. I think they were washed on the 4th.

Did you connect that with his illness at all—that he got a chill or anything of that kind?—No.

You did not know any cause for his illness?—Not at all.

On the 8th he complained of feeling ill, and went away?—Yes.

Did Mrs. Bartlett write to you constantly during his illness?—Nearly every morning I had a short note.

Did you keep those notes?—I did not.

Just notes to tell you how he was getting on?—Just " Not quite so well," or something of that sort.

I don't know whether you saw him before Sunday, the 13th?—I don't think so; I cannot call to mind.

Had Mrs. Bartlett asked you to call on the 13th? Did she say in a letter he would be glad to see you on that Sunday?—I don't think so. I might have said, perhaps, when I had written, I would call on Sunday afternoon.

There was no special reason for your going that day?—Oh, no.

Then on the 13th, I think you said, you found him very ill indeed?—Yes.

Was he much depressed and low?—He appeared so, for he was scarcely able to speak.

And do you know that the doctor visited him three times that day?—I do not.

I suppose at the time, perhaps at the time you went, he had only been twice, but have not you been told he was coming more than once a day?—I believe they told me he had been more than once.

Did he complain of sleeplessness?—Yes.

Adelaide Bartlett.

Edwards Baxter

You understood, did you not, thoroughly from Mrs. Bartlett that he was sleepless and restless?—Yes.

And on the next Sunday when you saw him—on 20th December—did you hear the doctor was giving him sleeping draughts? —I believe they told me to that effect.

Now, on the 27th—the following Sunday—you saw him again? —Yes.

Was he in a very bad state then?—No, sir, very much better.

Was it on that day he told you something about worms?— Yes, I believe it was on that date he alluded to them.

Did he tell you that he had passed worms, and that he could feel them wriggling up in his throat?—Yes.

Had you known anything of his ideas about mesmerism?— Not at all.

Nor had you, I suppose, known anything about his exceptional ideas of marriage?—No, not at all.

He had never made a confidant of you in that way at all, I suppose?—No, not at all.

What was about his income from the business, Mr. Baxter, do you think? Can you tell me what he used to draw?—About £300 a year.

Do you know anything about whether he had any property at all?—No; I am not aware he had any.

FREDERICK HORACE DOGGETT, examined by Mr. POLAND—I live along with my wife at 85 Claverton Street. I am Registrar of Births and Deaths for the district. 85 Claverton Street is my private address. In the early part of October last I had the drawing-room floor to let. It consists of two rooms, communicating with folding-doors, the front room being the sitting-room and the back the bedroom. The deceased, Mr. Bartlett, and Mrs. Bartlett took those apartments, and they continued to occupy them down to the date of his death. As far as I knew, they lived as man and wife. During the time they were living there I saw Mr. Dyson on two or three occasions. He was a friend of theirs, and used to come there.

On the morning of 1st January of the present year I was called up by the prisoner about four o'clock in the morning, as near as I can remember. I knew that the deceased had been ill for some time. I never saw the deceased to speak to during his lifetime. About four o'clock in the morning I heard a knock at the door, and I went to the door and found the prisoner at the door. She asked me to come down. She said, " Come down, I think Mr. Bartlett is dead." I had never spoken to the prisoner before. I at once got up. I put on my dressing-gown and went down to her room. She had gone down before me. It was then

Evidence for Prosecution.

Frederick H. Doggett

about ten past four by the clock on the drawing-room mantelpiece. I went into the front drawing-room. The prisoner was there. She asked if I thought Mr. Bartlett was dead. I saw him lying on the bed in the room, in the corner of the room next to the fireplace. I at once went up to him. He was lying on his back with his left hand on his breast. I put my hand on his breast. His nightshirt was pulled back and his breast was bare. I found him perfectly cold. I put my hand over the region of his heart. Mrs. Bartlett asked me if I thought he was dead, and I said, " Yes, he must have been dead some two or three hours. He is perfectly cold." She then said, " I had fallen off to sleep with my hand round his foot, and I woke up with a pain in my hand," or " arm," I do not know which, " and found him lying on his face. I put him in the position in which you saw him, and tried to pour brandy down his throat—nearly half a pint." I do not recollect whether Mrs. Bartlett said that he had swallowed any of it or not. After that I think Dr. Leach came. My wife came down before Dr. Leach arrived. I noticed the deceased's eyes. They were closed. I asked the prisoner whether she had closed his eyes, and she said, " Yes," and had put him in the position in which he then was. His jaw was dropping. Dr. Leach had been sent for before my wife came down. The servant went for him. I noticed a strong smell when I went into the room; it struck me as being chloric ether. I did not smell anything else. I looked round the room. There was a tray with some tumblers on it, and a glass jug containing water on the table.

What else?—I fancy—I am not quite certain, but I think there was a bottle on the tray containing some white powder. I also saw a wineglass. The wineglass was on the mantelboard. It was three-quarters full.

What did it smell like?—Evidently brandy, with some other drug in it; it smelt like ether or paregoric. I put it back where I found it. The wineglass was on the mantelpiece at the corner nearest the bed. That was all I noticed that I can call to mind. The only bottle I noticed was the one on the tray with the white powder. I looked round the room for the purpose of seeing what was there when Dr. Leach came.

And are you able to say, on looking round the room in that way, whether there was any other bottle on the mantelpiece, or table, or any other part of the room?—None that I saw.

After Dr. Leach came in did he speak to the prisoner, and did you afterwards leave the room?—I did.

Did Mrs. Bartlett remain or not?—I suggested that she should leave the room, but she remained with Dr. Leach. They had some conversation in a corner of the room. Before I left I assisted Dr. Leach to tie up the deceased's jaw and put his legs

119

Adelaide Bartlett.

Frederick H. Doggett

straight. His legs were cold, and the left leg was slightly drawn up. Dr. Leach examined the deceased's body while I was present, and said he could find nothing to account for death. I did not notice how the prisoner was dressed; I did not pay particular attention. When I went into the room I think she had a skirt or an underskirt on, and a loose sort of jacket. There was a large fire in the grate. It had evidently been tended within a very short time of my coming into the room. After assisting Dr. Leach I went downstairs, and shortly afterwards Dr. Leach came down—about a quarter of an hour afterwards. After that I went back to my room, and my wife and I went to bed. We left the prisoner in the back room where the bed was. On the following morning I saw the prisoner writing out some telegrams. It would be about a quarter of nine.

There is a matter which I passed over. I ought to have asked you—before you left the room that night did you see any Condy's fluid?—Yes. I rather think it was on the tray. There was more than half a tumblerful poured out.

By Mr. Justice Wills—When did you notice that?—The same night. I had noticed it before I went to bed that morning.

Examination continued—I did not see any other bottle. The next morning—or rather later the same morning—before I saw the prisoner writing the telegrams I saw a small bottle inverted in the tumbler of Condy's fluid. It had been brought down by the servant on the tray. It was an ounce bottle; there was no label on it. I handed the tumbler in which the bottle was inverted to the coroner's officer, Ralph. After that the telegrams were written and sent off, one to the father, one to the partner, and one to some lady at Dulwich. The bottle and the contents of the tumbler were both handed to Ralph. The contents were put in the bottle by myself, and Ralph and I sealed it with my seal, and the coroner's officer took charge of it. (Shown bottle)—That is something like the size of the bottle.

Mr. Justice Wills—A 2-ounce bottle?

Mr. Poland—Yes, my lord, I believe we shall trace it that that is the bottle.

Examination continued—Afterwards I heard of the post-mortem examination.

You know the bed where the man was lying near the mantel-piece. Have you been on the bed and tried it yourself?—Yes.

If you are lying on your back on the bed, can you reach the mantelpiece?—I can just reach it.

Anybody leaning on the bed could easily reach the mantel-piece?—Undoubtedly.

Or sitting up even?—It would be rather more difficult sitting up. I can just reach it sitting up.

Cross-examined by Mr. Clarke—The head of the bedstead

120

Evidence for Prosecution.

Frederick H. Doggett

was near the mantelpiece; was the foot of the bed towards the middle of the room?—It was lengthways.

But not actually level with the front wall of the room?—Yes.

Was not it turned round a little?—No, it was horizontal, or rather longitudinal, with the front wall of the room.

My learned friend asked you more than once whether Mr. and Mrs. Bartlett lived there as man and wife; you knew that they were man and wife when the rooms were let, did you not?—I presumed so.

But as far as their manner of living with you, you had not seen them?—I had only seen Mr. Bartlett one night to speak to.

You have mentioned something about the fire to which I wish to direct your attention. You were examined before the coroner on 4th February?—Yes, I was.

When you were examined on 4th February at some length you did not mention the fire at all?—I could not say from memory whether I did or not.

The first time you were examined you did not say a syllable about the fire, did you?—That I cannot recollect.

Don't you recollect on 4th February, after your wife had been examined, you were recalled, and the express question was put to you about the fire—you were asked about the fire and about nothing else?—Yes.

And when you went into the room, did you smell a smell which you say was something like chloric ether?—Yes.

That was the smell you traced to the glass on the mantelpiece?—No.

You saw a glass on the mantelpiece 6 inches from the corner, did you not?—I did not say 6 inches from the corner; it was close to the end of the mantelpiece; I don't think I said 6 inches.

When you saw that glass, you say it was three-quarters—you have said two-thirds—full of the liquid which you took to be brandy?—Yes.

And when you smelt it you smelt the same smell which you smelt on coming into the room?—Hardly.

You say, " a wineglass, containing some coloured liquid which I took to be brandy, about two-thirds full. I took it up and smelt it; it smelt very like the odour which pervaded the room—chloric ether "?—I think I said it smelt like paregoric.

Mr. JUSTICE WILLS—You said paregoric before the coroner.

Cross-examination continued—You said chloric ether before the magistrate, but you said when you went to that glass and smelt it, it smelt very like the odour which pervaded the room?—Yes.

You took it up and smelt it and replaced it on the mantelpiece, did you?—Yes.

121

Adelaide Bartlett.

Frederick H. Doggett

Did it remain there till Dr. Leach came?—Yes.

It stood there while you were all looking about the room?—Yes.

And it was brought down by your servant on the tray in the same condition in the morning? Was the liquid still in it?—Yes.

You saw the tray when it had come down, and you took the inverted bottle and the glass of liquid and handed them over to Ralph, the coroner's representative?—No, not exactly; when the tray was brought down I saw it by accident in the morning; I saw the bottle sticking out of the liquid, and I took it out with my fingers and locked it up in a cupboard, and I afterwards gave it to Ralph.

You thought it would be right that the bottle should be taken care of?—I did.

It did not occur to you to do the same with regard to the wineglass?—No.

When Dr. Leach came, you looked about the room; did you see any bottle on the mantelpiece at all?—No.

May there not have been a bottle on the mantelpiece without your having seen it?—I don't think so.

This is not a very long mantelpiece, is it?—It is rather a long mantelpiece. There is a mantelboard on the mantelpiece which makes it longer.

There is a looking-glass, is there not, with a little sort of a shelf at the end?—Not that I am aware of.

Is there not a little sort of a shelf by the looking-glass on which bottles might be put? You had not been in the room before?—Yes, I have.

Not while Mr. Bartlett was there?—No.

Perhaps the looking-glass being stood on a mantelboard would constitute a shelf, and come a little farther out from the looking-glass?—Certainly.

There is a clock in the middle of the mantelboard, I believe?—Yes.

Was there a photograph there, did you notice?—I think there was; I would not swear that.

There were two photographs in frames on the mantelpiece, I believe?—There were photographs.

There were two small vases, one on each side of the clock, which stood in the middle?—Yes.

And at each end of the mantelboard was there a tolerably large vase, say 7 inches wide and 15 inches high—a pair of large vases?—I don't know the exact size; they are large vases.

In your examination before the coroner, did you not say, "The doctor and myself examined the glass and also the bottles in the room"?—The bottle, the only bottle I saw, was the one on the tray which contained some white powder.

122

Evidence for Prosecution.

Frederick H. Doggett

I have it copied " bottles "—possibly it may be a mistake in copying. I have it, " The doctor and myself then examined the glasses and also all the bottles in the room, and there was no bottle on the mantelpiece " ?—There was the bottle of Condy's fluid; that is the only bottle I examined with the doctor—it was on the floor—it was a wine-bottle, three parts full of Condy's fluid.

Then, although this was taken down, it is not what you said— " Also all the bottles in the room " ?—There was one on the tray, and one of Condy's fluid.

One on the tray and one on the floor—two bottles ?—Yes, that is all I saw.

By Mr. JUSTICE WILLS—You say, one of Condy's fluid on the floor ?—Yes.

By Mr. CLARKE—You were telling us what Mrs. Bartlett said to you; you used the word " pain "; did she say she felt cramp in the hand ?—" Cramp." I think that was so.

Did Mrs. Bartlett tell you her husband had breathed heavily in the evening ?—Yes.

Mrs. CAROLINE DOGGETT, examined by Mr. WRIGHT—I am the wife of the last witness, Mr. Doggett, and I live with him at 85 Claverton Street. I remember Mr. and Mrs. Bartlett coming to lodge there on 3rd October. I remember Mr. Dyson coming there. The first time he came was within a week after 3rd October. He did not come often at first. The arrangement with the deceased was that he was to come to dinner once a week. The deceased arranged that when he took the rooms; he said a gentleman would dine once a week—Mr. Dyson.

Did he mention the name ?—No, but Mrs. Bartlett said it was only a clergyman. He came twice and three times a week, and sometimes more. He came at all times. He has been as early as half-past nine in the morning.

How long used he to stay ?—He has stayed all day. The deceased went out in the morning at from eight to half-past eight, and he returned to dinner between five and six.

When Mr. Dyson came early in the morning did he stay till Mr. Bartlett came back ?—Sometimes.

Did he have lunch with Mrs. Bartlett ?—Yes.

Did Mr. Dyson and Mrs. Bartlett go out together ?—Sometimes.

How was Mr. Dyson dressed when you saw him in the house ?— Twice I saw him in a lounge coat. I don't know the material it was made of; it was a blue coat—a serge coat. It was kept in the house—I believe for his use. There was also a pair of slippers left for him in the house. I remember Mr. Bartlett becoming ill about the beginning of December, but I cannot fix the date. I think he was not well two or three mornings before Dr. Leach was

Adelaide Bartlett.

Caroline Doggett

called in. He kept his room from the very first day of Dr. Leach's coming. Mr. Dyson used to go up to his room on some occasions, but not always. When he called he would see Mrs. Bartlett downstairs.

On the last day of December—the day Mr. Bartlett died—he, Mr. Bartlett, went out in the evening. Before that he had dined at home about three or half-past three. He had jugged hare for dinner. He had tea that night about nine o'clock. That was after I had seen him and after he had been out in the evening. He had been out to have his tooth taken out. I saw him when he came back. I went into his room and sat down. I had seen him very much worse than he was that night. He told me he thought the worst was over, and he would get better. Mrs. Bartlett was there at the time. Mr. Bartlett told me that Dr. Leach had given him orders to go to the seaside for a change—I think he said Torquay. Mrs. Bartlett said that she thought the journey would be too long. After that Mrs. Bartlett asked me if I had ever taken chloroform. I said that I had years ago. She then asked me if it was a nice or a pleasant feeling. I said I did not think I knew very much about it. Mrs. Bartlett said that Mr. Bartlett was in the habit of taking some sleeping drops; ten was a strong dose, but she should not, or did not, hesitate in giving him twelve. She told me what the drops were, but I do not remember the name. Mr. Bartlett then thanked me for his dinner, and said he had enjoyed it. He said that he had eaten all that was sent up, and he had so enjoyed it that he would eat three dinners a day. He also said that the mornings were getting lighter, and he should get up an hour earlier the next day. Mr. Bartlett had a tea supper that night; he had half a dozen oysters, and bread and butter, and cake. I do not know whether he also had some chutney. After that conversation I went out of the room.

I was called early next morning, about four o'clock. I went into Mr. Bartlett's room and saw him lying dead. I asked Mrs. Bartlett if she had given him these drops, and she said, " I have given him nothing." My husband was in the room when she said that, but he was looking round the room, and I was by the side of the bed. I noticed that the fire was a very good fire. I remember having a conversation with Mrs. Bartlett that same morning about a will. That was on the 1st of January. I went up to ask her if she would come down to the dining-room to have a little breakfast, as she had not rung for it, and then she said how strange it was that Mr. Bartlett had not long made his will.

Anything else?—I said, " Are you thinking about money? " She replied, " It is necessary," as her money which she had before she was married was in the business, and it was before the Married Women's Property Act.

Evidence for Prosecution.

Was there anything said at that time?—No; Mrs. Matthews came in at that time and I went downstairs.

Cross-examined by Mr. CLARKE—You had kindly gone up to see if you could get her to take some breakfast?—Yes.

Her own breakfast had gone up and had not been touched?—No; she had not rung for any breakfast.

And then she mentioned that about the will?—Yes.

All her means of livelihood had come from the business?—I understood from her that the money she had before she was married was in the business.

It had gone into the business?—Yes.

You thought that her thought was she was dependent upon the business, and the business man was dead?—Unless there was a will she could not have his money, because it was before the Married Women's Property Act.

Did she come down and have breakfast with you?—No; Mrs. Matthews came in, and I left her in the front drawing-room.

Has it ever been your sad lot to watch in a sickroom at night? —Yes, I have.

Do you know very well that that night the fire was made up for the night and packed?—Yes; but the bed was so near the fire it would have been too hot for Mr. Bartlett; and the gas was alight.

You know perfectly well that at night, with a view not to disturb anybody, the fire is packed for the night?—Yes.

And if after several hours you touch it and break it, it becomes a strong fire?—Yes.

The fire you saw was a strong fire, was it not?—It had been attended to; it had not burnt hollow at all.

So that either fresh coal had not lately been put on, or a well-packed fire had been disturbed by the poker?—Yes; but there was a bright light; the coals were quite lighted.

That would be the result of stirring with the poker; a well-made fire, was it not?—I should think so.

With regard to that conversation. Mrs. Bartlett was reading, was she not, while you and her husband were talking?—Yes, she was reading a book.

You know he had been out that day to have his tooth operated upon?—Yes; he told me about the tooth, and said it was a sound one.

Did he tell you that he had taken gas?—No.

Was nothing said about gas?—Not by Mr. Bartlett; not to me.

By anybody?—I never heard it.

Pray be careful. Mr. Bartlett had been out that day; do you know now as a fact that he had taken nitrous oxide gas?— From Dr. Leach.

Mr. Bartlett talked to you about the tooth?—Yes; but not that he had taken anything.

125

Adelaide Bartlett.

He talked to you about the tooth that had been taken out an hour or two before?—About two hours before.

What did he say about the tooth?—He said it was a sound tooth.

Did he say anything about the pain in having it pulled out? —That is what he said; the worst was over, and he thought he was getting better.

Did he say anything about the pain in having it taken out?— Not that night, but the other operation he had. He had seven taken out one day, and he said they had frozen his gums, and he did not feel very much pain, and two days before that he had had thirteen out.

Was it on that evening on which the conversation took place that he told you about the thirteen and the seven?—Each time.

On each occasion?—Yes.

When he had the seven taken out he told you that they had frozen his gums?—Yes.

Did he say it was by ether spray?—No; that was all he said.

Did not he tell you how they had frozen his gums?—No.

Did not you ask how they had frozen his gums?—No; he began saying that it was very wonderful, after going through the operation, he could eat some of Mrs. Bartlett's hot buttered toast— he smelt it, and he asked for some.

On which occasion was that?—When he had the seven out.

And on that occasion he told you that they had frozen his gums, and that it was wonderful he could eat the buttered toast, did he?—Yes.

Did he say that the result of freezing his gums was that he did not feel pain?—Yes.

On another day he had no less than thirteen stumps taken out, had he not?—That was the first operation—the thirteen.

On that occasion did he tell you about their freezing his gums?—No; I did not see him then.

Do you mean that they froze his gums twice?—He said that that was what they did on both occasions; he had had his gums frozen, and therefore did not feel much pain.

By Mr. JUSTICE WILLS—He had his gums frozen on each of these two occasions?—Yes.

Cross-examination continued—Try and recollect; on this evening, the last evening before his death, when he spoke to you about having one taken out, did you ask him if he had had his gums frozen again?—No.

Did he say anything about it?—No; he began telling me that Dr. Leach had said he ought to go away for a change.

Did he tell you anything about having the tooth out, and that instead of having his gums frozen he had had nitrous oxide?—No.

You do not remember all the conversation, do you?—It was

126

Evidence for Prosecution.

very late; the boy brought the medicine, and I had to leave the room.

You do not remember the name of the medicine?—No.

But the name was mentioned?—Yes, by Mrs. Bartlett.

Was it spoken of as a placebo—ten drops of a placebo?—Ten drops is considered a strong dose.

You say you cannot remember the word; was it a placebo?—I don't know what name she said.

Did she say that Dr. Leach had given a prescription for ten drops to be given if the pain was urgent, or if sleep was required, or anything of that kind?—No.

The Court adjourned.

Second Day—Tuesday, 13th April, 1886.

Evidence for the Prosecution—continued.

ALICE FULCHER, examined by Mr. POLAND—I am servant to Mr. and Mrs. Doggett, 85 Claverton Street. I remember Mr. and Mrs. Bartlett coming to live there some time in October. I waited upon them. The first week after they came I saw Mr. Dyson there. He used to come once or twice a week, and then about a fortnight or three weeks before Mr. Bartlett's illness he came three or four times a week. I have known him to be there as early as nine or half-past nine, and sometimes later. Mr. Bartlett sometimes went to business about eight or half-past eight, and returned between five and six in the evening. He sometimes went out again. Sometimes Mr. Dyson stayed till dinner time and dined with Mr. and Mrs. Bartlett. The usual time for dinner was between five and six o'clock. Mr. Dyson had an old coat that he used to put on which was kept in the back drawing-room. He had also a pair of slippers there. I have sometimes gone into the room while Mr. Dyson and Mrs. Bartlett were together.

Have you noticed anything about the room when you have gone in?—Yes, I have seen the window curtains pulled together and then pinned.

Have you seen when Mrs. Bartlett and Mr. Dyson have been there anything to attract your attention when you went in?—I have seen them sitting on the sofa together, and I have also seen them sitting on the floor together.

In what position on the floor?—I have seen Mr. Dyson sitting on a low chair and Mrs. Bartlett sitting on the floor with her head on Mr. Dyson's knee. I do not remember when that was, nor could I say how long it was before Mr. Bartlett's death. I do not know what I went into the room for. I never found the door locked.

When you went in and saw Mrs. Bartlett with her head resting on Mr. Dyson's knee, did they do anything at all when you went in?—No.

Or say anything?—No, they still sat as they were. I think that was the only occasion that I noticed anything of that kind when I went into the room. Sometimes Mr. Dyson would stay and have lunch with Mrs. Bartlett between twelve and one, and leave before Mr. Bartlett came home. I do not think there was anything else that I noticed.

On the day of Mr. Bartlett's death I took up the dinner about half-past two or three o'clock. I had seen him from time

128

Evidence for Prosecution.

Alice Fulcher

to time during his illness. He had been out that day. The dinner consisted of jugged hare. Later on in the day he had tea. He had for luncheon at twelve o'clock half a dozen oysters, bread and butter, and tea and cake. I did not hear him say anything about himself while Mrs. Bartlett was with him and I was in the room. His appetite appeared to be pretty good.

Was there any chutney with the supper or dinner?—The plates had been used for chutney at supper both by Mr. and Mrs. Bartlett. Mrs. Bartlett gave me orders for breakfast for next day when I cleared away the things; he asked me to get him a large haddock.

By Mr. JUSTICE WILLS—Do you mean after tea or after supper? —There was tea and supper both together. It was after the last meal.

Examination continued—The order was given when I was clearing the things away and he said that he should get up an hour earlier at the thought of having it. He sat up at the table and took his meals. He was walking round the room when he gave me the order. The last time I went up to the room was at twenty-five minutes to eleven, when I was taking coals in. Mrs. Bartlett asked me to take the coals up for the night, and she put her finger up and told me not to go into the room again. She told me to take a basin up for the beef tea, and to put it on the table outside on the stair landing. The basin I put on the table was empty. Mrs. Bartlett had Liebig's essence in the room.

As a rule, used you, while Mr. Bartlett was ill, to take in the basin the last thing?—Yes, always. I went to bed that night some time past twelve, and I was wakened about four in the morning by Mrs. Bartlett coming to my room. I got up and she asked me to go for Dr. Leach. She said, " Alice, I want you to go for Dr. Leach, I think Mr. Bartlett is dead.'' I think that is all she said. I replied, " Don't say that! " but she made no reply. She had a light-coloured dress on. She was not wearing that dress when I left her overnight. I got up and at once left the house and went for Dr. Leach—about five or ten minutes' walk. I roused him and told him what was the matter, and brought him back. Mrs. Doggett opened the door to me. I had not seen any one except Mrs. Bartlett before I left the house to fetch Dr. Leach. I had to stand knocking for Dr. Leach for some time, and I could not say what time elapsed between the time Mrs. Bartlett came to me and the time that Dr. Leach came back with me to the house. When Dr. Leach arrived he went into the room upstairs. I went into the room—the drawing-room —about half-past five or six o'clock in the morning. I saw a lot of things on the table in the room. The tray was there. I did not remove any of the things at that time. I left the tray

Adelaide Bartlett.

Alice Fulcher

till about half-past eight or nine o'clock. It had several glasses on it, and I took them downstairs to the ante-room, the smoking-room, and left them there. I washed them all except one.

What sort of glasses were they?—Some were tumblers and some wineglasses. I noticed that one wineglass was about half-full of something which I thought was brandy, judging from the smell and the colour. I washed it away. The glass that I did not wash was given to the coroner's officer; it was a tumbler containing some liquid with a bottle turned downwards in it. The coroner's officer, Ralph, took charge of that. That same morning Mrs. Bartlett gave me some letters to post; one was addressed to Mr. Dyson and one to Mr. Wood. I think I posted these in the morning, but I am not quite sure whether it was in the morning or night. I did not take any telegram. I saw Mr. Dyson the next day, Saturday, the 2nd. He came to the house in the morning while Mrs. Bartlett was in. He went up into the room where Mrs. Bartlett was. I do not know whether I showed him up or whether he just went up. Mrs. Bartlett had slept in the house. I did not hear anything that passed between Mr. Dyson and Mrs. Bartlett on the Saturday. Mrs. Bartlett left the house after that, on the Saturday, while Mr. and Mrs. Doggett were out. The next time I saw her was on Wednesday, 6th January. Mrs. Matthews came with her. She came for some of her things.

Cross-examined by Mr. CLARKE—Can you remember when it was that you say you saw the curtains pinned together?—No.

How long before Mr. Bartlett's death?—I could not say.

You cannot say whether it was a week or a month or three months?—No, I could not.

These were long white curtains, were they not, that came down to the ground?—Yes.

And generally hung close together?—Yes.

From top to bottom?—Yes.

That was their usual condition, was it?—Yes.

Then they would hang close and cover the window whether they were pinned or not?—Yes, sir.

Can you tell me how long it was that Mr. Bartlett was sleeping on the iron bedstead in the front room?—From the beginning of his illness.

From the very first time that Dr. Leach came to attend to him, I suppose?—Yes.

And after that time did you know that Mrs. Bartlett was sleeping on the sofa or chair in the front room where he was?—Yes, sir.

She did not use the bed in the back room?—No.

But used to be in the front room, and, as you know or believe, attend to him, make beef tea for him, and so on?—Yes.

And he slept on a little low iron bedstead?—Yes.

130

Evidence for Prosecution.

Alice Fulcher

Was that bed near the fireplace?—Yes.

And was there often a stool or chair at the bottom of the bedstead?—No, sir; the piano was mostly there at the foot of the bed.

The piano was at the other window when you went in at the door. The front room, the drawing-room, had two windows. When you went into it from the staircase there was a window opposite you?—Yes.

And then the fireplace was to your right?—Yes.

The room stretched away to the right?—Yes.

The bed was by the fireplace?—Yes.

And the piano was in the corner of the room on the left-hand side as you went in?—Mrs. Bartlett moved it against the foot of the bed along the side.

When do you say it was moved?—I do not know when it was moved, but it was moved.

Just remember; there was a bookcase between the windows?—Yes, and Mrs. Bartlett moved that, too, to the other side of the room.

There were folding doors between the two rooms, I think?—Yes.

And the sofa that I have mentioned was a heavy sofa, I think, against the folding doors?—Yes.

So that it kept them closed?—Yes.

And Mrs. Bartlett, going from one room to the other, would have gone out on to the staircase?—Yes.

Do you know about the washing basin in the back room, whether it was often used quite late at night by Mrs. Bartlett?—Yes.

I do not know whether you drew the inference—perhaps you would—that before settling herself for the night she would go into the back room and wash?—Sometimes.

She would sometimes, would she?—Yes.

You knew that the basin was used?—Yes.

Whether it was or was not used on the night of the death, I think you do not remember?—No, sir, I do not.

Now, just one word with regard to this matter, about finding Mr. Dyson sitting on a chair and Mrs. Bartlett with her head on his knee. When you went into the room on that occasion you had been summoned to the room by Mrs. Bartlett?—I do not know what I went up for—whether I went up to take letters or not.

You were examined with regard to this two months ago nearly at the Police Court?—Yes.

Did you say this—" I believe it was in the afternoon when I saw Mrs. Bartlett's head on Mr. Dyson's knee. I could not say the time; I would have been rung for at the time for dinner. I do not recollect that I was rung for, whatever was the cause.

Adelaide Bartlett.

Alice Fulcher

I had been sent for by Mrs. Bartlett"?—Did you say that?—Yes. Well; I could not say whether I had been rung for or not now.

Were there books on the table?—Yes.

Was Mr. Dyson sitting near the table?—He was sitting in front of the fire—that is, near the table.

You usually took, I think, a supply of coals for the night late in the evening?—Yes.

And on this evening Mrs. Bartlett told you to bring up the coals and to bring the empty basin?—Yes.

Just try and recall this. Did she tell you at one and the same time about bringing the coals and about bringing the basin? —Yes.

Can you remember how long it was before you took the coals up?—Well, I think I went for Mr. Bartlett's breakfast before I took the coals up.

You did not take the coals and the basin up together?—Yes, I did.

Are you sure—just try and remember; when you took the coals up you went into the room?—Yes; and I think I left the basin outside until Mrs. Bartlett told me, and then I took it in.

Do try and remember. I do not think you quite mean that. You think you left the basin outside until Mrs. Bartlett told you? —No. I took the coals up, and then Mrs. Bartlett told me to take the basin and not to take it into the room.

That is what I was trying to remind you of. Mrs. Bartlett told you about the coals and the basin at the same time. Is it not a fact that you took up the coals without the basin?—Yes; and I went for the basin.

Having been told to bring up the coals and the basin, you brought them up and took the coals into the room?—Yes.

But you had not brought the basin?—No.

At that time Mr. Bartlett had not gone to bed?—When I took the coals up Mr. Bartlett was in bed.

Then it was when you were told about the coals and the basin that he was walking about, was it?—When I was clearing away the tea I said Mr. Bartlett was walking about.

Then you took the coals and you went into the room while he was in bed?—Yes.

And not having brought the basin in with you, Mrs. Bartlett told you that you might put it on the table and not come in again? —Yes.

And you would pass the basin in the ordinary course of things as you went up to your bedroom?—Yes.

You did put the basin on the table?—Yes.

And you found it there untouched the next morning?—Yes.

Do you remember when it was you put the basin there? Was it when you went up to bed?—Before.

132

Evidence for Prosecution.

Alice Fulcher

You did not go up to bed for some time afterwards, I think?—No.

Did Mrs. Bartlett usually go out in the daytime at some time or other for a walk?—Yes.

And she had been out with her husband that day to the dentist's, had she not?—I do not know.

Well, in the evening when you were there they were having supper, and she had a walking dress on, had she not?—Yes.

And when she came to call you at four o'clock in the morning she had a light and looser dress on?—Yes, sir.

Was it a sort of loose jacket?—It was the dress she used to go out for a walk in sometimes.

Are you sure of that?—Yes.

Be careful; you have said she went out with a walking dress in the evening?—Yes.

And you said she had a looser dress in the morning?—Yes; but she had been out for a walk in that dress.

How long before?—Several times.

How long before?—Not the same night.

Was that a looser dress?—It was the same as any other dress, only a different colour.

You have been asked about the length of time that elapsed before you brought back Dr. Leach. I suppose you jumped up as quickly as you could?—Yes.

And went as quickly as you could for him?—Yes.

And brought him back as quickly as you could get him?—Yes.

I do not know whether you went to bed again after that or not?—No; I did not.

Then you took the glasses down and Mr. Doggett saw them before anything was done with them, did he not?—Yes.

Did you help pack Mrs. Bartlett's boxes when she went away?—Yes, sir.

You did not see any medicine chest or anything of that kind, did you?—No, sir.

ANN BOULTER, examined by Mr. MOLONEY—I am a charwoman, and live at 1 Great Peter Street, Westminster. I am sometimes employed by an undertaker. I went to 85 Claverton Street on New Year's Day, between seven and eight in the morning, and I washed and laid out a dead body, with the assistance of Mrs. Bartlett. I noticed that the legs were tied. I asked Mrs. Bartlett if he had had a fit, and she asked why I asked that.

What did you say?—I thought he might have struggled, as his legs were tied. Mrs. Bartlett said, " No, poor dear, he suffered very much with his head, also his teeth for some time." She remarked it was curious or funny that he should make his will a day or two previous to his death. I remarked how odd that it was so, and asked if it was in her favour, and she said " Yes."

133

Adelaide Bartlett.

Cross-examined by Mr. CLARKE—Is that all she said to you about his illness?—Yes.

That his head had been bad, and that he had suffered very much with his teeth?—Yes.

Did you notice the teeth at all?—No, I did not; his mouth was closed.

The body was covered up when you went in, I suppose? Did you call her attention to the fact of his legs being tied together?—I did.

Was there more conversation than you have told us?—No, I think not.

Are you quite sure she said two or three days, and not two or three months?—No; that was all she said to me.

Are you quite sure she said two or three days?—" A day or two previous to his death " is what she said.

Do you know that while you were there a letter came for Mr. Bartlett?—Yes.

Did Mrs. Bartlett open it?—Yes.

Did she say where it had come from?—I understood her to say it was from his brother—the deceased's brother.

Where from?—I do not know where from.

She did not say?—No.

Did she say, " Oh, how cruel! " or " This is cruel "?—Yes, sir.

And did you ask her what she meant?—I asked her what was cruel.

And did she say?—It was a letter from his brother.

That a letter had just come from his brother wishing him a happy New Year?—Yes, sir.

And she said how cruel it was?—Yes; that was what made me notice her. I thought it was strange to make that remark.

That the letter should arrive while he was lying dead?—Yes, while I was washing the body.

Re-examined by Mr. MOLONEY—She did not say from which brother?—No, she did not—from his brother, I understood her to say.

WILLIAM CLAPTON, examined by Mr. POLAND—I am a Fellow of the Royal College of Surgeons, and reside at 27 Queen Street, City. I am one of the medical officers to the British Equitable Insurance Company. In the month of November, 1880, I examined Thomas Edwin Bartlett for the purpose of insuring his life. The insurance was effected. It was a policy for £400, and on the usual premium—a first-class life. I examined him in the ordinary way to ascertain whether his was a good life to take.

At that time did you find that, as far as you could judge, he was a sound man, suffering from no illness?—No ailment what-

134

Evidence for Prosecution.

ever. I passed him as a first-class life. The policy describes him as a grocer, of Herne Hill, and the exact date of it is 3rd December, 1880; I examined him on 15th November, 1880.

Rev. GEORGE DYSON, examined by Mr. POLAND—I am a Wesleyan minister. At the beginning of this year I was living at 18 Parkfield, Putney, and had been there since the beginning of September. I first made the acquaintance of Mr. and Mrs. Bartlett about twelve months last January or February. They were then living at The Cottage, Merton Abbey, and I was in charge of a small chapel in the High Street, Merton. Mr. and Mrs. Bartlett attended the services. After seeing them in my chapel I called upon them as members of my congregation, and that was how I made their acquaintance. They continued to attend until they left the neighbourhood. My second call upon them was in the following June, when I had tea with them at The Cottage, Merton Abbey. After that I called on them frequently.

Was there any reason for that? Had anything been said when you took tea with them on that occasion about calling again? —That same evening Mr. Bartlett requested me to call oftener than I had done previously. I believe I called on the following Wednesday, and spent the evening with them. Mr. and Mrs. Bartlett left The Cottage at Merton Abbey about the end of August or the beginning of September. I was in Dublin for about a week in June, and I took the degree of Bachelor of Arts at Trinity College there. On my return, Mr. Bartlett told me that he would like Mrs. Bartlett to take up her studies again, and he requested me to take the supervision of them. In consequence of that, I called upon her from time to time and gave her lessons in Latin and history, and also in geography and mathematics. Besides calling on Mrs. Bartlett in that way, she called on me at Wimbledon, or, rather, I should say that I took her to my apartments with her husband's knowledge. I came to be on very intimate terms with both Mr. and Mrs. Bartlett.

I remember their going from Merton Abbey to Dover at the beginning of September. They were away there for about a month. Mr. Bartlett requested me to go down and see them there, and he took me with him, paying my fare. I went down twice, but I believe that on the second occasion I paid my fare myself. Of course, I knew him as a man of business, well to do in business. All the time that I knew them, and at Dover, they lived together as man and wife, as far as I could judge. While I was at Dover Mr. Bartlett wrote to me, and I think I replied to his letter. (Shown two letters)—One of these is Mr. Bartlett's letter to me and the other is my reply. They are as follows:—" 14 St. James Street, Dover, Monday. Dear George,—Permit me to say I feel great pleasure in thus addressing you for the first time. To me

135

Adelaide Bartlett.

Rev. George Dyson

it is a privilege to think that I am allowed to feel towards you as a brother, and I hope our friendship may ripen as time goes on, without anything to mar its future brightness. Would that I could find words to express my thankfulness to you for the very loving letter you sent Adelaide to-day. It would have done anybody good to see her overflowing with joy as she read it whilst walking along the street, and afterwards as she read it to me. I felt my heart going out to you. I long to tell you how proud I feel at the thought I should soon be able to clasp the hand of the man who from his heart could pen such noble thoughts. Who can help loving you? I felt that I must say two words, ' Thank you,' and my desire to do so is my excuse for troubling you with this. Looking towards the future with joyfulness, I am, yours affectionately, Edwin."

" 18 Parkfields, Putney, September 23, 1885. My dear Edwin,—Thank you very much for the brotherly letter you sent me yesterday. I am sure I respond from my heart to your wish that our friendship may ripen with the lapse of time, and I do so with confidence, for I feel that our friendship is founded on a firm, abiding basis—trust and esteem. I have from a boy been ever longing for the confidence and trust of others. I have never been so perfectly happy as when in possession of this. It is in this respect, among many others, that you have shown yourself a true friend. You have thanked me, and now I thank you, yet I ought to confess that I read your warm and generous letter with a kind of half fear—a fear lest you should ever be disappointed in me and find me a far more prosy, matter-of-fact creature than you expect. Thank you, moreover, for the telegram; it was very considerate to send it. I am looking forward with much pleasure to next week. Thus far I have been able to stave off any work, and trust to be able to keep it clear. Dear old Dover, it will ever possess a pleasant memory for me in my mind and a warm place in my heart. With very kind regards, believe me, yours affectionately, George."

On leaving Dover, Mr. and Mrs. Bartlett went to 85 Claverton Street. I was then living at 18 Parkfields, Putney. I had a season ticket from Putney to Waterloo, which was given to me by Mr. Bartlett. At this time I had a fresh chapel at Putney, larger than the one I was in before. My name was put up as the minister on the notice board in front of the chapel. I do not think that Mr. and Mrs. Bartlett came over to that chapel, but I used to visit them at Claverton Street from time to time.

Upon your first visit there, do you remember some conversations that you had with Mrs. Bartlett about her husband. Just apply your mind and state fully everything you remember she said?—I remarked, I remember, how her husband seemed to throw us together, and asked how it was. I thought it was remarkable. She told me that his life was not likely to be a long

Evidence for Prosecution.

one, and that he knew it, and she repeated what he had told me himself, that his friends were not kind to her—that they did not understand her, being a foreigner; that he had confidence in me and affection for me—I am giving the words as near as I can recollect—and that he wished me to be a guardian to her. He knew I should be a friend to her when he was gone.

I want you to state, if you can remember, more in detail what she said about her husband's state.

Mr. CLARKE—What he has given us is repeating what he has heard from Mr. Bartlett.

Examination continued—I want all she said. You had heard it before from Mr. Bartlett, you say? Just repeat all you can remember what she said about Mr. Bartlett's illness, and what was the matter with him?—I do not know whether it was then or later. I asked her what was shortening his life, and she told me that he had an internal complaint, and that he had had this for some five or six years, I think; that she herself had been his nurse and had doctored him by his express wish. She said that he was very sensitive about this affliction, and on that account he had had no regular doctor to attend him.

Did she say anything that had happened while she was attending him while he had this internal complaint?—I do not remember her saying anything then.

Anything about the chloroform?—Not then, not at that time. I do not recollect anything more that she said then.

Afterwards what more did she say, when you have been to Claverton Street, about her husband?—Later she told me that the disease caused him very great pain, and to soothe him she had been accustomed to use chloroform. She told me that she went for advice to Dr. Nichols, in Fopstone Road, Kingston, or Earl's Court. I cannot recollect what she said—simply that she gave me to understand that he gave her advice. She mentioned that Annie Walker came to see him occasionally and brought him what medicine he needed.

By Mr. JUSTICE WILLS—Annie Walker was a lady nurse.

Examination continued—She told me that Annie Walker had nursed her husband in one of the earlier attacks which he had. I do not remember her telling me how she first became acquainted with Annie Walker. She told me on one occasion that Annie Walker had brought her chloroform. I frequently spoke to her about Dr. Nichols, as I was interested in him.

By Mr. JUSTICE WILLS—Did you know him?—No, but I was interested to know something about him.

Examination continued—I did not know Dr. Nichols at all.

Did you know that there was such a person?—No. I cannot say what I said to Mrs. Bartlett about Dr. Nichols.

At this time was not the doctor, as far as you know, attending on Mr. Bartlett at the house?—No, not that I know of.

Adelaide Bartlett.

Rev. George Dyson

Do you remember anything further that was said by Mrs. Bartlett about Mr. Bartlett's illness?—She said it was an internal complaint; I remember nothing more.

Was anything said about his death, as to how long he might live?—Oh, yes, that Dr. Nichols had said he might die within twelve months. I do not remember anything more being said as to when Mr. Bartlett might die.

By Mr. JUSTICE WILLS—I mean that Mr. Bartlett might die within twelve months from the time that Mrs. Bartlett was speaking. She did not say when Dr. Nichols had seen him last.

Examination continued—I do not remember anything more that was said. Up to that time, when this conversation took place at Claverton Street, Mr. Bartlett had seemed to me to be in good health, as far as I could judge, except that he was very weary in the evening when he returned from business. He returned from business at various times, sometimes at ten o'clock at night, and at other times he would return to dinner about five. He appeared to me to have a very severe pain in his left side; I have often seen him place his hand there convulsively.

Did he say anything to you as to what was the matter with him?—Yes, he told me that he had suffered from dyspepsia severely. He mentioned that some years previously he had had a severe illness, and that on that occasion his wife sat up for a fortnight with him and nursed him very faithfully. As far as I recollect, he said that it was dyspepsia or dysentery that he suffered from then. During my visits to Claverton Street I continued to give instruction to Mrs. Bartlett. I used to go there two or three times a week, generally about three o'clock in the afternoon. On one occasion only I went at half-past nine in the morning, and Mr. and Mrs. Bartlett and I left about half-past ten to go to the St. Bernard Dog Show. When I went in the afternoons I usually stayed until about half-past four if I had an evening engagement, otherwise I should remain the evening. I still continued on very intimate terms with both Mr. and Mrs. Bartlett.

I knew of Mr. Bartlett's illness, commencing about 10th December. I think I saw him on the day he was laid up, or just about that time—probably two or three days before. He seemed then to be very wearied and very much depressed. I saw him several times during his illness. The first time I saw him he was on the small bed in the drawing-room, and Mrs. Bartlett was nursing him. I first heard that I was the executor under his will about the middle of September, as far as I can fix the date. Mr. Bartlett informed me of that. I heard that Dr. Leach was attending him during his illness, and I heard that he was suffering from dysentery.

Anything further?—I heard that he was suffering from worms.

138

Evidence for Prosecution.

Rev. George Dyson

He told me so himself—indeed, I heard the whole course of the illness. He seemed to be troubled with sleeplessness as much as anything else.

During the Christmas week I went to my home at Poole, and I returned on Saturday, 26th. I went to the house then, and I saw Mr. Bartlett. He was up. He seemed very prostrate, and he told me that he suffered from great sleeplessness, and that he regretted that, because it kept Mrs. Bartlett from having any sleep. He said he was glad I had returned, as he was afraid she was breaking down with nursing him, and he told me about worms. I called about two o'clock that afternoon, and remained till about seven or eight in the evening.

From his conversation and manner, how did he appear to be as to spirits?—He seemed very depressed. As far as I recollect, I was in the room all the time. I must correct one thing I have said; he was depressed on the Sunday.

When was it that Mrs. Bartlett said anything to you about the chloroform?—On the Sunday night, the 27th. Mr. Bartlett was in the room at Claverton Street. My conversation with Mrs. Bartlett took place while she and I were going to the post, about nine or half-past nine. She told me she wanted some chloroform, and that Annie Walker had brought the chloroform to her before. She said that she wanted it to soothe her husband, to give him sleep, and she asked me if I could get some for her. I told her I would, and I did.

First of all, I want you to apply your mind to the conversation on that Sunday night. Was anything more said, that you remember, about it? Did she say how the chloroform was to be used?—She said she wanted it for external application. She told me that Annie Walker had gone to America, and that she knew of no one else that could get it for her but me. I do not recollect anything more.

By Mr. JUSTICE WILLS—Did it not occur to you that there was a doctor in attendance?—Oh, yes, and I asked her to get it through the doctor.

Examination continued—She told me that he did not know that she was skilled in drugs and medicines, and, not knowing that, he would not entrust her with it.

Was her medicine chest mentioned at any time?—She had mentioned to me before, on one of my visits to Claverton Street, that she had a medicine chest. She had mentioned the medicine chest at other times, and, as far as I recollect, she did mention it then.

What about it?—She spoke of the fact that she understood medicine. I agreed to get the chloroform for her.

By Mr. JUSTICE WILLS—She said she wanted the chloroform to soothe her husband, to get him to sleep.

Adelaide Bartlett.

Rev. George Dyson

Did she give any explanation of what she meant by external use?—Yes, that she used it with a handkerchief.

You mean by inhalation, then?—I suppose so. She said she sprinkled it on a handkerchief.

Examination continued—I was to get a medicine draught bottle. She said that it was volatile, quickly used, and that she would require that amount. She did not state the size of the bottle, but I understood her to mean the ordinary draught bottle. I do not recollect anything further that was said by her about the chloroform on that occasion. We returned to the house in about a quarter of an hour's time. She gave me money to buy the chloroform—I think she gave me a sovereign, but I cannot be sure about the amount. Nothing was said as to how much it would cost. When we got back to the house, somewhere about nine or ten, I saw Mr. Bartlett. I think I left the house about half-past ten.

By Mr. JUSTICE WILLS—I did not say anything to Mr. Bartlett about this intended purchase of chloroform.

Examination continued—When I left the house on the Sunday night, 27th December, I wrote to a medical student, Theodore Stiles, asking if he would get me some chloroform. He was at Poole at that time, and I wrote to him there. He is not in town now that I know of. He is at the Medical College in Bristol. I did not keep a copy of my letter to him. I did not receive any answer to that letter. I telegraphed to him at Bristol. He was a friend of mine. I did not get any chloroform from him.

On Monday, the 28th, did you purchase the chloroform yourself?—Yes, on the Monday. I went into an oil and colour shop first, mistaking it for a chemist's. As I did not get it there, I went to Mr. Humble's, next door—Mr. Humble, the chemist, 190 Richmond Road, Putney. I think I went there between nine and ten o'clock. His shop is about four or five minutes' walk from where I live. I had passed the shop every day, but I had never been into it before. The chapel, of which I was the minister, was about 50 yards away from the shop. I purchased an ounce bottle full of chloroform.

What did you ask for?—I asked for chloroform. I was served with it, and I paid 1s. or 1s. 3d. I was asked whether I wanted camphorated chloroform, and I said, "No, pure chloroform." I was first shown a half-ounce bottle, but, as I wanted a larger quantity, I bought an ounce.

By Mr. JUSTICE WILLS—Why did you not say at once, "I want a 6-ounce bottle, a regular medicine bottle"?—I asked him for some chloroform; I did not mention any particular quantity.

You said you understood you were asked to purchase a medicine bottle full. I do not understand why you did not ask straight out for a medicine bottle full?—I do not remember what

140

Evidence for Prosecution.

Rev. George Dyson

was in my mind at the time. I did not mention the quantity to him.

Examination continued—Did you say what you wanted it for?—I did not give the right reason. He asked me whether I wanted camphorated chloroform, and, as far as I remember, he touched his mouth so as to know whether it was for the teeth. I did not answer that question. But I asked, " Is it good for taking out grease stains?" I think he told me that it was. I then bought it and paid for it. The stopper was in the usual way, with a leather top tied over it. It was labelled " Chloroform." Some bottles had " Poison " on, but I cannot say whether this one had. There was also the usual chemist's label on giving the name and address. I next went to Mr. Penrose's shop at Wimbledon. That is the business of Cadman & Co., The Ridgeway, of which Mr. Penrose is the manager. I should think that would be about three miles from Mr. Humble's shop. I had known Mr. Penrose for about eighteen months. He was an occasional hearer at a chapel where I officiated, and I knew him very well.

What did you say to him about the purchase of chloroform—for what purpose did you want it?—For taking out grease stains. I forget whether I asked for the quantity or not.

Did you tell him how you had got the grease stains?—On being down in the country, down at Poole. He made up an ounce bottle, and then I asked him for another one. I bought the two bottles of one ounce each, but I do not remember the price. These bottles were properly labelled, " Chloroform, Poison," and also the usual chemist's label giving the name and address. I then went to Mr. Mellin's at 36 High Street. Mr. Mellin is a chemist, and I have known him for about eighteen months. Mr. Mellin was a member of my congregation. I asked him for some chloroform.

For what purpose?—I gave him the same reason. I bought one bottle containing 2 ounces or an ounce and a half. I am not sure which. I do not remember what price I paid to Mr. Mellin. The bottle I bought at Mr. Mellin's was a blue bottle, with the words " Poison, not to be taken " on the bottle. My last purchase was about two o'clock in the afternoon. I took the four bottles to my own house at Putney, and I poured the chloroform from them into one bottle—a light, colourless, square-shaped bottle similar to the one which is now shown to me. I had got that bottle from my landlady. I cannot remember whether I cleaned it out, but it is probable that I would do so. I took the label off the blue bottle, as far as I remember, and put it on to this bottle in which I had poured the chloroform. I think the words on the label were " Chloroform, Poison," because it was a long label, but I cannot be quite sure as to whether " Poison " was on it. Certainly the word " Chloroform " was on the bottle.

Adelaide Bartlett.

Rev. George Dyson

On the following day, Tuesday, 29th, I took the one bottle containing the chloroform to Claverton Street. I should think this would be between two and three o'clock in the afternoon. I saw a visitor there—a Mr. Hackett, I believe. Mrs. Bartlett was there. I gave her the bottle containing the chloroform whilst we were out for a stroll on the Embankment. I asked her if that would do, and she said it would. I think I told her some of it was methylated.

Had she told you what sort to get?—No, just chloroform. I knew that some of the chloroform I had purchased was methylated. After asking her if it would do, I do not remember anything more that was said. I had had a sovereign from her and I gave her the change, but I do not remember when. I went back with her to the house in Claverton Street, and saw Mr. Bartlett there. I stayed with him until six or seven. He was up and dressed then.

How did he appear to be on that Tuesday?—He seemed very weak. He seemed brightened by the fact that he had gone out for a drive, but he was still troubled with his sleeplessness. I called again on the Wednesday. He was then in bed, and appeared to be about the same; I do not recollect any difference. I saw Mrs. Bartlett when I called on the Wednesday, and I apologised to her as she was offended at something I had said on the previous day, Tuesday.

What was it?—I had advised her to get a nurse to assist her, consequent upon her telling me that the friends were saying unkind things about her—that she was not giving him full nursing attention. I do not know that she mentioned any names. I told her that it would be better in the eyes of the world if she were to have a nurse with her—meaning that that would stop them. She was offended, and said that I suspected or did not trust her. I told her that I trusted her thoroughly, and Mr. Bartlett overheard. This conversation took place in the room after the return from the walk. Mr. Bartlett did not hear the whole of the conversation. But he heard that exclamation and saw I was distressed with it.

By Mr. Justice Wills—Did he hear that she told you the friends were saying unkind things, and that you advised her to have a nurse. Did he hear the whole of that?—Oh, that I cannot say. He was walking about the room at the time; but I know he heard those words " respect " or " trust."

Mr. Clarke—There was one conversation on Wednesday, and another conversation had taken place on Tuesday which on Wednesday was apologised for. The question is whether Mr. Bartlett heard both those conversations.

Examination continued—The conversation about getting a second person to nurse was, I understand, after you returned from the walk on the Embankment. You were in the room?—Yes. Mr. Bartlett was walking about there, and she said, " You don't

Evidence for Prosecution.

Rev. George Dyson

trust me." He said, " Oh yes, you may trust her. If you had twelve years' experience of her as I have, you would know you could trust her." It was in consequence of that that I returned on the Wednesday morning. I was troubled about it. Mr. Bartlett was in bed alone when I was shown into the front room, and I told him I wished to see Mrs. Bartlett. I then apologised to Mrs. Bartlett for what had taken place on the previous Tuesday.

By Mr. JUSTICE WILLS—Mr. Bartlett requested the servant to show me downstairs when I told him that I wished to speak to Mrs. Bartlett.

Examination continued—I saw Mrs. Bartlett downstairs, and told her that I was distressed that she should say such a thing. I do not remember saying anything more. This would be between ten and eleven o'clock in the morning. I then left, and did not return until the next day, Thursday, the 31st, about two or three o'clock in the afternoon. I saw Mr. and Mrs. Bartlett. He seemed nervous, and he was in great pain from his teeth. He said he was expecting the doctor, and he asked me to call and tell him to come. I went to Dr. Leach, but I did not see him. I think I saw the servant-maid, and I left a message. I returned direct to the house at Claverton Street. I saw Dr. Leach there, in the front room. After he left Mrs. Bartlett told me that the doctor had said that mortification of the jaw had set in. I left about six or seven o'clock.

By Mr. JUSTICE WILLS—Mrs. Bartlett told me that in his room, the front room. I think Mr. Bartlett was present, but I cannot swear to that.

Examination continued—About what time did you leave?—I left about half-past four or five. That was the last time I saw Mr. Bartlett. He was up then and getting ready to go to the dentist, if I remember rightly. I did not go to the house the following day, the Friday. I received a letter from Mrs. Bartlett that day, but I destroyed it within a few days of receiving it.

As near as you can remember, what was stated in that letter to you? How did she address you?—I cannot remember—I think as " Dear Mr. Dyson." She said that it was her grief to tell me that Mr. Bartlett had died somewhere about two o'clock, as far as she could judge, and she requested me to call and see her on the Saturday, about the middle of the morning. I believe she addressed me in that letter as " Dear Mr. Dyson."

By Mr. JUSTICE WILLS—Surely you can tell. You are not likely to forget a thing of that sort, I should have thought. How was she in the habit of addressing you in her letters?—She used my Christian name in some letters, but I cannot swear to this particular one.

Examination continued—I called on the morning of Saturday, 2nd January, about eleven or twelve o'clock, and I saw Mrs. Bart-

143

Adelaide Bartlett.

Rev. George Dyson

lett in the front room upstairs. I did not write to say that I was coming. Mr. Bartlett was lying in the back room.

Now, Mr. Dyson, state fully what passed between you and Mrs. Bartlett on this Saturday morning about the death, and everything she said?—She asked me whether I did not consider it was sudden. I said it was very sudden. She then described the night of his death and said, " I was sitting by the bedside reading and had my hand or arm round Edwin's foot," and I think she said she dozed off to sleep, and when she woke through the feeling of pain in her arm she found Mr. Bartlett turned over; she expected that the turning over had caused this cramp in her arm; she gave him brandy, and then she roused the household. That was the account she gave me.

Eh?—That was what she told me of the death.

Anything said about the doctor?—About the doctor?

Yes?—That he had ordered a post-mortem, and she told me that it was to be held that afternoon. I asked her what he had died from.

Was this before the post-mortem?—This was before the post-mortem. She said the doctor told her that he thought some small blood vessel must have broken near the heart or on the heart—I cannot be sure of which. I do not recollect anything more.

How long did you stay with her on that occasion?—I remained to the post-mortem, which was held in the afternoon. I was downstairs during the post-mortem, and Mrs. Bartlett was downstairs also.

Did anything further pass between you on the subject of her husband's death?—Not that I remember.

By Mr. JUSTICE WILLS—Mr. Wood, the solicitor, and my co-executor, was also downstairs with us. I think he came in the afternoon, but I cannot be sure about the time.

Examination continued—He came before the post-mortem. After the post-mortem we went upstairs to hear the result. Mrs. Bartlett went upstairs with us. Mr. Bartlett, sen., was there the latter part of the time of waiting. We all went up into the front room to hear the result. Besides the doctors there were present Mrs. Bartlett, Mr. Bartlett, sen., Mr. Wood, and myself. Dr. Leach said that they had conducted a careful post-mortem examination, and had failed to discover the cause of death. He said that the rooms were to be locked and sealed and handed over to the coroner.

Did Dr. Leach in the presence of Mrs. Bartlett say anything else about the cause of death—anything that had happened at the post-mortem?—Not to my knowledge. I went away with Mrs. Bartlett to Mrs. Matthews. I think we left the house about four or five o'clock. I took Mrs. Bartlett to Mr. and Mrs. Matthews, at 98 Friern Road, East Dulwich, they being friends of Mrs. Bartlett's. On the way I had some conversation with her. I asked

The Rev. George Dyson.

Evidence for Prosecution.

Rev. George Dyson

her if she had used the chloroform, and she said, " I have not used it. I have not had occasion to use it. The bottle is there just as you gave it me." She also said, " This is a very critical time with me." She told me to put away from my mind the fact that she had possessed this medicine chest, and that I had given her the chloroform. She told me that I must not worry her about it.

By Mr. JUSTICE WILLS—What did you say to her when she said it was a critical time and you must put away the fact that you helped her to have chloroform?—I cannot remember what the answer was.

Examination continued—I told her on our way to the Matthews that I should see the doctor and would ask him about the post-mortem. I do not recall any more conversation on the way. When we got to Mr. and Mrs. Matthews I went into the house and saw Mrs. Matthews. I do not think I had any conversation with Mrs. Bartlett in the Matthews' house. She introduced me to Mrs. Matthews as Mr. Dyson, and then she told Mrs. Matthews of the post-mortem, and she told her of the fact that she had come to stay with her. Nothing further passed in the house that night about the death or about chloroform, so far as I recollect. I next saw Mrs. Bartlett on the morning of Monday, the 4th, at Mrs. Matthews. She was alone when I first saw her. I had seen Dr. Leach that day, and he had shown me some notes of the post-mortem. I went direct from Dr. Leach and asked Mrs. Bartlett what she had done with the chloroform.

What did she say?—She was very angry with me for troubling her about it.

But what did she say?—She said, " Oh, damn the chloroform! "

How did she behave? What did she say or do?—She was angry. She stamped her foot on the ground, and she rose from her chair, and then Mrs. Matthews came in. Mrs. Matthews left the room again, and I had a further conversation with Mrs. Bartlett.

By Mr. JUSTICE WILLS—Was nothing further said when Mrs. Matthews came in during the time she was in the room?—Mrs. Matthews asked her what she was troubled about, but I do not remember her reply. Mrs. Matthews then left the room, and I told Mrs. Bartlett about my having seen Dr. Leach, and that either chlorodyne or chloroform, some drops of it, had been found in the stomach of the deceased Mr. Bartlett. Then she asked me to tell her which it was—either chlorodyne or chloroform—and I told her I was not sure, that I confused the two.

Examination continued—I then spoke to her about her husband's sickness, of which she had told me. I asked Mrs. Bartlett whether she had not told me—or, rather, I emphasised the fact to her, that she had told me that her husband was suffering from

L   145

Adelaide Bartlett.

Rev. George Dyson

this internal complication, and probably then I spoke of the fact that nothing was said about this complication in the post-mortem, and I asked her if she did not tell me that her husband's life would be a short one. I said, " You did tell me that Edwin was going to die shortly."

By Mr. JUSTICE WILLS—Well?—She said she did not.

Examination continued—What did you say?—I said that I was a ruined man.

What more, if anything?—Mrs. Matthews was in the room at that time. She had come in.

What more?—She said I had better leave.

Did you say anything more, do you remember, about a ruined man?—No, I do not think I said anything but that. I then left.

Before you left was anything said about a piece of paper? —I do not remember it—I cannot remember everything that was said.

When Mrs. Matthews was in the room was there anything said about poetry?—Yes, I did mention to Mrs. Bartlett a piece of poetry—I asked her for a piece of poetry that I had given her. I am not prepared to swear it was on this occasion I asked her that. To my recollection it was on the Wednesday. When I did mention it she said it was at Claverton Street. It was some verses about herself that I had written, and had given to her some few weeks previously. Her husband read it. I do not recollect anything more that passed on Monday, the 4th. I saw her again the same night. She spoke about the chloroform then.

What did she say?—I told her I was going to make a clean breast of the affair, that I should tell everything I knew about it. I cannot say if that was on that occasion, or whether it was earlier in the day that I said it. She said she did not wish me to do so. She did not wish me to mention the chloroform. I cannot recall her exact words, but the substance of it was that I was not to say anything about the chloroform. I repeated my intention.

How did you repeat your intention? What was the substance of what you said?—The substance was this, that I was puzzled, I was very much perplexed and alarmed, and the best thing I could do in this matter was to tell what I knew of the matter and of my having bought the chloroform. I do not remember what was said to that, I cannot remember whether she made any answer. I returned her a watch which she had given me on the Saturday, and which she told me her husband had left to me, as it was his wish that I should have that watch in memory of him when he was gone. She gave it to me before the post-mortem.

Did anything more pass between you on that Monday?—Yes, I gave her money for a cheque that I had changed for her. She had asked me to change a cheque for £5, signed by her husband.

146

Evidence for Prosecution.

Rev. George Dyson

I had received that sum two or three weeks before the death. It was for expenses which I had been put to when I was with them at Dover. She told me it was Mr. Bartlett's wish that I should not suffer any expenses owing to my connection with them. The cheque was for £5, and I gave her back £4 that evening. Nothing more happened that evening. I cannot remember when I gave her the change for the sovereign which I had received to buy the chloroform with. The four bottles which had contained the chloroform were still at my lodgings. I did not see Mrs. Bartlett on the Tuesday, but I saw her on Wednesday, the 6th.

Where do you say the bottles were on the evening of Monday, the 4th?—On the evening of Monday they were on Wandsworth Common. When I said that they were at my lodgings I thought that Saturday was the day that was being referred to. On the Sunday morning I had thrown the four bottles away on Wandsworth Common on the way to chapel at Putney. I pointed out to one of the officers in this case where I had thrown these bottles away. I threw them away as I walked along the path. As far as I know I took the label off the one bottle, and the others would have the labels on, I presume. On Tuesday, the 5th, I went to see the solicitor, Mr. Wood. He gave me some letters for Mrs. Bartlett, and I left these at Mrs. Matthews' house on the Wednesday.

Were these unopened letters which had come by post, or were they a bundle of opened letters?—They were some sorted letters— two or three dozen, I should think.

By Mr. JUSTICE WILLS—They were letters that I had been sorting with Mr. Wood at his office. They were old letters to Mr. Bartlett from various people.

Examination continued—I gave Mrs. Bartlett the letters on the Wednesday. Mr. Wood showed me the will, but whether then or later I do not know. The first time I saw it was in Mr. Wood's possession at the office, but whether on the Tuesday, or later, I cannot say.

On the Wednesday Mrs. Matthews and Mrs. Bartlett were going to Claverton Street, and, as it was snowing heavily, I fetched a cab for them, and went with them to Peckham Rye Station. I do not remember anything passing between me and Mrs. Bartlett.

Do you remember whether on the Wednesday any conversation took place between you and Mrs. Bartlett?—There was sure to have been some conversation.

Anything about Mr. Bartlett's death and the chloroform?— Probably, but I really cannot remember. On that day Mrs. Bartlett and I came down to Victoria by train, and I went to buy some cord for Mrs. Bartlett's boxes, arranging to meet Mrs. Bartlett and Mrs. Matthews at Dr. Leach's. When I went to Dr.

147

Adelaide Bartlett.

Rev. George Dyson

Leach's I found that they had gone on to Claverton Street. I saw Dr. Leach, and I inquired for Mrs. Bartlett and Mrs. Matthews. He told me that they had gone on to the house, and as I was leaving he gave me Mrs. Bartlett's keys and told me that the coroner had done with the rooms, and requested me to take the keys to her. I went on to Claverton Street, but I was not allowed to go into the house. Afterwards I saw Mrs. Bartlett outside the door at Claverton Street, and I gave her the keys and said that the doctor had sent them for her. She, Mrs. Matthews, and I returned to Dr. Leach's house. Nothing passed between Mrs. Bartlett and me then.

I attended the inquest before the coroner, Mr. Braxton-Hicks, on 7th January. It was held at Pimlico, near the Buckingham Palace Road. Mrs. Bartlett was also present. I was not represented on that occasion, but I heard the witnesses examined. The inquest was adjourned to 4th February.

Up to that time had you told anybody except Mrs. Bartlett that you had purchased this chloroform?—Yes.

To whom had you mentioned it——

Mr. CLARKE—I object.

Mr. JUSTICE WILLS—I think it is inadmissible at this stage. Something may occur to make it evidence, but at this stage we cannot go into it, I think.

Examination continued—After the inquest Mrs. Bartlett and I had dinner together in a private room at Mrs. Stuard's, the confectioner's shop. I should think we were together there for about an hour. We discussed the recent events which had happened—the post-mortem, and my having bought the chloroform, and so forth. She told me I was distressing myself unnecessarily, and I gave her to understand that I thought I had reasons to be alarmed. I remember one thing she said—that if I did not incriminate myself she would not incriminate me. I told her I was aware of my perilous position, but I was not afraid to stand to the truth as it affected me, and I should persist in my intention to make a full and complete statement. I was aware that the contents of the stomach had been sent to be analysed. I next saw Mrs. Bartlett on Saturday, the 9th January; I met her accidentally at Mr. Matthews' place of business, and returned with both of them to Mr. Matthews' house. On that occasion we discussed the subject; I was anxious to know what really had become of the chloroform, and I told her that I was puzzled. She was indignant at me, and asked me why I did not charge her outright with having given it to him. I do not recollect anything more that was said about the chloroform.

By Mr. JUSTICE WILLS—When she said, " Why do you not charge me outright with having given it to him," what did you say?—I cannot tell you every word that I said, but it was to the effect that I was not prepared to do such a thing as that. I believe

148

Evidence for Prosecution.

Rev. George Dyson

it was on that occasion that she told me she had poured the chloroform away and thrown the bottle out of the carriage window as she was coming from London on Wednesday, 6th January.

Examination continued—That was in the train returning from London to Peckham Rye, which is the station near to the Matthews. I cannot remember anything more that was said on the 9th. The funeral took place on the Friday, and I saw Mr. Matthews that day. The communication I made to Mr. Matthews was not on that day; it was on Wednesday, the 6th. I did not see Mrs. Bartlett after the 9th.

I attended the adjourned inquest on 4th February. Mrs. Bartlett was there. I was legally represented, and I presume Mrs. Bartlett was also represented. The inquest was again adjourned to 11th February. I was called as a witness before the coroner then, and I presume that I was cautioned.

Were you called at your own request?—I was *subpœnæd* to attend as a witness. I believe Mrs. Bartlett was arrested that day after I had been examined. I was examined again on the 15th, and again on the 18th, when there were one or two questions put to me. I was arrested on the 18th on the charge of wilful murder, and I was afterwards taken before the magistrate and committed for trial.

I am twenty-eight years of age now. I have kissed Mrs. Bartlett in her husband's presence.

I believe by the rules of your body, the Wesleyan body, the earliest period at which you can marry after you enter the ministry is two years?—There is a prohibition of from six to seven years. I could have married next October or thereabouts.

By Mr. JUSTICE WILLS—In June last I was lodging at 12 Thornton Road, Wimbledon.

Cross-examined by Mr. CLARKE—The last day that you had any conversation with Mrs. Bartlett was Saturday, 9th January, I understood you to say?—It was.

On that day you spoke to her about the chloroform?—Yes.

And she was indignant?—Very indignant.

And she said, why did not you charge her outright with having given chloroform to her husband?—Words to that effect.

It was from her lips you first heard that suggestion?—Yes.

Had you made the suggestion before?—No, I had not; it was from her lips I first heard it.

In an indignant tone?—Very, indeed.

And since that day you have never conversed with her?—Since that day, not up to my arrest.

You have just said, in answer to my friend, that you have kissed her, and kissed her in her husband's presence?—I have.

Was there any secret between you, or any secret understanding between you, apart from her husband?—None.

You knew nothing of Mr. Bartlett and his wife until you

Adelaide Bartlett.

Rev. George Dyson

had seen them at the chapel at which you ministered?—No. I understood the learned counsel asked me the question with regard to a secret understanding, too, in reference to marriage, and I answered it in that regard.

As to marriage, it was not a secret understanding?—It was not a secret understanding.

There was no secret understanding with regard to marriage. Was there any impropriety of conduct between you and Mrs. Bartlett?—There was not; that is to say, I kissed her.

That would be an impropriety—you do not defend that?—No.

By Mr. Justice Wills—You mean to say it was only in her husband's presence?—And out of his presence.

Cross-examination continued—Whatever your relations were with regard to Mrs. Bartlett, they were relations that were known to her husband?—Oh, yes.

We have the letter which you wrote in September in which you addressed him as " My dear Edwin "?—You have.

And about that time you had taken to speak of him as Edwin? —Yes.

And he of you as George?—Yes.

Did he speak of his wife to you as Adelaide?—Yes.

I see in that letter you say, " I have from a boy ever been longing for the confidence and trust of others, and I have never been so perfectly happy as when in the possession of this," &c. " You have shown yourself a true friend." Had he at the time that you wrote that letter placed implicit confidence and trust in you?—He had; so I judged.

And you believed?—Yes.

And, in your belief, did he continue to repose that implicit confidence and trust in you to the very last hour of his life?—He did.

Now, in that letter you say—" I respond from my heart to your wish that our friendship may ripen with the lapse of time." That was your real and sincere wish, was it?—That was my wish.

And did you down to the last day of his life endeavour to reciprocate his friendship and to deserve his confidence?—I did.

Were you sincerely solicitous for his welfare?—Yes.

And do you believe that every day of that illness you and his wife were both anxious for his welfare and tried to serve him?— I do.

You have said just now that you have lately ascertained— that is, since you were examined at the coroner's inquest—that only one year instead of two had to elapse before you were allowed to marry?—That is so.

Down to the time that you were examined on 11th January you believed, did you not, that you could not in any case be allowed to marry till October, 1887?—I had that belief.

Evidence for Prosecution.

Rev. George Dyson

You had never inquired particularly?—What do you mean by a particular inquiry?

You told my learned friend, when you were examined before the coroner, that you had inquired, and you found your previous impression was a mistaken one?—I did not inquire, but I was told so.

Told so by some one who, in your belief, knew?—Yes.

And you believe that your present impression is the true one? —Yes.

Then you had never inquired before you were examined before the coroner as to whether your impression was the true one— whether you knew you could be married before 1887?—No, I never made any inquiry.

Had you ever mentioned to Mr. Bartlett the question of the time at which you could be married?—Never.

Or to Mrs. Bartlett?—I may have done so.

And, if you did so, you mentioned your then impression that you could not be married until October, 1887?—That I cannot swear.

Try and recall your thoughts. You have told me, down to the time when you were examined before the coroner, that was your belief?—Yes.

Then, if you mentioned the matter to Mrs. Bartlett, you would have mentioned the date you believed to be the true one?—Yes; but I cannot swear that I did.

You have no distinct recollection of having mentioned it at all; is that what you mean?—No; I have a recollection of mentioning it, but I have no recollection of what you ask, namely, that we could not be married till October, 1887.

I am suggesting to you that, if you mentioned it, you must have mentioned the date which, in your belief, was the true one. You would tell her the truth about it, would you not?—Certainly.

Then was it this that you mentioned to her, that you could not be married for two years?—Yes.

Was it that you did not recollect that you mentioned the date? —Yes.

You did not mention the date, but you mentioned that, according to the rules of your body, you could not be married for two years?—Precisely.

The subject of marriage had been mentioned and talked about between you and Mr. Bartlett during his lifetime?—Marriage in general, do you mean?

We will begin with marriage in general?—Yes.

And you became aware that at a very early period of your acquaintance he had peculiar ideas on the subject of marriage?— Yes.

Your earliest visit was paid to him in your pastoral character —it was that which induced you to call?—It was.

151

Adelaide Bartlett.

Rev. George Dyson

And very early in your acquaintance did he ask you whether you thought the teaching of the Bible was distinctly in favour of having one wife?—He did.

Did he suggest to you that his idea was that there might be a wife for companionship and a wife for service?—He did.

And you combated that view, and told him that the teaching of the Bible was distinctly contrary to it?—The general tenor of the Bible.

By Mr. JUSTICE WILLS—What do you mean by a wife for service? Is it household drudgery?—Yes; he explained it household duties—the general management of the household.

And what did companionship mean?—He explained that he thought the companion should be educated and intelligent, and should be his confidante in all matters.

I really want to understand what he meant; were both of them to be his bedfellows?—He never mentioned that to me, my lord.

Did he say that neither of those two wives was to be his companion in that sense?—He did not refer to that question at all.

Cross-examination continued—Just let me ask you, Mr. Dyson, did you not clearly understand that the suggestion was that one was to be the wife to him; or do you mean that he suggested to you, when visiting him in that character and talking to him about Scriptural matters—he suggested to you that a man should have two wives in that full and complete sense?—Yes; so I understood him.

That would have struck you as a most outrageous suggestion, would it not?—It struck me as a very remarkable suggestion.

What suggested itself as the explanation to you—moral obliquity or simply carelessness?—Oddity.

Because that is the man to whom afterwards you wrote in the terms I have read to you in that letter. Do you mean to suggest that the man you wrote to in those terms had actually suggested to you, a Christian minister, that he should be allowed any sexual connection with two women?—No; he never asked me such a thing; he simply asked me whether the Bible admits polygamy.

But he never suggested it for himself?—No.

He suggested it for nobody?—Yes; I understood it to be a general suggestion.

By Mr. JUSTICE WILLS—Did not it strike you as an unwholesome sort of talk in the family circle?—Not coming from him, my lord; he was a man who had some strange ideas.

Cross-examination continued—He made no secret of them?—No; he told me not.

And he would refer to those ideas from time to time, would he?—He did once or twice; not frequently.

In his wife's presence?—I think not.

One moment. Do you mean to say that there was nothing

Evidence for Prosecution.

Rev. George Dyson

between you and Mr. Bartlett which was kept secret from his wife?—I am sorry I cannot undertake to say yea or nay to that.

But to the best of your belief, was there any matter of secrecy or confidence between you and Mr. Bartlett from which his wife was excluded?—Your question does not touch the case.

Will you answer the question, and not judge it? Was there any matter of secrecy or confidence between you and Mr. Bartlett from which his wife was excluded?—I know of no secret.

By Mr. JUSTICE WILLS—Was this serious talk, or was it as a man might say joking, " I think it would be a good thing to have two wives; one for show and one for work "? He might say that in a joking sort of way. Was it that, or was it seriously said?—It was said tentatively to me, half playfully, the first time; but I have a recollection of his speaking more seriously of it on some later occasion.

Cross-examination continued—You told us that you have noticed that he put his hand on his side, and complained of some convulsive pain, I think you said?—Yes.

How early did you notice that?—I think all through the time of my knowledge of him.

Would it be as early as June or July, to begin with?—Yes; I think I noticed it at Merton Abbey.

Did you notice that a clutching occurred at other times, or on special occasions?—Yes; when he has taken wine I have seen him put his hand to his side sharply, in that way.

And did he tell you what it was that was affecting him?—No, he did not.

Did he not say anything about it?—No; I do not remember that he did.

Of course, that happened before his wife, when his wife has been there?—Yes; at the dinner hour, for instance.

When that happened to him, what did he do? Did he get up from his chair, or leave off taking wine, or what did he do?—He would leave off taking wine.

And continue his dinner?—Yes.

And the thing would pass off, whatever it was?—Yes, apparently.

How early was the question of the possible duration of his life mentioned in his presence or by him?—I cannot say how early.

Was not it at Dover?—I cannot swear that he mentioned the question of the duration of his life at Dover.

Did not he mention to you at Dover something about his condition, his health—having regard to that matter?—He did.

What was it he said at Dover?—He told me that he was not the strong man that once he was. I am not giving you the exact words.

I do not ask for the exact words. I only ask to be allowed

Adelaide Bartlett.

to hear what you say. Did he say what had been the cause of the change in him?—He attributed it to overwork.

Do you know that while he was at Dover he was working extremely hard?—I think he used to get up at three in the morning, and go to business from Dover.

He would get up at three in the morning and come up by the tidal train—the boat express?—Yes.

And go back to his wife, at what time of night?—I have known him come back at ten.

By Mr. JUSTICE WILLS—How long were you at Dover?—I spent two or three days there on two or three occasions.

Six or seven days?—Yes.

Cross-examination continued—And it was between your two visits to Dover that you wrote the letter to which I have referred? —Yes.

Referring to the first visit, you say " Dear old Dover," &c. " Thank you for the telegram. I am looking forward with much pleasure to next week." Next week you were to visit him again, were you not?—Yes.

Was that which you have told us the only reference he made while you were at Dover to the matter of his health being broken? —That is all that I remember.

But he was depressed and low-spirited from time to time, was he?—Yes; he seemed to me to be. I am not stating quite the correct thing. You say from time to time; it was more latterly— the last two months that I knew him.

But even when he was at Dover, were not there times when he was depressed and despondent?—I did not notice it.

The statement you have made about his saying he was not the strong man he was—that is all you recollect him saying at Dover? —With regard to his health.

His wife had told you, in his presence, that Edwin was very low-spirited, and did not think he would live long?—I can swear to her having said he was low-spirited. I cannot swear to her having said that he could not live long—that is, in his presence.

How early, then, was it that you were told by anybody that his life was not likely to be a long one?—When I first went to Claverton Street.

Not until then?—I cannot swear, but it is possible.

I am suggesting to you that, as early as your visit to Dover, that was the conversation in his presence about his life not being likely to be a long one. Will you swear that that did not happen? —I cannot swear to that.

You say that he was an odd man, or a man with curious ideas —I forget the phrase?—I did not say that; I beg pardon; I said it was an odd question, in answer to my lord.

Mr. JUSTICE WILLS—You said more than that; you said it was an oddity.

154

Evidence for Prosecution.

Rev. George Dyson

Cross-examination continued—A man of strange ideas in connection with the married state?—That is so.

And the terms upon which people should live in married life; is that so?—Yes.

Do you know of books which he used to read with regard to that matter?—I do not.

By Mr. JUSTICE WILLS—I had better ask it now, or I shall have to ask it afterwards. What do you mean by that—a man of strange ideas in connection with the terms upon which persons should live in married life? Tell us what you mean?—I thought the question referred to what I said before—to having two wives.

Do you remember anything more?—No.

Cross-examination continued—You were on the closest terms of intimacy with him—as brother to brother?—Yes.

Did he talk to you about the books he read?—Yes.

Did he never talk to you about this book? It is called "Esoteric Anthropology; or, the Mysteries of Man"?—It is the first time I have heard of the book.

Are you sure?—Certain.

Do you mean to say you never saw it in his possession?—Not to know it.

Just look at it (handing the book up to the witness)?—This is the first time I have seen that book.

Do you mean to say that Mr. Bartlett has not talked to you about Dr. Nichols?—No; Mr. Bartlett never mentioned him to me.

Do you mean to say that Mr. Bartlett never mentioned the name of Dr. Nichols to you?—Never.

Are you certain?—Yes; I never heard him mention Dr. Nichols.

Well, now, had he any other strange ideas with regard to marriage?—I never heard him offer any.

Did he ever make reference to marriage between you and Mrs. Bartlett after he should be dead?—Yes.

How early did he make that reference—how early in your acquaintance?—I should think it would be about the latter end of October.

They were then at Claverton Street?—I must explain; he did not mention the words there. I have conveyed a wrong impression.

If you think any answer of yours is doing yourself or, still more, anybody else, injustice, correct it?—He has made statements which left no doubt on my mind but that he contemplated Mrs. Bartlett and myself being ultimately married.

And, to the best of your recollection, was that statement first made in October?—About that time.

By Mr. JUSTICE WILLS—I must ask you to be a little more definite, and tell us what he did say. It was a very remarkable conversation, probably such a one as never occurred in the ex-

155

Adelaide Bartlett.

perience of any man in Court before, and therefore must be impressed upon your mind. What was it he said?—I can remember this; he had been finding some fault with Mrs. Bartlett, not angrily, but correcting something, and I said to him, " If ever she comes under my care, I shall have to teach her differently," or some such words.

Cross-examination continued—Well, go on?—He smiled and said something to the effect that he had no doubt I should take good care of her. I have a clear impression of such words passing between me and Mr. Bartlett.

By Mr. JUSTICE WILLS—Is it possible that this was the first of such conversations? It seems very extraordinary for a man to suggest to another man, if ever his wife came under his care, that he should have to teach her differently. Was that the first time?—The first time that I can recollect.

Cross-examination continued—Let me suggest challenging your recollection, only trying your memory. According to you, the first conversation began by your saying, " If ever she comes in my care "?—Yes.

Does not that remind you that there must have been some conversation, at some previous time or other, about her becoming your wife?—Not necessarily.

You were speaking of it as a thing assumed and known between you as likely to happen?—Precisely.

Was it assumed by you?—I so understood it.

Then there must have been a previous conversation?—Not touching the question of marriage.

What previous conversation can you suggest as having established that understanding in consequence of which you have spoken?—Conversations; one was Mr. Bartlett's letter to me.

Now, I have reminded you that letter is dated 23rd September, and was written by you while they were at Dover?—Yes.

Let me read it again; it may help you : " My dear Edwin,—Thank you very much for the brotherly letter you sent me yesterday. I am sure I respond from my heart to your wish that our friendship may ripen with the lapse of time," &c. ?—Yes.

Now, what was the conversation upon which you say that letter was founded?—A conversation which took place at Putney, when Mr. Bartlett came to see me.

Was that the conversation when he told you that he had made his will and made you the executor?—It was.

What was the conversation?—This is a very delicate matter for me.

Mr. JUSTICE WILLS—No, no; we have long outstepped the bounds of delicacy.

Cross-examination continued—When he came to see you at Putney he had come up from Dover. He came to tell you he had

Evidence for Prosecution.

Rev. George Dyson

made a will, leaving his money to his wife and leaving you as his executor ?—Yes.

Now, then, what did he tell you at that time about you and his wife?—Well, I told him that there was no denying the fact that I was growing very attached to her, and that I wished to let him know it; that it was disturbing me in my work; and I asked him whether it would not be better for me to discontinue my friendship with them, and he said, " Why should you discontinue it? "

Well?—He told me I had been a benefit to her; she liked my preaching, and it had helped and had benefited her. He showed me one of her convent letters, which she had written to him from the convent, which was a very devotional letter; and he said he should like me to endeavour to lead her back more closely to that frame of mind or disposition of heart. He said he had confidence in me, and that he should be pleased if I would continue as friendly as I had been with them. That was the substance of what he said.

What did he say with reference to the possible future?—He did not mention the future, except that he looked forward to it.

To what?—He said nothing very much; but what he said of the matter was, that he hoped we should have some pleasant inter-course.

Mr. JUSTICE WILLS—There is nothing in that.

Cross-examination continued—What about his will?—He mentioned the will to me, and said that, as a proof of confidence in me, he had selected me, with his legal man, to act as executor.

Just let me remind you; you were telling the husband that you had become attached to his wife, and you say that the husband expected you, did you not, to continue the intimacy?—Precisely.

He desired that it should continue?—Yes.

He spoke of appointing you executor to his will?—He did.

Was it not then that he said that, if anything happened to him, you and Mrs. Bartlett might come together?—No; that was later—at Claverton Street.

And you told us that, so far as you can remember, nothing more was said at that interview in September?—Not touching upon that matter; but we had a long conversation together not pertinent to this inquiry.

Not touching upon future relations between yourself and Mrs. Bartlett?—No. I must correct one thing. You asked me if he did not say, " If anything happens to me, you two may come together." Those words have gone down upon the deposi-tions; but the coroner put it in that way. I suppose he said that; and I said, " Yes; something very much like that." But I did not say that he used those words.

That being suggested to you as the meaning, you accepted it?—Yes.

Adelaide Bartlett.

Rev. George Dyson

And accept it now?—I do.

Can you remember what the words were in which it was clothed, because it is not a usual thing to take place?—No, I cannot.

There is one question I ought to ask you. I need scarcely ask you, as a gentleman, you had at that time said nothing to Mrs. Bartlett about your feelings independent of Mr. Bartlett?—I regret to say that I had.

Did you tell him that you had?—Yes.

You said that you had. Did he ask you to write to her?—He asked me to write to her before, when they went away to Dover.

But the situation was altered?—Yes; I understand you. He did ask me on one occasion to write to her.

And you wrote?—Yes.

And is that the letter to which he referred in the letter which has been mentioned, which I will read again—" Dear George,—Permit me to say that I feel great pleasure in thus addressing you for the first time," &c. That letter had been read to him, as he said, by his wife?—Yes.

After that, you wrote letters to her from time to time?—I did.

Which she, at your request, returned to you?—No.

What?—Do I understand the question, that she had returned the letters I wrote to her?

That she has returned your letters to you?—No, not one that I remember; no, I should surely recollect it.

Did not you ask her for them?—I remember her showing me one of my letters.

Did you ask her for them?—No.

Do you say that?—I say that.

By Mr. Justice Wills—Why were you so anxious to get that piece of poetry?—Because it was sentimental.

Cross-examination continued—Were not the letters sentimental?—No, not as that is; they were affectionate, but not sentimental.

Now, Mrs. Bartlett had told you that she had no friends of her own?—Yes.

And that her husband's friends were not kind to her?—Yes.

And you have told us that she said they did not understand her, she being a foreigner, and that her husband had confidence and affection for you, and so on, and that he knew you would be a friend to her. On that occasion that was said in his presence, was it not?—Not in his presence.

Did not you know from him that his friends were not kind to her?—Yes.

When had he told you that?—I believe he told it me at Merton—at least not so strongly at Merton; he said that they did

158

Evidence for Prosecution.

Rev. George Dyson

not understand her, and he was accounting for the quietness of their lives, and he gave that as a reason.

Did he mention her being a foreigner?—Yes.

And he told you she was at a later period?—Yes; he emphasised that at a later period.

And did he express to you at all times, as to the future, that he hoped you would be a friend to her when he was gone?—I remember Mrs. Bartlett telling me that.

In his presence?—No; he was not present.

Where was it?—At Claverton Street.

After the illness?—It was when they first went to Claverton Street.

Now, he told you of her having nursed him affectionately previously?—Yes.

I think you gave us the expression that if you had known her, as he had, for twelve years, and known how affectionately she had nursed him, you would not have doubted her?—Yes.

Earlier than that, had he spoken to you of the previous illness during which she had nursed him?—Yes.

When did he speak to you—what did he tell you?—He spoke of it after hearing me preach at Merton; that would be in August. I must correct myself.

By all means?—It was after my return from Dover they came to hear me preach at Merton.

Shall we alter it from Merton to when he came to hear you preach at Merton?—Yes.

And brought her with him?—Yes.

And it was after the service—what did he tell you after the service?—I was troubled with indigestion, and he said he had suffered himself from dyspepsia, and she had nursed him during the illness.

Did he say where this had been?—No.

Did he say when it had been?—Some years before that time.

Did he tell you where they had lived at the time?—Probably he would.

Do you remember?—I do not remember.

Did he tell you what doctor had attended him?—He did not mention any doctor attending him.

You can tell us no more about it, then?—No.

Did he ever tell you, or speak to you, about Mrs. Bartlett's one confinement?—I think he did.

When did he tell you of it?—At Merton.

Did you learn from him then that some few years before she had for the only time in their married life been pregnant?—He told me nothing about that.

What did he tell you?—Simply that she had this child which died.

Adelaide Bartlett.

Rev. George Dyson

Did he tell you that was the only one?—No; I do not think he mentioned more than that.

No, I suppose not; there were no more to mention, you know; that was the only child she had?—Yes.

You knew that from him?—Yes.

Was it spoken of by him in Mrs. Bartlett's presence on any occasion?—Not that I remember; indeed, I may say no. I only remember his mentioning it to me once.

Do you know that Annie Walker attended Mrs. Bartlett in her confinement?—Yes.

Who told you that?—Mrs. Matthews.

That was long afterwards; did not you know it before his death?—No, not before his death.

Are you sure about that?—Certain.

Annie Walker was mentioned?—Yes.

By Mrs. Bartlett?—Yes.

Do you mean to say that Mrs. Bartlett never said Annie Walker attended her in her confinement?—She said that Annie Walker attended her husband in his sickness.

Do you mean to say that she did not say that Annie Walker attended her in her confinement?—No.

Are you positive?—Positive. I am upon oath, and I say so; I am positive.

Tell me the date that Annie Walker was first mentioned?—I cannot.

Did you ever speak to Mrs. Bartlett about that one child?—She spoke to me about it when we were passing the cemetery at Merton.

How early in the acquaintance?—That would be before we went to Dover.

Just try and recall when Mrs. Bartlett told you about the birth of the child. Mrs. Bartlett spoke to you about it when you were near the cemetery. Was not Annie Walker's name mentioned in reference to that matter?—No; I cannot swear that it was.

Do you undertake to pledge yourself absolutely that it was not?—I think I may.

You think you may?—Yes; she was often spoken of.

Excuse my suggesting to you if she was so often spoken of, that makes it more likely. Do you undertake to swear that she was not spoken of with regard to that?—She may have been, but I cannot swear to it. I cannot pledge myself to what I am not certain of.

She was so often spoken of; and Dr. Nichols was so often spoken of—so frequently, that you say you were interested in him?—Yes.

Was that before Mr. Bartlett?—No; I never remember Dr. Nichols being mentioned before Mr. Bartlett.

160

Evidence for Prosecution.

Rev. George Dyson

Let me ask you again. You have told me you had no secret with Mrs. Bartlett from her husband. Were not you in the habit of talking in the most friendly and affectionate way with Mr. Bartlett about his illness and his business?—Excuse me; I do not think I have stated that I had any secrets with Mrs. Bartlett which her husband did not know of. You asked me about an expression of marriage, and I qualified it in that way.

Do you mean to say that you had a secret with Mrs. Bartlett about Dr. Nichols?—Yes.

How early?—After they went to Claverton Street.

Why? Had you anything to do with Dr. Nichols?—Nothing.

I do not understand. If you were in the fullest confidence with Mr. Bartlett, why did you not talk about Dr. Nichols with him?—Because Mrs. Bartlett said he might not like my mentioning it to him because of an internal affliction.

You understood that Dr. Nichols had never seen him?—No.

By Mr. JUSTICE WILLS—What had the internal affliction to do with it?—He advised Mrs. Bartlett when Mr. Bartlett was worse.

Without seeing him?—Yes; and he prescribed as to the nursing, and so on.

Cross-examination continued—Now, as soon as Mr. Bartlett was taken ill, you saw Dr. Leach?—Yes.

You were at that time on honest and true friendship with Mr. Bartlett?—Yes.

Did you ever say to Dr. Leach that it would be as well for him to see Dr. Nichols?—I did not.

Mr. JUSTICE WILLS—For him to see Dr. Nichols?

Mr. CLARKE—Yes.

The WITNESS—It never occurred to me to suggest such a thing.

Cross-examination continued—You knew his name and you knew his address?—Yes.

And you did know as a fact that Dr. Nichols was to be found at the Fopstone Road?—Yes.

Why did you not suggest to the doctor that it would be as well for him to know what Dr. Nichols had prescribed?—I never made any suggestion to the doctor.

What for?—I should have considered it impertinence.

Impertinence, when you were on terms of brotherhood with the man who was ill?—Yes; I should have considered it impertinence.

Do you really mean to say that, in your relations with Mr. and Mrs. Bartlett, you would have considered it impertinent to suggest what another medical man's opinion might be?—Yes, I do.

Now, Mr. Bartlett told you he had been suffering from dysentery, did he not?—He did.

That, according to his account, he used to suffer from that?—

Adelaide Bartlett.

Rev. George Dyson

I told you just now it was some years before I got to know Mrs. Bartlett.

We do not understand that that had anything to do with the internal disease?—I did not understand you as referring to the internal disease.

And you did not understand that he mentioned distinctly that that had nothing to do with the internal disease?—I did not know of the internal disease then. I knew of the dysentery before we went to Dover.

No name of a disease was mentioned, was it?—No.

But only something upon which Mr. Bartlett would be sensitive?—That was how it was explained to me; it was put to me in that way. Mrs. Bartlett put it that he was sensitive as to a question of his sickness.

You were with him at the very beginning of his illness, were you not?—Yes.

I think you went with him and his wife to the Dog Show?—I did.

On the 9th of December?—Yes.

And was he taken ill in the course of the evening?—He was.

Had he appeared to you before that time to be getting into an ailing and low condition?—He seemed very much worn out at night when he returned.

I think you describe him to us as being very weary, very much depressed, and complaining of suffering from sleeplessness?—During the sickness.

From the beginning of the sickness—at the beginning of the sickness?—Yes; not before the sickness.

You just said that he seemed ailing up to the time, and then, when it began, you describe him as very weary, very much depressed, and suffering from sleeplessness?—Yes.

Did he from that day up to the last time you saw him complain of sleeplessness and pain?—Yes; throughout the sickness.

As that sickness wore on did he become more depressed?—He varied.

You have seen him crying, have you not?—Yes, once.

Are you sure it was only once?—I am certain about it; I only remember seeing him once.

Could you say what date that was at all?—I think it was just before I went home before Christmas.

When did you go?—I went on the Monday in Christmas week.

That would be Monday, 21st December?—Yes.

Now, did you see Dr. Leach early during the time of the illness?—In the first week of it.

Can you tell me about how many days after he was taken ill you had any conversation with Dr. Leach?—I should think five or six.

Evidence for Prosecution.

Rev. George Dyson

Do you know anything of Dr. Leach being called in—how it was he was sent for?—Because Mr. Bartlett was so unwell.

Why was he selected? It was not anybody he knew before?—I do not know why he was selected.

You say that Monday, 21st December, was the day when he was crying?—No; I did not name the day. I said it was some time just before I left.

I thought you did?—No; I could not name days.

Mr. Justice Wills—He gave the date of his own journey.

Cross-examination continued—At the time he was crying, was he in very low spirits, and talking about not recovering?—He spoke very little indeed, and I can recollect nothing that he said to me.

Nothing that he said about being alarmed about himself, or anything of that kind?—No; I cannot remember it.

Is not it the impression on your mind that at that time he was very low-spirited, and that he should not recover?—Yes; I have the impression that he thought he would not recover.

When you came back on Saturday, 26th, you found him still worse, did you not?—Not worse.

You said that you came back on Saturday, 26th, and he was very prostrate, there was great sleeplessness, and that he said he was glad you had returned, and he was afraid his wife was breaking down in nursing him?—Yes, he said that.

Did he tell you on that day, Saturday, of his having had worms?—No.

On the Sunday—the next day?—Yes.

You told us you were there from two o'clock to seven or eight on Saturday. You went again on Sunday—at what time?—About nine or a quarter-past in the evening.

And then he was still worse, and more depressed, was he not?—No; I thought he was brighter on the Sunday.

You told me he was depressed on the Sunday?—On the Saturday.

You correct yourself, then; you said he was brighter on Saturday, and much depressed on Sunday. I am putting it to you whether on this visit, Saturday and Sunday, he was very ill, very prostrate and depressed?—Well, it is difficult to tell you; he contradicted himself.

Contradicted himself?—Yes; he asked me on Sunday whether any one could be lower than he was without passing away altogether, and he attributed that to the medicine for worms.

He asked you whether you thought it possible for a man to be lower than that without passing away altogether?—Yes.

And that very great depression you attributed to the appearance of the worms?—I cannot say it was very great depression. He had that impression of his state, but he did not seem cast down in spirits. He seemed to be bearing up well.

163

Adelaide Bartlett.

Rev, George Dyson

According to that expression, he was thinking of himself as one actually on the edge between life and death?—Yes.

But he was cheerful?—He seemed to bear up very well against it.

Did you see the doctor on the 26th or 27th?—What days would that be?

The Saturday or Sunday?—No.

How long were you there on the Saturday, as far as you remember?—I called about three, and I was there till between five and six.

Between five and six in the afternoon?—Yes; I spent the afternoon there.

On the 26th did not Dr. Leach visit him three times, on the third occasion staying several hours, because his condition was so bad?—So Mr. Bartlett told me on the Sunday. He did not tell me he visited him three times; he told me he was there that length of time.

Several hours?—Several hours.

Did he tell you the condition of his bowels was such that on the 26th he had taken two purgative draughts and also a dose of croton oil, and that he also had been galvanised in the abdomen?—Yes; he described that to me.

And that he had taken santonine as well?—No; he did not.

At all events he had taken purgatives and croton oil, and had been galvanised, and had hot tea and coffee, and did he tell you all had been no use?—Yes.

Did he tell you that the doctor had given it up in despair?—Yes; that he was going to try later in a day or two.

Now, with regard to the sleeplessness, did you know he had been having frequent injections of morphia?—Yes.

Did he tell you that even that would not give him sleep, and that he got up and walked about in the night?—Yes.

And was it with regard to that that he spoke of his wife being likely to break down under the strain of nursing him?—Yes.

Now, on the evening of the 27th you have told us that Mrs. Bartlett spoke to you about chloroform. I think you said you went out together. As a matter of fact, your going out together was an accident, was it not?—Yes; that is to say, as I came to the door, I found her going out to post some letters; and I went as far as the post, and then returned to the house with her.

I must just ask one other question on this with regard to Annie Walker; you have spoken of Dr. Nichols, and Annie Walker has been mentioned several times, and you said Mrs. Bartlett told you Annie Walker had gone to America. Will you undertake to say it was not Dr. Nichols who was mentioned as being a doctor in America—an American doctor—and that that was the way America was mentioned?—Yes; I understood he was an American—an American by extraction.

Evidence for Prosecution.

Rev. George Dyson

You must have understood that from Mrs. Bartlett?—Yes.

Well, then, she mentioned America to you in connection with the name of Dr. Nichols?—Yes, but it was rather a jumble. Do you mean, did she do that at any time or on any particular occasion?

I say at any time?—Oh, yes, she did.

Now, you see that Mr. Bartlett told you morphia would not give him sleep, and he used to get up and walk about. Did you have any conversation with him about mesmerism?—I think it is likely I did.

You alone can tell us whether you did or not—did you?—Yes, I did at Merton.

At Merton?—Yes.

Did you know him then as being a believer in mesmerism?—No.

What?—I did not know him as being a believer in mesmerism.

Did not he tell you he believed in mesmeric force?—I do not remember his telling me he believed in it; he asked me if I did.

Did he suggest he had mesmerised anybody, or that you had mesmerised him?—No.

Did he?—I cannot remember him doing that.

Cannot you tell us what sort of a conversation it was about mesmerism?—I told him a story in connection with mesmerism on this occasion.

Am I to take it you introduced the subject, or did he ask you if you believed in it?—I believe I introduced it.

You believe you introduced it?—Yes.

Did you ascertain that it was a subject to which he had given attention?—No, I did not.

Did you ever hear that he believed in mesmeric influences of a very singular kind?—No.

Did he never tell you almost at the close of his illness that that very night, the 28th, when he was so desperately ill he had got up and stood for two hours waving his hands about over his sleeping wife?—No, he did not tell me that.

Do you mean you never heard anything about that before that at all?—In evidence I have.

I am not speaking of evidence?—No, I have never heard that.

Nothing at all?—No.

Not before you were examined—not before the inquest took place, at all events?—No.

Do try and remember?—I do not remember.

You mean to say you never heard of mesmerism at all, or anything of that kind?—No; not till I heard it in evidence.

What was your income?—About £100 a year.

Had you mentioned that to Mr. Bartlett or to Mrs. Bartlett at any time?—They both knew it; yes.

It is no reproach. I do not mean it at all unpleasantly,

Adelaide Bartlett.

Rev. George Dyson

but they knew you were not competent enough to bear extra expenses—expenses of travelling, and so on, and Mr. Bartlett offered you the season ticket to Dover ?—Yes.

Which you declined, and then afterwards he gave you a season ticket by which you travelled from Putney to Victoria ?—Yes; Putney to Waterloo.

Did you, during his life, ever say anything to Mrs. Bartlett to suggest that you would marry her immediately on his death if he should die ?—Never.

The understanding that at some time or other you and she might come together, you tell me, was known to him ?—Yes.

There was no more than that understanding between you and Mrs. Bartlett, was there ?—No more.

Now, you have told us that Mrs. Bartlett mentioned to you the way in which chloroform was to be used, about sprinkling it upon a handkerchief; was it for the purpose of soothing her husband ?—Yes.

Did you understand that her husband was at all violent, then ? —Yes; she told me that in a previous sickness he was violent.

And she was in some apprehension of that state of things recurring ?—Yes—described it as a paroxysm.

And was it by way of soothing him and quieting him in these paroxysms you understood it was to be used ?—Yes; to give him sleep.

Now, you have told us about your getting the chloroform; at the time you got the chloroform, and you went to the chemist's whom you knew, and wrote to your friend, and so on, was there the faintest or the remotest idea in your mind that it could be used for any dangerous or improper purpose ?—Not the faintest.

I mean there was no such idea of that kind crossing your mind with regard to danger from the misuse of this chloroform you were getting ?—Not in this case; no.

You had never seen Mrs. Bartlett with a medical book, had you—" Squire's " ?—Yes, I have seen her with that.

You have seen " Squire's " ?—Yes.

Mr. JUSTICE WILLS—You speak of " Squire's " as one which everybody knows; is it a book of domestic medicine?

Mr. CLARKE—It is a pharmaceutical book, my lord: the " Companion to the British Pharmacopœia."

Mr. POLAND—This is the very book that was found, my lord: " Companion to the British Pharmacopœia."

The WITNESS—Yes.

Cross-examination continued—Where had you seen that ?— At Claverton Street.

You yourself had some knowledge and some studies in medical science, had you not ?—Not medical; no.

But do you know much about chloroform ?—I know very little about it, if that was in the sense you ask.

Evidence for Prosecution.

Rev. George Dyson

Have you ever seen it administered?—No.

You put it not in the sense I ask. You may know, not the chemical properties of chloroform, but the medical property, as anæsthetic, and the limits with which it might safely be used, and all that?—No; what I knew was that chloroform was used for soothing and sleeping purposes; nothing more.

And your idea was that putting a few drops on a handkerchief was a thing for which, as far as your knowledge went, chloroform might be safely used?—Yes.

You say you did not mention it to Mr. Bartlett that you had got the chloroform, and you understood that Mrs. Bartlett did not desire it to be mentioned to him?—Not specifically the chloroform.

What?—Not that the chloroform was not specifically to be mentioned, but the disease, the affliction, for which she wanted it. I understood from her these paroxysms arose from that.

She never asked you not to mention you had got the chloroform?—No. I think I ought to state, in justice to myself, there was a visitor there, and I could not give it to her in his presence.

If the visitor had not been there, would you have given it to her in the presence of Mr. Bartlett?—I cannot say. I might or might not.

At all events, she had not asked you to keep it secret?—No.

Now, I should like to clear this. Was it on that very day when chloroform was given to her that there was this—I forget what you called it—disagreement, or whatever it was—misunderstanding—between you and Mrs. Bartlett?—No.

You suggested that she might as well have a nurse?—Yes.

And you knew at that time that for more than a fortnight, I think, this lady had never had a proper night's rest?—Yes; I was under that impression.

From what you had heard from Mr. Bartlett?—Yes.

He had spoken of the probability of her breaking down?—Yes.

And could you see yourself, from her appearance and manner, that she was tired and strained with the work?—Yes.

And, besides that, she had told you about the friends complaining that he was not properly nursed, hadn't she?—She had.

Taking those two things together, you suggested that a nurse should be obtained?—Yes.

And she was indignant—angry at the suggestion?—Yes.

And you said you did not trust her, or something of that kind?—Yes.

Was there at that time in your mind, or in your suggestion, the smallest distrust of Mrs. Bartlett?—There was not.

At every time when you had been there during her husband's illness, had you seen her giving diligent and affectionate attention to his wants?—Yes.

167

Adelaide Bartlett.

Rev. George Dyson

And did he himself ever suggest that a nurse would have given him better attention and care?—I cannot remember that he mentioned that.

Cannot you remember? He told you that the wife was tired and broken down. Did he suggest a nurse being fetched?—He did not then.

At any time?—I do not remember his doing so.

Why, the moment he heard of this conversation, his answer to you was, if you had known her for twelve years you would not have hesitated to trust her?—Yes.

Do you suppose he would have listened for a moment to anybody else doubting her?—I do not suppose he put any construction on it. I do not quite understand your question.

The following day that question of a nurse was mentioned before Mr. Bartlett, and you explained that you wanted to apologise to Mrs. Bartlett, and then he said that he had known her for twelve years—" You can trust her; if you had had twelve years of experience you would know you could trust her." That is what he said?—Yes.

Did not you gather from her that he was not only satisfied with, but that he praised and desired to continue, that attention that she was giving him?—That was the impression it left on my mind.

She was angry with you that you made this suggestion to her?—Yes.

So angry, that you went. You returned, as you said, the next morning, in order to apologise?—Yes.

You thought you had offended her?—Yes.

And then, let us understand, so little was there any reserve between you and Mr. Bartlett that you told him—you found him in bed alone, and told him you wanted to see Mrs. Bartlett alone and apologise to her; and then I think he sent the servant to show you downstairs that you might make the apology. That was so, was it not?—Yes, that was it.

We hear that in some of Mrs. Bartlett's letters to you she addressed you as George; from the time when, in September, this understanding was set up between you and the husband, was he in the habit of calling you George?—Yes.

And were you spoken of as George when you three were together?—Yes.

By Mr. JUSTICE WILLS—What did you call her in his presence?—By her Christian name.

Cross-examination continued—Adelaide?—Yes.

You habitually called her that before him?—Yes.

And in his presence? Now, on the Saturday evening you say she spoke to you—it was after the post-mortem examination—and said you were to put away from your mind the fact that she possessed a medicine chest. I just want to call your mind to that con-

Evidence for Prosecution.

Rev. George Dyson

versation.   At that time you had the bottles which you had bought?
—Yes.

You threw them away as you went to church on the Sunday
morning?—I did.

Did you tell her you had thrown them away the next time
you saw her—on the Monday?—No.

Are you sure?—Yes, I am sure of that.

Why did not you tell her?—I could not say at this time.

Why?—Probably because it never occurred to me to tell her.

Were you in great anxiety and distress at that time about
your position?—I was.

You were afraid the effect of your having bought the chloroform might get you into trouble?—Precisely so.

So that you thought you had better get rid of the bottles?—
No.

Why did you throw them away?—Because it was the horror
that seized me when I imagined what might have happened.

That is what I was suggesting; you thought you had better
not have the bottles in your possession?—No; that was not the
motive in my heart when I threw them away; the sight of them
was hateful to me, and in a panic I threw them away; it was not
the motive of self-protection.

What did you mean when you said you were a ruined man?
—Because I had in my mind what might have happened.

You had in your mind what might happen to yourself?—Yes;
what might be the cause of Mr. Bartlett's death.

What might happen to yourself?—I was going on to say the
thought was in my mind at the time, possibly it was the chloroform I had bought had been the cause of Mr. Bartlett's death.

Did that first occur to you on the Saturday morning?—It
would be difficult to say when the thought first came.   I think on
Saturday night it grew on me.

And, thinking that, you thought you would be a ruined man
if the matter came out?—I thought I should be a ruined man if
the matter came out—you mean about the chloroform?

Yes?—I thought I should be a ruined man if my fears were
true.

And if you were associated with the matter?—I saw that
danger.

And was it that that suggested to you the throwing away the
bottles?—No.

Now, then, why did you not tell her on the Monday that you
had thrown the bottles away?—I presume because it never occurred
to me to tell her.

Do you mean to repeat that answer—it never occurred to you?
—I do.

It did occur to you to ask for the piece of poetry?—Yes.

And you got it?—Yes.

Adelaide Bartlett.

By Mr. JUSTICE WILLS—When did you get it?—On the Saturday, I believe.

Let me see where we are. That is the 9th?—After the inquest, I think it would be—it was then, or the Wednesday.

Cross-examination continued—Just think. The 9th was the last time you ever saw Mrs. Bartlett to speak to—the day she was indignant, and suggested you might as well charge her with giving chloroform. Do you mean it was that day?—Yes, I think it was that day.

There had been a conversation about it before, had not there? Do you remember the conversation partly in Mrs. Matthews' presence, and partly when Mrs. Matthews was out of the room? Were not you then trying to get that piece of paper?—I have said I cannot swear whether it was on the Wednesday. I heard Mrs. Matthews give in evidence that I was there.

You have heard Mrs. Matthews give in evidence it was then, and I understand you to say whatever was the paper spoken of in Mrs. Matthews' presence was this piece of paper?—Yes.

There was no other piece of paper you were trying to get back?—No; it was this piece of poetry.

You say that Mrs. Bartlett told you not to say anything about chloroform?—Yes.

Was that at the time the piece of poetry was mentioned?—No; that was on the Saturday night.

That was the first Saturday after the post-mortem examination?—Yes.

The 2nd of January. What was the day on which you gave your evidence about purchasing the chloroform; do you remember?—I believe it was the third sitting of the coroner's inquest.

That was in February?—Yes, it would be.

11th February, I think. Was Mrs. Bartlett the only person who had advised you to say nothing about the chloroform?—No.

Mr. Matthews had, had he not?—Yes. Understand me, nothing about the chloroform, not altogether; nothing about it immediately. He recommended me to wait the result of the analysis.

Mr. Matthews, to whom you spoke, advised you to say nothing about the chloroform until the result of the analysis was known?—Yes.

And you took his advice, and did not?—No, I did not.

Re-examined by Mr. POLAND—When was it you mentioned it to Mr. Matthews that you had purchased chloroform for Mrs. Bartlett?—On the Wednesday evening.

You mean the Wednesday, the 6th?—Yes.

6th January; that was the day before the inquest?—Yes.

Where had you mentioned that to him?—Walking between his house and Peckham Rye Station in the evening.

What had you said to him about that?—I told him briefly the

Evidence for Prosecution.

Rev. George Dyson

facts of the case, and I said that I had my fears, and that my idea was to give the facts.

You mean by the facts of the case that you had purchased chloroform?—Yes.

And what you had done with it—that you had given it to Mrs. Bartlett?—Yes.

What did you mean by your fears?—My fears?

Yes?—As to what had become of it; what use had been made of it; or, rather, as to what its effects had been.

You say it was then Mr. Matthews advised you to await the result of the analysis before you said anything about it?—Yes; and really to await my being called by the coroner, and give my evidence in due order—that was the advice.

Was Mr. Matthews the first person to whom you mentioned you had purchased this chloroform and given it to Mrs. Bartlett?—Mrs. Matthews was the first.

Then you had previously mentioned it to Mrs. Matthews?—Yes.

When had you mentioned it to her?—At Dr. Leach's house, when I was waiting in the ante-room.

Which day?—Wednesday.

Did she advise you at all?

Mr. CLARKE—My friend is carrying his suggestions a little too far.

Mr. JUSTICE WILLS—I think so.

Re-examination continued—At any rate, you did mention the fact to her. Had you mentioned the fact to any one else?—Do you mean on that day?

Yes?—No; I had mentioned it to none then.

Then had you mentioned it to any one else before you were called before the coroner on the 11th?—Yes; to the Wesleyan minister at Poole, my home.

Had you been down there?—Yes.

I only want to know—it is right you should mention it—you had also mentioned it to another minister of your own body?—Yes.

Then, on the first day you were called and examined before the coroner you mentioned about this chloroform?—That is so.

Was it the first day?—The first opportunity I had; not the first day.

Now, I want you just to tell me a little more fully what was said when you told Mr. Bartlett you were growing much attached to Mrs. Bartlett, and you had better discontinue the visits, and he said you had better not, because your preaching had affected her. Describe that more fully. How had it affected her?—He did not describe the particular way, but thought it had benefited her; since you ask the question, in a spiritual way.

By Mr. JUSTICE WILLS—I want to know why you went to

Adelaide Bartlett.

Rev. George Dyson

three different shops to buy the chloroform?—Because I did not get as much as I wanted at one shop.

Why did not you say to the first man, " You have given me a little bottle; I want four or five times this quantity "?—Because I thought he would want to know what I wanted it for, and I did not wish to enter into a long explanation.

Why not?—Because I thought he would not understand that Mrs. Bartlett was skilled in the use of medicines.

Why did you say it was for taking grease spots out of clothes? —He asked me what I wanted it for.

Do not let us have any nice distinctions between telling a falsehood and acting it?—I do not defend that, my lord; it was simply that I wanted to avoid an explanation. That was the only idea I had in my mind.

What was your notion of what this very large quantity of chloroform was wanted for, for you say you went to three druggists, and, except that from each of them the quantity you were asking for appeared excessive, nothing appears as to what was your notion of what such a large quantity of chloroform would be necessary for?—This way. I knew chloroform was used by amateurs. I heard of its being used for the gums—toothache, for instance.

What do you mean by amateurs?—That is, by any one.

Yes, for toothache. Well?—And I knew that—at least, I had an idea—this would be sold to doctors; at least, to people who understood the use of it for the other purposes for which it was wanted.

You see, that answer does not meet my question quite. You say, three chemists you went to in succession; and you seem to have been conscious that each one of them would think that quantity you really wanted to get was a very large quantity. What was your own notion of what such a large quantity was wanted for? —Oh! I understand. I thought it was used very quickly in the way Mrs. Bartlett mentioned. I knew it was volatile. I had an idea that a very few applications would exhaust the amount.

A very few sprinklings on a handkerchief?—Not a few sprinklings. I thought it was more than that.

Did you think the whole handkerchief was to be saturated with it?—Not saturated, but well moistened in it. I had never heard how it was done, and knew nothing of how it was done.

When you went to Mrs. Bartlett with the chloroform in your pocket, you say a visitor was there. Who was that?—A Mr. Hackett was there—I believe the name is.

How long did he stop?—He was gone when I returned.

You left him there?—I left him there with Mr. Bartlett.

The Court adjourned.

Third Day—Wednesday, 14th April, 1886.

JOHN BAWTREE HUMBLE, examined by Mr. MOLONEY—I am a chemist at 190 Upper Richmond Road, Putney. I know Mr. Dyson by sight. I saw him pass my house on several occasions before 28th December. I recollect his coming to my shop on Monday, 28th December, about twelve o'clock, and asking for some chloroform. I asked him whether he required camphorated chloroform for teeth, and he said "No, pure chloroform." I then took up a 2-drachm bottle and asked him if that would be sufficient. He said he wanted more, and I showed him a ½-ounce bottle, but he said he should like more than that. I then showed him a 1-ounce bottle, and he said that that would do. I ultimately gave him 1 ounce of methylated chloroform in a white glass bottle, which I labelled. He paid me 1s. 3d. for it.

Was that a large or an ordinary quantity to sell to one person at one time?—I should have considered it rather a large quantity without a prescription.

THOMAS SAMUEL PENROSE, examined by Mr. POLAND—I am a chemist, and I manage the business of Cadman & Co., The Ridgeway, Wimbledon. I have known Mr. Dyson for about eighteen months. He came to my shop about twelve o'clock on 28th December, and I sold him two bottles of methylated chloroform of 1 ounce each, for which he paid me 1s. 6d. There was a label on the bottle, "Chloroform, Poison," and there was also one of my trade labels on it. Mr. Dyson took these bottles away with him.

JOSEPH RICHARD PHILLIPS MELLIN, examined by Mr. POLAND—I am assistant to my father, Joseph Mellin, a chemist, at 36 High Street, Wimbledon. I have known the Rev. Mr. Dyson for about eighteen months. He came to our shop on 28th December about midday, and purchased 1½ or 2 ounces of pure chloroform. The price was 2s. an ounce, and the chloroform was in a small blue bottle with the words, "Poison, not to be taken," on the glass. In addition to that, it had a label pasted on it, "Chloroform," and also one of our ordinary trade labels with the name and address. The bottle would hold 2 ounces I think, but I do not remember whether it was full or not.

Mrs. ALICE JANE SELBY MATTHEWS, examined by Mr. R. S. WRIGHT—I am the wife of Mr. George Frederick Matthews, and I live at 98 Friern Road, East Dulwich. I have known the prisoner, Mrs. Bartlett, for about five years, and intimately for about three and a half years. I also knew her late husband. When I first

Adelaide Bartlett.

Alice J. S. Matthews

knew them they were living at Herne Hill, and afterwards at Lordship Lane, East Dulwich, where I was in the habit of going to visit them. They afterwards went to Merton Cottage, and I continued to visit them there. Last July my husband and I stayed for a week in their house. So far as I could see, Mr. and Mrs. Bartlett lived on very affectionate terms, and apparently as man and wife. About three years ago Mr. Bartlett suffered from neuralgia, but I could not say for how long; it may have been a day or two or it may have been longer.

By Mr. JUSTICE WILLS—He did not lie up. At other times the state of his health was very good. I did not see them at all in Claverton Street in the autumn of last year.

Examination continued—On the morning of 1st January I received a letter from Mrs. Bartlett, and I went to the house about twelve o'clock. I went upstairs with Mrs. Bartlett to the room where the body was. She gave me an account of how the death had taken place.

By Mr. JUSTICE WILLS—That was in the front room.

Examination continued—Mrs. Bartlett said to me that the night previously her husband was in bed and she sat by his side, with her arm round his foot, and that she was wakened by feeling a cramp in her arm. She said it was after twelve before she had gone to sleep, because she heard the people downstairs wishing each other a happy New Year. When she was wakened by feeling a cramp in her arm she found her husband lying on his face. She turned him over and tried to give him brandy, but she did not tell me whether he swallowed any of the brandy. I asked her what he died from, and she said, " We don't know. There must be a post-mortem." I do not remember anything else that either of us said about the death at that time. I stayed in the house all day with her, except that we went out together in the afternoon to get some mourning. We went back to the house in the afternoon, and I stayed there until about nine o'clock at night.

On the next day, Saturday, 2nd January, Mrs. Bartlett and Mr. Dyson came together to my house at Dulwich after tea. I had never seen Mr. Dyson before, but I knew that there was such a person. I cannot remember from whom I had heard that there was such a person.

By Mr. JUSTICE WILLS—Do you mean you had heard of him in connection with the Bartletts or independently?—In all probability it would be in connection with the Bartletts, but I cannot say.

Examination continued—Mrs. Bartlett said to me that the doctors were not agreed with regard to the cause of death, and that the rooms were to be sealed, and so she had come to me. I do not remember anything of any importance in connection with the next day, Sunday, the 3rd. Mr. Dyson did not come that day, but he came on Monday, the 4th, before lunch. Mrs. Bartlett

Evidence for Prosecution.

Alice J. S. Matthews

was out at the time he came. He stayed until she came in, and I left them alone for a minute or two.

As you came back to the room where they were was your attention attracted by anything?—Yes, I heard a noise in the room, like some one stamping. I went into the room, and I saw Mrs. Bartlett stamping round the room. I asked her what was the matter. She did not answer for some minutes, and then she said that Mr. Dyson was bothering her about a piece of paper. I went out of the room for a few minutes, and when I returned I heard Mr. Dyson saying to Mrs. Bartlett, " You did tell me that Edwin was going to die soon," and she said, " No, I did not." Mr. Dyson then bowed his head on the piano and said, " Oh, my God! " After a bit I asked him whether he had not better go.

By Mr. JUSTICE WILLS—There was nothing more said.

Examination continued—As he went out he said, " I am a ruined man." I do not remember asking Mrs. Bartlett what he meant by all that, but I remember asking her what the paper was, and she told me it was a piece of poetry. On Wednesday, the 6th, Mr. Dyson came to my house. Mrs. Bartlett and I were going to London when he came, and he went with us. Mrs. Bartlett and I left him at Victoria Station, and then we went to Dr. Leach's, but found him out. We then went on to Claverton Street. Mr. Dyson came there in the afternoon. About three o'clock the three of us went to Dr. Leach's house. Mrs. Bartlett went alone into one room to see Dr. Leach, while Mr. Dyson and I remained in another. Mrs. Bartlett left us alone for about an hour, and during that hour I had a conversation with Mr. Dyson. On Saturday, the 9th, Mr. Dyson came to my house.

Was Mrs. Bartlett staying with you?—No. She went up to town, and went to my husband's place of business to bring him home. Mr. Dyson went there also to see my husband, and they all came down together. I cannot say that Mrs. Bartlett told me what she had been seeing Dr. Leach about on Wednesday, the 6th, but I understood she was to go and hear the result of the post-mortem. On Saturday, the 9th, in the evening, there was some talk going on in my house. Mr. Dyson was in a great state because he said he would be ruined and would have to leave his ministry, and so on. Mrs. Bartlett and my husband were present. I cannot recollect the whole of the conversation, but I know Mr. Dyson said, " Suppose it should be proved——" and he hesitated and did not finish. Then Mrs. Bartlett said, " Do not mince matters. Say I gave him chloroform if you want to." She said it very indignantly. That is all I remember about the 9th. On the Saturday or the Monday—I do. not recollect which—I asked Mrs. Bartlett why she told Mr. Dyson all those lies. I did not tell her what it was that Mr. Dyson had said, but I knew that she knew what he told me.

How?—Well, about—I cannot remember now what was said.

175

Adelaide Bartlett.

Mr. CLARKE—I must object to this.

Mr. WRIGHT—I am entitled to ask what he said.

Mr. CLARKE—Oh, no.

Examination continued—Well, you asked her why she told Mr. Dyson all those lies?—Yes. She said he had bothered her so, that he did not believe her when she told him the truth.

Did she say what the truth was?—Yes.

That Edwin was going to die?—And so she told him the lie.

By Mr. CLARKE—Told him what?—Told him the lie.

Examination continued—That is all that I remember.

By Mr. JUSTICE WILLS—Just listen to me. Don't say anything you know from any other source. Has anything passed between you and her to indicate what you were talking about?—No, I do not remember; but I should like to say this, that I said to her then I did not know that Edwin thought he was going to die soon, and she said that he did think so latterly.

Examination continued—Did Mrs. Bartlett ever tell you that she had any chloroform?—Yes. She said she had had the chloroform to soothe Edwin, but that she had never used it. I cannot say that she told me where she got it, but, of course, I understood. It was either on the Saturday or the Monday that she told me about the chloroform—it was after we were at Dr. Leach's. She told me she had poured the chloroform on the rails as she came from Victoria to Peckham Rye on the 6th, and that she had thrown the bottle into Peckham Rye Pond. I passed Peckham Rye Pond on the 6th; it was frozen. There were some boys on the ice at one end, but I could not say whether it was frozen all over. Mrs. Bartlett left my house on the 11th, and went to lodgings in Weymouth Street, Portland Place. She paid me two or three visits, but I do not remember anything that was said. On the 20th, when she came to see me, she said she had asked Dr. Leach about giving Edwin chloroform, and he had told her she could not possibly have given him chloroform, because it would have shown in his brain if she had given it to him by inhalation, and if she had given it to him to drink it would have burnt his throat all down, and his screams would have alarmed the house.

Mr. CLARKE—I have no questions to ask.

The FOREMAN—There is one question I should like to ask—Mr. Bartlett, in his evidence, stated that his son, the deceased, had told him that he intended to alter his will on 1st January in his favour. Is there any proof of that beyond his own statement?

Mr. JUSTICE WILLS—No, there has been none given.

The FOREMAN—You can easily understand why I ask the question, I think.

Mr. CLARKE—Perhaps it was with reference to a question that was asked. I do not think he said he intended to alter his will, but to make him an allowance.

Evidence for Prosecution.

Alice J. S. Matthews

The FOREMAN—To alter his will, I think it was.

Mr. JUSTICE WILLS—I will refer to it. It strikes me as new. My memory may be wrong.

Mr. CLARKE—What he said was that there was not room for him at the house—" I had no allowance from him "—he was to give him an allowance this year. It was after I had read a page over to him.

Mr. JUSTICE WILLS—I think he did say something in answer to your question. I remember his answer to it—" He had never, in fact, made me an allowance, but I had from him what money I wanted. He was the tenderest of sons." That is the passage, I think, but there was nothing said about altering his will.

A JUROR—We are still under the impression that he stated so, and that it was an allowance. Was there any proof that he promised that besides his own statement?

GEORGE FREDERICK MATTHEWS, examined by Mr. MOLONEY—I am the husband of the last witness. I have known Mr. and Mrs. Bartlett for about three and a half years. I visited them at Merton Abbey, and stayed some time with them. Up to the time of Mr. Bartlett's death his general health was very good, so far as I know. I did not notice anything peculiar about his ideas. So far as I could judge, he and his wife lived as man and wife. I saw him during his last illness on 15th December. He seemed very prostrated. Mrs. Bartlett told me that he was suffering from slight mercurial poisoning, and also from verdigris. She said he might possibly have got it from moving things in the warehouse—he had been hunting rats. That was the last time I saw him alive.

On 1st January I went to Claverton Street and saw Mrs. Bartlett there. After having tea she said that Dr. Leach had said that he could not grant a certificate. Later on in the evening it was said that Dr. Leach and Mrs. Bartlett had come to an understanding that morning that there must be a post-mortem. Mrs. Bartlett came to my house on 2nd January with Mr. Dyson. In the evening she spoke to us about how her husband died; she told me that she must have fallen asleep sitting near the foot of the bed, and she had his foot under her arm; she was wakened by feeling cramp in her arm, and found her husband lying on his face; she turned him over and endeavoured to give him some brandy, and, becoming alarmed, she proceeded to rouse the house and also send for the doctor. Mrs. Bartlett stayed at our house that night.

On the Sunday, speaking to her about the death, was anything said by you about having got poison?—Yes, we talked about the death, and I asked her if it was possible that he might have taken poison himself or if he could have got at any poison himself, and she gave me to understand that she did not think he could have done so.

Adelaide Bartlett.

George F. Matthews

Did she say why?—Yes, she said she did not think there were any poisons in the house.

Did she say anything as to the smell of chlorodyne at the post-mortem?—Yes, I believe she said the doctor had told her that there was a smell of chlorodyne, which might be accounted for by her husband having used chlorodyne.

Was anything said about arsenic?—Yes, I was told that there was a smell of garlic. I asked her if it was possible that he could have got at any arsenic, and she said no. There is nothing more than that that I can remember.

We had a visitor, and, of course, there was not much said. I remember seeing Mr. Dyson on 6th January when I was coming home from business. I walked with him to the station, and had a long conversation with him. Mrs. Bartlett was not present at that conversation. Mr. Dyson and Mrs. Bartlett came to my house on the evening of 7th January, the day of the coroner's inquest. We discussed the evidence which had been given at the inquest, but nothing more that I can remember. Mr. Dyson came to my place of business in the city on Saturday, 9th January.

Did Mrs. Bartlett also come to your warehouse that day?—Yes, Mr. Dyson came about eleven o'clock in the first instance. I was too busy to see him, and asked him to call again when I was about to leave—at two o'clock. Mr. Dyson and Mrs. Bartlett went with me to my house that afternoon, at my request. In Mrs. Bartlett's presence there was a conversation about Mr. Dyson's position; he told me that he was ruined, so far as his prospects in the ministry were concerned. I endeavoured to combat the idea, and he proceeded to explain that it was impossible for him to do otherwise than resign; that, according to a system that existed with them, certain superintendents of every district were responsible for the condition of the ministers in each district; and that the slightest breach of anything on the part of the minister would cause him to be called before, what I understood to be, a sort of council. Turning to Mrs. Bartlett, he said, "Supposing that it turns out——" or "Suppose it should be proved that you——" and then he hesitated. Mrs. Bartlett said, "Don't mince matters; say it, if you wish to say, I gave him chloroform." He said, "Well, to put it hypothetically, supposing it was discovered that you gave him chloroform, and I gave it to you——" Then, I cannot say exactly the words, but he made an action as much as to say, "What would be the opinion of the world? How should I come out in such a case?" and he moved his hands so (showing). Mr. Dyson went away almost immediately after that.

By Mr. JUSTICE WILLS—I cannot recollect anything that Mrs. Bartlett said to that.

Examination continued—Mrs. Bartlett left my house on 11th January. I saw her with my wife at my house on 20th January. She told us that Dr. Leach had said that it would be impossible

178

Evidence for Prosecution.

George F. Matthews

for her to have given her husband chloroform by inhalation without it showing in the brain, and she could not have given it to him as a drink, because he would have burnt his throat all down, and he would have aroused the house with his cries.

Cross-examined by Mr. CLARKE—You have been, I believe, for some years a friend of Mr. Bartlett's?—Yes.

You believed that you were in perfect confidence and intimacy with him?—Yes.

You had every reason to think so?—Yes.

Did he ever talk to you about medical matters?—No.

Did he ever communicate with you his strange ideas on the subject of marriage, or anything connected with it?—No, never.

He never lent you any books, or showed you any book?—No.

Did you ever hear of Dr. Nichols' book?—Yes, I have seen it. There?—Yes; Mrs. Bartlett handed it to me, once.

Mrs. Bartlett?—Yes.

Is that the book (holding one up)?—I cannot say.

Was it a queer sort of book?—Yes; scarcely in my line of business. I did not read it—yes, that is the book.

How long ago was that?—Two years ago, quite.

And did he ever talk to you about magnetism?—No, never.

Or mesmerism?—No.

And you had no knowledge of his having strange ideas about marriage, or about his having ideas about magnetism?—No, nothing of the kind.

Is that the only medical book you have known of belonging to him and Mrs. Bartlett?—No; I have seen "Squire's Companion" there.

Where have you seen that—at Merton?—At Merton Abbey.

Re-examined by Mr. POLAND—You say that is the book which you saw her with?—Yes.

How long ago?—Two years.

Where?—At my house.

She lent it to you?—Yes.

What did she say about it?—Mrs. Bartlett was a believer in the hydropathic system; and I do not know, but I rather think that the book was about that, and she gave it to me so that I should read something on the subject. I am not certain, because I never read the book, but I know so well that it was a book on hydropathy.

By Mr. JUSTICE WILLS—I am glad you have told us the book; it was a book of a different kind?—I never looked at it.

Re-examination continued—Was it left with you?—Yes.

Did you read it at all?—No.

Did you return it to her?—I believe my wife did; I do not think I did.

Did you look at the book to see what it was about?—I have no memory.

Adelaide Bartlett.

George F. Matthews

Was the title of it " Esoteric Anthropology (The Mysteries of Man) : a Comprehensive and Confidential Treatise on the Structure, Functions, Passional Attractions and Perversions, True and False Physical and Social Conditions, and the Most Intimate Relations of Men and Women. By T. L. Nichols, M.D., F.A.S." ? —If I had read as far as that I should not have read any further : that was the reason she gave it to me; she was speaking of Dr. Nichols.

Did you know anything of Dr. Nichols yourself ?—No.

I think you said that you had never seen Mr. Bartlett with that book ?—No, never.

ANNIE WALKER, examined by Mr. POLAND—I am a midwife and a trained nurse, attached since October, 1881, to the London Association of Nurses, 62 New Bond Street. I received a letter at the Institute from Mrs. Nichols, the wife of Dr. Nichols, of Fopstone Road, Earl's Court. Mrs. Nichols is now dead. That letter made an appointment, and I went to see her. In consequence of what she said to me I went to see Mrs. Bartlett at Station Road, Herne Hill. I saw Mrs. Bartlett, and I was engaged to attend her in her approaching confinement. I attended her without a doctor in her house for four weeks before she was confined in November, 1881. The child was stillborn.

Had you spoken to her at all about having a doctor? —I am not quite certain whether I took the order from her. I went to her husband and asked him to let her have some medicine. He asked me if her life would be all right. I said I did not fear for her, but I feared if he did not have help at once the child would be stillborn. He said he would much rather that I took the case through. He would much rather not have any man interfering with her, and I agreed to go on. She had a very bad time at her confinement and suffered great pain. I begged Mr. Bartlett to send for a doctor, so as to be there when the child was born. A doctor was sent for, but the child was born before he arrived. I continued to attend on Mrs. Bartlett for three weeks. We spoke on the subject of the confinement, and she said that she never meant to have any more children, but she did not say why. When I visited her after her confinement I saw Mr. Bartlett. As far as I could judge, they were living together as man and wife, and they were on affectionate terms together. I visited them when they were at Lordship Lane, and also when they were at The Cottage, Merton Abbey. I stayed with them at The Cottage for a few days in September, 1884.

Did she say anything to you then about her husband ?—All I remember her saying was that she played and sang in the evening, and that he never appreciated enough what she did. She said that he did not appreciate her work. She worked very beautifully, but he always thought that she ought to do it better.

Evidence for Prosecution.

Annie Walker

By Mr. JUSTICE WILLS—Are you expressing the result of your own observation or what she said herself?—What she said herself.

Examination continued—Did she speak to you on that occasion about the will?—I cannot say whether it was on that occasion; it was on several occasions, and I think she even said it in the presence of Mr. Bartlett. She said, " Don't you think it is a shame? Edwin has made a will that the property will come to me, provided that I never marry again." I feel sure she mentioned that more than once, but I cannot be quite positive of it.

I have seen Dr. Nichols, but he has never seen me, so far as I know. I have never seen him about Mr. Bartlett at all, and have never had any communication with him. I know he is the husband of the lady who had originally written to me, and I know he is the gentleman who wrote a book, " The Mysteries of Man." I have seen that book lying about at the Bartlett's, but I have never seen any one reading it. I understood from Mrs. Bartlett that it was through reading that book that she wrote to Mrs. Nichols. I have never seen any other medical book in the house, nor have I seen any medicine chest.

I have never had any conversation with Mrs. Bartlett about chloroform, nor have I ever got any chloroform for her on any occasion. She has never asked me to purchase any chloroform or any medicine for her. I have never been out of England, and I have never spoken of going to America. I never knew anything of Mr. Dyson. I never attended Mr. Bartlett at all.

Cross-examined by Mr. CLARKE—There was no chloroform used at Mrs. Bartlett's confinement, was there?—No, sir; not any.

At any time when you have been there have you heard chloroform mentioned?—Never.

By her or before her?—Never.

So far as you know, she knew nothing about chloroform at all? —Not that I know of, in any way at all.

You came to be attending her through Mrs. Nichols, I think you said?—Yes.

Mrs. Nichols herself attended people, I believe, did she not?— I do not know if she did. She visited a lady that I attended once, but they were great friends.

Don't you know that she attended people herself?—Well, I have read it in the book.

You have read this : " In a large practice extending over many years . . . Mrs. Nichols has never directed treatment to be suspended "?—Yes. I do not know much about the book; I have just looked at it a little.

You only know Dr. Nichols as Mrs. Nichols' husband, and as the author of the book?—That is all.

You have looked through this book?—I have.

There is nothing immoral or indecent in this book, is there? —Not anything.

Adelaide Bartlett.

Annie Walker

And you have seen it at the place there while Mr. and Mrs. Bartlett were there?—Yes, while they were there.

There was no concealment about it?—Not at all.

It was lying about?—Yes.

Had you seen patients before through the recommendation of Mrs. Nichols?—Mrs. ——

Never mind the name; one or two?—Two.

Did you attend a patient afterwards through Mrs. Nichols? —No.

Now, in September you were four weeks in the house before this poor lady was confined?—Yes.

And were you living in the house with her?—I was living in the house, and taking my meals with them both.

Was she attentive and affectionate towards her husband?— Most affectionate.

And was she as attentive as she could be to him with regard to his meals in the morning?—Very. She would get up very early, and see that he had his breakfast at seven, before he started, comfortably.

Although she was expecting her confinement to happen some little time before it really did?—Yes.

And did you form some attachment for her?—Yes.

I think you gave her your photograph?—Yes.

In your nurse's dress?—Yes.

And do you know that that photograph was put in the album? —No, I do not know that. I have never seen her since I went to the house last October twelve months.

You say that once, after the confinement, Mrs. Bartlett said that she should never have another child?—Yes.

It had been a very painful time?—Yes.

She had a very bad time, and a time of great suffering?— Yes.

Altogether, you were seven weeks in the house, I believe?— Yes.

And you were really anxious at the time of the confinement?— Very anxious.

With regard to her life—her life was in danger, was it not?— Well, I did not see any reason for fear. She was keeping up very well.

But you were anxious, and, even after what Mr. Bartlett said, you again insisted on having a medical man?—Yes.

Have you nursed a great many ladies in labour?—A great many. I have been fourteen years nurse.

It is not a very uncommon thing for a woman to say that she hopes never to have another child, is it?—No; not at all.

Re-examined by Mr. POLAND—You say that you know they were living together on the terms of man and wife?

182

Evidence for Prosecution.

Annie Walker

Mr. CLARKE—Do not keep repeating that, or I must ask my learned friend to define what he means. It is a phrase he uses so frequently.

Mr. JUSTICE WILLS—It is a phrase that I shall have to point out the illustration of when it comes to my time. Among ordinary people you know what passes in the ordinary relations of life, but you know nothing of what passes in the bedroom, or how the bedroom is arranged with reference to the specific matter which is the only thing we can inquire into. The mere opinion is worthless on this point.

Re-examination continued—After the statement she made that she would not have another child, did she ever say anything to you as to the terms upon which she was with her husband?—No.

They occupied the same room and the same bed, did they?—When I was with them.

By Mr. JUSTICE WILLS—When you paid your visit?—Yes.

I suppose, whenever you paid your visit, you have been up in their room?—Yes.

Did you use chloroform at all at the confinement?—No.

You say that they occupied the same bed; was there anything exceptional, as far as you know, between them as man and wife? —No.

As I understand you, Mrs. Bartlett never made a statement to you in reference to herself and her husband as to the terms upon which they cohabited. That is what you mean?

Mr. POLAND—Yes, I will put it that way.

The WITNESS—No.

By Mr. JUSTICE WILLS—Let me ask you one other question. I had a very cursory glance at that book, but there are parts of it which do tell married people how to live together without having children, are there not?—Yes.

Mr. CLARKE—I am sure your lordship wishes me to be correct. Your lordship will find that the book contains nothing objectionable. The answer is vague.

Mr. JUSTICE WILLS—I will take the opportunity, Mr. Clarke, of looking at the book this evening myself. I will just point out to you at once the passage which caught my eye.

Mr. CLARKE—Yes.

Mr. JUSTICE WILLS—It was opened there; that is how I came to see it.

Mr. CLARKE—" Abstinence.—There is one way that is natural, simple, and effectual. It is to refrain from the sexual act. It is easily done by most women, and by many men. In every civilised community thousands live in celebacy, many from necessity, many from choice. In England and the older American States there is a large surplus female population. In Catholic countries the whole of the priesthood and a great number of religious of both sexes take

183

Adelaide Bartlett.

vows of perpetual chastity. This practice has existed for at least sixteen centuries. I have shown that in the ordinary cases conception can only take place when connection is had a day or two before, or ten days, or, for safety's sake, say sixteen days after, menstruation. There is then a fortnight each month when the female is not liable to impregnation."

Mr. JUSTICE WILLS—I am much obliged to you.

Mr. CLARKE—" And it is also to be observed that the natural period for sexual union is when it is demanded for the purpose of procreation; and that the use of marriage or the sexual act for mere pleasure, and using any means to avoid impregnation, are unnatural. It is questionable, therefore, whether we can morally justify the use of any means to prevent conception. If it can ever be justified, it is when a woman is unwillingly compelled to submit to the embrace of her husband while her health or other conditions forbid her to have children."

Mr. JUSTICE WILLS—I am much obliged to you for correcting my impression; it was formed on hastily opening the book.

THOMAS LOW NICHOLS, examined by Mr. WRIGHT—I live at 32 Fopstone Road, Earl's Court. I was a graduate at New York in 1850, but I have no degree entitling me to practise here. I have been for about twenty-five years in England, mostly in London. There is no other Dr. Nichols that I know of in Fopstone Road, Earl's Court, or in any part of Earl's Court. The book entitled "Esoteric Anthropology," which has been mentioned in Court, is one of my books. I first saw Mrs. Bartlett, the prisoner, at the Westminster Police Court. I cannot remember having any communication with her or her husband by letter or otherwise. I do not know any one of the name of Bartlett in this country, nor do I know any nurse or midwife of the name of Annie Walker. This morning I saw the witness called Annie Walker; I have never seen her at all before to my knowledge.

Did you ever make any statement to anybody that anybody of the name of Bartlett would die within twelve months?—Certainly not.

Or any statement of that sort?—I could not make any such statement unless I had examined the patient.

Cross-examined by Mr. CLARKE—You have no qualification here, I think?—I am not registered; my diploma was just too late to be registered.

But you have lived for some years in England, have you not? —For twenty-five years.

You used to live at Malvern, I think?—Yes.

And it was while you were living at Malvern, in the year 1873, that you issued the English edition of this book?—Quite so. It was written about 1853, in America.

184

Evidence for Prosecution.

And it was published in America, and largely circulated, I think?—Very largely—all over the world, I believe.

Did Mrs. Nichols, your late wife, write a book and publish a book?—Oh, yes.

It was called, I think, " A Woman's Work in Water Cure and Sanitary Education "?—Yes; that was the English reproduction of a previous work called " Experience in Water Cure," published in America.

In the year 1853, I think, you were giving lectures in New York, at the American Hydropathic Institute?—Yes.

And you were then teaching students in anatomy, physiology, and hydro-therapeutics, and assisted by Mrs. Nichols either in teaching or writing books?—In both. She wrote her own books, and did her part of the teaching for both sexes.

Then I understand that the American book which she wrote was called " Experience in Water Cure," and the English book " A Woman's Work in Water Cure "?—Yes, in England.

And was again largely circulated?—Yes.

I think the first book you wrote was called " Human Physiology the Basis of Sanitary and Social Science "?—That was later. That was written at Malvern.

That was a larger book, was it not?—Somewhat larger—twice the size.

I think it is only right that I should read to you a passage from the preface of the English edition in order to found a question upon it. " ' Esoteric Anthropology,' though covering a portion of the same ground, yet varies widely from my recent work, ' Human Physiology the Basis of Sanitary and Social Science '; it treats more particularly of disease and more practically of treatment—especially of the conditions and diseases of the reproductive system and of gestation and childbirth. ' Human Physiology ' treats more of social science, and three of its six parts are devoted to matters which are but slightly touched in the ' Anthropology.' One may therefore well be the sequel or companion of the other. I have honestly tried to make both of them thoroughly good and useful books—true in science, pure in morals, and containing the principles of the highest welfare of man and of humanity." Does that truly represent your intention in writing the book?—Most certainly it does.

And the character of the book?—Most certainly it does.

Did Mrs. Nichols practise largely in England?—Most of the patients came to her.

At page 302 I see you are dealing with some matters of the troubles of women, and you say, " The treatment of this condition will alarm such persons as think they must not touch cold water . . . bad consequences." It was a large practice in-

185

Adelaide Bartlett.

Thomas L. Nichols

volving hundreds of cases?—Including America, yes. She had more practice here than I had.

You did not know Miss Walker at all—the last witness?—I did not. She may have visited at my house, but she might have seen me without my noticing her at all.

The practice which the late Mrs. Nichols was carrying on was a practice that would in the ordinary course of things lead to communication with Miss Walker without your recollecting it?—Quite so. She had her own patients, who, as I said, usually came to her, and she saw them in a different apartment.

And ladies might come and consult her, I need scarcely ask you, without your knowing their name or anything of the kind?—Certainly.

Have persons occasionally come to consult you for your advice?—Sometimes persons who read the book came to me. I did not lay myself out for practice, nor wished it; I was engaged in literary work.

It is again only fair that I should read this sentence from the preface—"I write, not to get consultations, but to prevent their necessity; not to attract patients, but to keep them away and to enable them to get health without my further cure."—That is so, that was my intention.

And, to the best of your ability, you carried out that intention?—I wished to make my book as perfect as I could.

But from time to time persons did come to you for advice, which was given?—Yes.

Would that be sometimes for matters, or generally for matters, involving very private considerations?—They might; that might come in some cases.

You never visited patients, I think?—Very seldom. I have sometimes been prevailed upon to see a patient.

However, you never held yourself out as a practitioner?—Not at all. I always gave persons to understand what my position was. If they insisted upon my seeing a child or a patient that I thought I could be useful to, I ordinarily went, but that was very rare.

Did you practise in America?—I had some practice there.

Did you keep a record of those who visited you in England?—I never did.

Not even a record of the names, or whether they were real or assumed names?—I never kept any records at all.

I believe Mrs. Nichols died in 1884?—In May, 1884—nearly two years ago.

Re-examined by Mr. WRIGHT—Your wife used to attend patients of a certain kind?—She attended usually to ladies who called.

In London, did she ever receive male patients?—She may have seen gentlemen who may have wished to speak to her; I cannot say with regard to that positively.

Evidence for Prosecution.

Not to your knowledge?—No—not often. I do not know that I quite understand. She very seldom visited any patients : if they were not able to come to her, when she drove out she may have sometimes called.

THOMAS ROBERTS, examined by Mr. MOLONEY—I am a dental surgeon practising at 49 Charlwood Street, Pimlico. I was called to see Mr. Bartlett on 16th December, and I went to 85 Claverton Street. I saw Mrs. Bartlett on the landing outside the door, and I asked her if her husband was in the habit of taking mercury in any form. As far as I recollect, I think she said " I do not know." I saw the deceased, Mr. Bartlett, that day. I examined his mouth, and I looked at the gums. According to my judgment he was suffering from mercurial poison. His teeth were loose, and I extracted the two upper central roots. I went to see him again on the 17th, along with Dr. Leach, and extracted about eleven more roots. On the 21st I extracted four lower incisors. I used a solution of cocaine on his gums. Cocaine is a new drug lately used ; I cannot say whether it is a mineral or a vegetable drug. The object of painting Mr. Bartlett's gums with cocaine was to produce local anæsthesia, to dull the sense of pain in the jaw and make the operation more easy. When I saw Mr. Bartlett on the 21st I thought that the signs of mercurial poison had lessened. On the 31st December Dr. Leach and Mr. Bartlett came to my house, between five and six, and I extracted a tooth. Dr. Leach used nitrous oxide gas, and I should think he was about half a minute under its influence. On 31st December, which was the last time upon which I saw him, I should say that his condition was much better. I noticed in the lower jaw, the front portion, the gums had separated and receded from the central ridge of the alveolus, the bone of the jaw ; the alveolus is the bony process in which the teeth are inserted. I said to Dr. Leach, " I think this looks very much like necrosis setting in." Necrosis means the death of the bone. It had extended between two lower canines about an inch and a half or an inch and a quarter, and the decay had gone down the whole socket of each of the teeth which I had extracted before.

Was the disease of the bone what you call extensive?—Not at all so. I should say it was only commencing.

Cross-examined by Mr. CLARKE—Did you have some trouble on the last day in administering the nitrous oxide gas?—He took more than patients would ordinarily do ; he inhaled more gas.

Did you help to apply it several times?—No ; only once.

How long did it take before he went off, do you think?—Three or four minutes, I should think. I did not take the time.

As a rule, two minutes is quite sufficient, is it not?—Yes.

You noticed the condition of the bone of which you have told

Adelaide Bartlett.

us. Did you also notice a fungoid growth in the mouth?—Yes; round the necks of the teeth.

There were very few teeth remaining, were there not?—Very few teeth. Of what date are you speaking; of the first time I saw him?

No, the last time.

By Mr. JUSTICE WILLS—How many teeth did what you extracted answer to?—I extracted eleven teeth and stumps on my second visit; but I cannot say how many teeth or how many stumps.

Cross-examination continued—There were only two left on each side?—No, more; I know there were more.

How many?—I cannot say exactly. I know one was left on the lower left side and one canine on the lower right.

How many were left in the upper jaw, right and left?—I cannot say how many.

The larger teeth at the back of the jaw had gone, had they? —I believe they had.

Was the breath very foul?—I did not notice at the last visit. It was extremely so at the first and second.

When did you notice this fungoid growth?—At each visit; each time I saw him.

Was it found in the hollow space where the teeth had previously been?—No; I should say not.

Will you tell me where it was?—Around the necks of the teeth on the margin of the gums.

Around the necks of the teeth that still remained, do you mean?—Yes.

By Mr. JUSTICE WILLS—Was that the growth of the bone or of the gum? I do not quite understand what fungoid growth is?— It was principally tartar, I should say.

Cross-examination continued—You tell us you said to Dr. Leach you thought necrosis was setting in—was that said after the operation had been performed?—Before the last operation had been performed.

Was it said in Mr. Bartlett's presence?—It was.

Will you first tell us, supposing necrosis not to be stopped, how does it progress? You say it is the death of the bone?—It goes on—that is, the dead part of the bone separates from the healthy part, and then you can take it away. It separates entirely, and you can remove it.

How much of the structure of the bone may be involved in that, I suppose, depends upon the condition of the person, the circumstances of his life, and so on?—Certainly.

I mean it might go on in a way which would cause the death practically or the destruction of the jawbone?—It might do so.

Which of course would be a very terrible thing to contemplate?—Very.

188

Evidence for Prosecution.

Re-examined by the ATTORNEY-GENERAL—The portion that was decayed, you said, would have separated from the healthy portion —the portion where necrosis appeared, which was decayed or dead, would separate from the healthy portion?—I did not say that it had separated.

But it would?—It would, if allowed to have gone on.

There is also a means, is there not, by paring or removing the decayed part, of separating it from the healthy part, and preventing the spread of the necrosis?—Yes; I suppose it might do so. I cannot say for certain.

At all events, did you consider this a case involving any serious consequences, involving any serious operation?—Not at that time.

You did not think it sufficiently serious, then, to consider the question whether an operation would be necessary?—Not as to the necrosis portion of the bone.

You thought it would separate entirely naturally?—That is its process.

Leaving the rest of the gums healthy?—Yes.

As to this fungoid growth you have spoken of, did you find it necessary to suggest any treatment, or to do anything in relation to that?—No.

Why?—Except—I cannot say for certain—that I recommended the mouth to be rinsed out with Condy's fluid.

And was that an adequate treatment, in your opinion, for the case?—Well, I thought it was the best thing to do.

Did you attach any serious importance to that?—Not to this fungoid growth.

The deposition of Dr. THOMAS HENRY GREEN, sworn, was put in and read as follows:—I am a physician at Charing Cross Hospital. I was present at a post-mortem on the deceased Bartlett on the 2nd of January, and the post-mortem was made under my directions. I made no notes. I dictated the notes. I did not read over the notes at the time. I have read them since. I believe the notes contain what I dictated. I noticed the œsophagus (I cannot speak positively to the condition, unless I am allowed to refer to my notes); as far as I can remember, the lower part of the œsophagus was denuded of the epithelium.

The ATTORNEY-GENERAL—Your lordship does not need to have that explained to you, but perhaps it may be convenient to say that that long word means the gullet.

Mr. CLARKE—My lord, the deposition of Dr. Green is divided into certain portions. I should like the examination and the cross-examination to be read straight on without any interruption, if the Attorney-General consents.

Mr. JUSTICE WILLS—You mean without showing where the break is?

Adelaide Bartlett.

Dr. Thomas H. Green

Mr. CLARKE—Yes, my lord.

The ATTORNEY-GENERAL—Very well.

Deposition continued—It had come off in little patches here and there. The stomach was removed. It was tied before removal at both ends. The contents of the stomach were put into a large glass vessel; this vessel had no stopper to it, therefore a smaller glass-stoppered bottle was procured from the chemist, and the contents were transferred from the larger vessel to the smaller. I should think about half an hour elapsed before the transfer to the smaller vessel. The contents of the stomach smelt very much like chloroform. I compared it to a mixture of chloroform and garlic. I examined the cardiac end of the stomach and the mucous membrane. I examined them by my eyes, by means of a lens, and by my finger. The mucous membrane at the cardiac end of the stomach was covered with thick, tenacious mucus (I am speaking from memory). I believe it was unnaturally red—I am not sure—a dusky red, I believe. The capillaries were filled with blood. There was considerable injection of the mucous membrane at this part of the stomach. In the posterior dependent aspect of the stomach there was a distinct loss of substance—I should think over a space about the size of a shilling. I examined the intestines. I do not remember if the contents were run into any receiver. The smell of the contents of the intestines was similar to the stomach—much less intense. I examined the heart. I noticed the tissue. It was perhaps a little softer than I expected it to be so shortly after death. If I remember rightly, I said that the tissue is a little softer than natural, perhaps post-mortem. It was very slight. I noticed the cavities and larger vessels of the heart were much too deeply stained. The blood itself was fluid. That was not a normal condition, considering the time that had elapsed from death to the post-mortem examination. I was not present when the result was announced to the family. I was obliged to leave. I concluded that death was most likely due to the contents of the stomach. I suggested, before I left, that it would be wise to have the contents of the stomach sealed, and the coroner should be communicated with.

Cross-examined by Mr. EDWARD BEAL—My depositions taken before the coroner I looked through hurriedly and I signed. They were offered to be read to me by the coroner, but he did not read them. I read the notes of the post-mortem rapidly about two hours ago. I think I have not seen them since they were dictated. I cut open deceased's stomach myself. The inflammation at the cardiac end was obviously recent. It was obviously a recent change. I do not think acute inflammation could have lasted sufficient time in this case not to be characterised as recent. When I arrived, there were two large jars, which I carefully examined and smelt. They were glass and quite clean. I do not remember

Evidence for Prosecution.

Dr. Thomas H. Green

any more. A third small stoppered bottle was sent for from the chemist. I examined it. It appeared to be perfectly new. I don't know that I exactly saw the sealing of the jars. I was engaged in something else. I cannot say I saw them labelled. The skull-cap was removed. The *dura mater* did adhere to the skullcap rather more than it ought to do. The brain was carefully examined throughout, cut up, sliced in every possible direction. I do not remember that the meninges were thickened. The ventricles of the brain I did not notice anything abnormal about. I did not notice any odour about the ventricles. We examined the brain most carefully, and, as far as I remember, there was nothing abnormal about it. The brain was examined after the stomach. It was examined last. I examined the larynx, and cut it all the way down. I believe there was nothing abnormal about it. I examined the trachea. I believe there was nothing abnormal about that. The kidneys I examined. They were quite natural. I examined the spleen. That was quite natural. I have no recollection of examining the bladder. I should think I did so, but I do not remember. There was nothing particular about the lungs; a little congestion behind; I fancy a post-mortem change; for all practical purposes they were healthy. I only looked at the skin with my eye. I did not notice ulcers about the leg. We noticed he was a healthy-looking man. I noticed no ulceration anywhere except in the stomach. The pyloric end of the stomach was inflamed. I believe the small intestines were perfectly healthy throughout. We cut them up and carefully looked at them. We weighed none of the organs; we had no scales, and I saw no special reasons for doing so. I can't remember the size and shape of the loss of substance in the dependent part of the stomach. It was about the size of a shilling—very shallow. The edges were certainly not clean cut. The loss of substance did not extend to the muscular coat. There was very marked congestion for some distance round the ulcer. All the appearances in the deceased's corpse were consistent with natural disease except the appearance of the stomach. Some of the appearances in the stomach I might attribute to natural disease—all the appearances of the stomach, except that of the ulcer and the mucous membrane in its immediate vicinity. I do not consider those appearances due to chloroform, but to some irritant—I could not say from chloroform. I inferred it from the smell. The whole of the stomach was slightly inflamed. I examined the mouth. I think we found nothing but the condition of the jaw—there was some slight necrosis—nothing in the mucous membrane of the mouth. I did not notice the teeth particularly. A good many were lost. I did not observe an abcess. I noticed the pharynx was quite natural, and the upper part of the œsophagus. He was a strong, well-nourished, healthy-looking man, powerful, well developed—I should say, as far as I could observe, a man capable of considerable physical exertion.

Adelaide Bartlett.

Dr. Thomas H. Green

By Mr. LICKFOLD—I cannot complain of my practice. I should imagine necrosis of the jaw is not a pleasant ailment. I expect to find it occur in a healthy person. I should not call a person suffering from necrosis in a healthy condition. I do not remember I heard Mr. Leach describe him as suffering from alarming symptoms of necrosis. Poisoning by liquid chloroform is, I believe, of very rare occurrence. I have never, in the course of my practice, had a case of poisoning by liquid chloroform. I have never seen a case in which I suspected death to have resulted from chloroform. I do not know what chloroform is considered. I believe it may destroy life very quickly in a liquid state. I do not know. I believe so now. I have not come to that conclusion. If I had been asked, I should have said it might destroy life quickly. I do not know that persons have taken 4 ounces and recovered. Taylor is a great authority. If I have referred to his book, it must have been when a student. I have no personal knowledge whatever of poisoning by liquid chloroform, nor of the symptoms it produces. Ulceration of the stomach does not commonly follow on gastritis. Gastritis is ulceration of the stomach— ulceration is one of the manifestations of gastritis. Ulceration of the stomach will sometimes cause perforation, and perforation sudden death. What I meant was that signs of acute inflammation might pass off—signs of acute inflammation of the stomach might pass off completely, or leave only signs which could not be distinguished from a chronic process. It would not pass off after death. I quite agree with the passage in " Taylor on Poisons," second edition, page 163, read to me. I do not know anything about the theory that chloral hydrate may be turned into chloroform by the action of the blood alkali. Chloral hydrate would not have the slightest smell of chloroform. If in the stomach—I do not know. I do not remember having heard the medical men say anything about the brain before what I have said to-day. I do not remember I said anything before the coroner about it. I have a very clear recollection of what I conceive to be the all-important facts of the case; of course I mean as to post-mortem appearances. The notion that there was chloroform in the system did impress me. I should not, to my knowledge, have expected to find something wrong in the brain in a case of poisoning by liquid chloroform. I believe the blood in chloroform poisoning is more or less altered and does not coagulate properly, and stains the tissues; but I have no knowledge. I do not think I have spoken to Mr. Leach since the post-mortem. Oh, yes, I did, when he asked me to come to the coroner's inquiry. We certainly had no medical discussion.

Re-examined—I first got a notion of chloroform as soon as we opened the stomach, after the thorax had been examined. Before smelling the stomach, no person had suggested to me there

Evidence for Prosecution.

Dr. Thomas H. Green

was chloroform. The notion came to me immediately I opened the stomach. There was no perforation of the stomach in this case; the ulceration was only superficial. The ulceration and the appearances surrounding the ulcerated part were, in my opinion, due to the recent action of an irritant poison. Chloroform is a very volatile liquid. It acts as a local irritant. It is used externally as a local irritant. I should not like to express any opinion as to whether any of the signs of inflammation of the stomach might have been due to an inflammation of the mucous membrane antecedent in causation to that caused by an irritant. What I mean to say is, that the signs of inflammation at the cardiac end of the stomach were to my mind so characteristic of the action of a local irritant that the slighter degrees of inflammation in other parts of the stomach might have been, or not, due to the irritant. I cannot distinguish in the pyloric part between inflammation due to the irritant, and any irritation due to any preceding gastric disturbance. The inflammation was recent, certainly. The inflammation at the cardiac end was certainly recent.

By Mr. LICKFOLD—Chlorodyne would not have nearly so pungent a smell as I smelt in the stomach. It has a slight smell of chloroform, I believe; but what I smelt was almost as strong as a freshly opened bottle of chloroform.

The WITNESS further says—I desire to say that all I have said has been from my memory, and without reference to notes.
(Signed) T. HENRY GREEN.

Dr. ALFRED LEACH, examined by the ATTORNEY-GENERAL—I am a licentiate of the Royal College of Surgeons, a licentiate of the Society of Apothecaries, and a licentiate of midwifery. I practise at 41 Charlwood Street, Pimlico, which is less than a quarter of a mile away from Claverton Street. On 10th December last I was called in between nine and ten in the morning by Mrs. Bartlett to attend the deceased. I had never heard either of him or of the accused. I arrived at 85 Claverton Street before eleven o'clock in the forenoon. The deceased was sitting up on the sofa in the drawing-room, and I think he had on a dressing gown. I found that he was suffering from diarrhœa, some pain in the left side, fœtid breath, and he was suffering from the signs of indigestion and sub-acute gastritis—one might call it mercurialism. Mercurialism is the effect of a dose of mercury in a person with an idiosyncrasy for that drug, certain persons being more liable to the injurious effect of mercury than others.

By Mr. JUSTICE WILLS—Does that mean that he had taken too large a dose of blue pill or something containing mercury?—Yes. It does not mean that he had been taking mercury chronically.

o

Adelaide Bartlett.

Dr. Alfred Leach

Examination continued—I cannot remember exactly what I prescribed for him. I think it would be chlorate of potash and bismuth, but I am afraid I am venturing to say too much even with that; I have not looked at my notes since I was at the Police Court, and I am speaking from memory only, which is fallacious. I gave the copy of my prescriptions to the Treasury. On referring to it I find the first prescription is " Bismuth cinchona, tincture of nux vomica," which may be correctly described as a stomach mixture. On the same day I also prescribed chlorate of potash and lemon syrup as a mouth wash, because of the state of the jaw. I called again on 11th December, and I directed that the bismuth should be suspended by a solution of bicarbonate of soda, bromide of ammonium (a mild sedative), nux vomica, and flavouring matter —compound tincture of chloroform at the end. That would contain two drops of pure chloroform in the entire prescription, which would again be described as a stomach and sedative prescription. I called on the 14th, and gave the patient a morphia pill to procure sleep at night, and I repeated the mouth wash or chlorate of potash. On the 15th I prescribed a tonic of gentian and nux vomica. I cannot say whether there was any injection that day or not. On the 18th I prescribed sulphate of magnesium and tincture of jalap—a fairly strong purgative of Epsom salts, but that was not taken, however. The bismuth mixture was repeated on the 18th with the bromide, and here for the first time I added some chloral hydrate—15 grains to be taken at bed time, which is a small quantity. On the 19th I added morphia to the chloral hydrate. On that day his condition had improved. On the 20th the chloral hydrate was increased to 20 grains, and the bromide and morphia remained the same. On the 22nd I see nothing except a mouth wash. On the 24th I gave him a mixture having no therapeutic action.

Why did you give it?—Because he would not sleep. I had tried a strong or fairly strong narcotic, and, judging the nature of my patient, I thought it might make him sleep by giving him a placebo, giving him ten drops at a time, and telling him that he was bound to sleep after it—in fact, a prescription for the imagination. On the 25th I prescribed a tonic, which was also calculated to act as a slight stimulant to the digestive organs and is a nervine stimulant also; it contained phosphate of strychnine. On the 26th I began the vermifuges—the worm medicines—santonine made up with a little combination of senna, to be followed by a draught of sulphate of soda and Urwick's extract. That failed to act, and then, at my suggestion, he swallowed the draught that was prescribed for him on the 18th, which he had not taken until this moment. He likewise had administered to him by himself two small globules, each containing a fairly good dose of croton oil for aperient purposes. These were all ineffectual, and I was

194

Evidence for Prosecution.

Dr. Alfred Leach

afraid to give him any more. On the 28th I gave him an emulsified preparation of iodoform with bismuth for the fungoid state of his jaws.

Is it a correct description of this treatment to say that it was addressed to the soothing of the stomach, sedative and aperient?—So far, you are quite right.

An innocent and ordinary treatment?—I hope so. I found that my treatment was successful, and that his health was improving every day. On the 16th December Dr. Roberts, the dental surgeon, was called in. He used cocaine, and on the 31st I administered nitrous oxide gas for the performance of the operation. The last time I saw Mr. Bartlett alive was about six o'clock on 31st December, in front of Dr. Roberts' door, 49 Charlwood Street. He had just had a tooth out, but previous to that I think I may say that he seemed better than I had ever seen him before. I cannot say that his spirits were better, but they were not bad.

From what did you derive the impression that he was better than you had ever seen him?—Chiefly from his acknowledging it, saying that he felt he was better, a thing he was very loath to do. On the 30th I said I would not continue to visit him, and the reason for that was that he had made up his mind to have continual medical attendance, and I was not inclined to continue. Of course, if he needed it, I would not mind attending, but I did not think that he continued to need it—to need it daily, I mean—and to see him twice a week would have been quite enough.

About 4 a.m. on 1st January Mr. Doggett's housemaid came for me. I asked her whether it was merely one of his notions or whether he was really ill, and I think she said he was dead, but I scarcely accepted that as true. She could only say, "I know nothing about it; Mrs. Bartlett only tells me he is dead." I got alarmed, and we jumped into a hansom and went to Claverton Street. When I went into the room I found Mr. Bartlett was dead. This would be about 4.30 in the morning. When I got there Mrs. Bartlett and Mr. Doggett were in the drawing-room; I am not quite certain whether Mrs. Doggett was there also. I found the deceased lying in his usual place—a camp bedstead near the window, where I had always seen him. I made a formal examination in order to see whether he was dead or not, although directly I entered the door I saw that he was dead. He had on a nightdress, and I think an undervest, and he was lying on his back with his arms across the abdomen. The legs were up a little; the fingers naturally closed, and the surface very pallid and very cold; the eyelids nearly closed, and the pupils, for him, very much dilated; natural for death. The mouth was open, and the tongue was very white. I calculated that he had been dead

195

Adelaide Bartlett.

Dr. Alfred Leach

for two or three hours. A little later, after thinking it over a day or two, I thought it possible that he might have been dead longer, but I think now, on giving the matter very careful consideration, three hours is as nearly accurate as I can give. I said to Mr. Doggett in the drawing-room that I thought he had been dead two or three hours; I am not sure if Mrs. Bartlett was present then. When I smelt the body I found that the chest smelt of brandy. I think it was moist, I am not sure of that. The mouth had no odour whatever. The brandy that I smelt was on the chest itself. It was a slight smell. I am not certain as to whether there was any moisture on the vest or nightdress. That was the only smell on the body that attracted my attention. In the room there was that natural close odour of a sleeping room, the odour of supper and of condiments and of brandy and of gas. The face was pale, but the expression was natural. The fingers of the hand were slightly flexed, as were also the legs.

Was there any appearance at all of any convulsive action, any paroxysms, or anything of that kind?—No. I looked for that. I looked for froth on the lips, but found none. The eyelids were so closed as to prevent an examination of the pupils without drawing up the eyelids. I lifted the eyelids of both eyes to see the pupils.

Lying back, as you have described him, his pupils would be in the direction of the ceiling?—No, they were more in the direction of the wall behind him.

By Mr. JUSTICE WILLS—Contracted in death?—Yes; the line of vision would have been distinctly above the horizontal if he had been standing up.

Examination continued—I could form no opinion at all as to whether his eyelids, in the state in which I saw them, were in the state in which he had died, or whether anything had been done to them. It is possible to draw down the eyelids so as to close them before cadaveric rigidity sets in.

About what time does it take?—A few minutes to many hours; roughly speaking, from six to eight. It depends on the cause of death, the state of the body before death, and on surrounding circumstances to some small extent.

The temperature of the room?—Yes, but very slightly, I think. I scarcely know that the surrounding circumstances are important. I believe the cadaveric rigidity differs between bodies immersed in water and others. I am not speaking from experience; only from reading on the subject.

Will you please describe the arrangement of the room? Was there any table near the bed?—No, the table was in the middle of the room, away from the bed. The head of the bed was towards the wall on which the mantelpiece was. The fireplace projected from part of the wall, which projected also, and that left a kind

196

Evidence for Prosecution.

Dr. Alfred Leach

of very shallow alcove. The head of the bed was in that alcove, as near the mantelpiece as the alcove would allow it to be.

Did you observe anything on the mantelshelf ?—Unusual ?

I did not say unusual. Did you observe anything ?—Yes, a looking-glass, a clock, some vases, and a small bottle of chlorodyne. That was all. The bottle of chlorodyne was either on the mantelshelf or a little bit on the other side, away from the bed. The size of the bottle would be about an ounce bottle. On the table there were the remains of supper and a brandy bottle, a bottle containing some white stuff, I think carbonate of soda—there was nothing of importance on the table. I satisfied myself that the bottle contained some brandy, but I do not remember how much. There was also a wineglass, with some brandy in it, on a table. I do not remember whether there was a whatnot or stand at the end of the room facing the mantelpiece. I certainly looked for anything that could throw light on the subject I had in hand, but I did not take an inventory of what was there besides the things of importance. I would call bottles things of importance.

Was there anything there besides the bottle of chlorodyne on the mantelpiece and the bottle of brandy on the table ?—Yes, the glass jar with white powder in it—carbonate of soda, I think— and the glass with a little brandy; beyond that I remember nothing. There was a little lock-up next the fireplace which I examined along with Mr. Doggett. I forget whether it was locked or not, but, if it was locked, we unlocked it. We did not have to ask for the key. There was nothing of a suspicious nature in that lock-up; there were no bottles in it. I smelt all the glasses in the room. Brandy, a smell of supper, and so forth were all the things noticeable to me. I saw a glass of Condy's fluid; I am not sure whether it was on the corner of the mantelpiece or on the floor just below it.

When you say a glass, do you mean a tumbler ?—Yes, with another bottle in it, but I am not quite sure. The chlorodyne bottle was labelled " Chlorodyne," and there was very little in the bottle. I looked round the room with care, and searched carefully to see whether there was anything in the place that might throw light on the matter, anything suspicious. The bedroom opened from the drawing-room by folding doors, but I do not think I entered it.

Was there anything whatever in the previous conduct of the deceased, in your observation of him continuously from 10th to 31st December, to suggest to you the probability of death from natural causes ?—No, nothing.

Did you say anything to Mrs. Bartlett, or did Mrs. Bartlett say anything to you, as to what could have been the cause of death ?—Yes, I asked her to give me an explanation—any assistance, any elucidation of the mystery, but she said she was unable. We then discussed several things, and then I spoke to her in a

Adelaide Bartlett.

Dr. Alfred Leach

low voice so that Mr. Doggett might take the hint to leave the room. When he was gone I thought perhaps some matters of delicacy which she did not like to mention before him might come out, but she was unable to give me any explanation, and then it was, I think, that we discussed the subject of chlorodyne.

Mr. CLARKE—If the witness has a note that may assist his recollection of that I am quite content that he should refer to it now.

The ATTORNEY-GENERAL—Either my friend wishes the witness's notes read or he does not. I am willing to take the course he thinks most desirable, but I thought it was best to get an independent recollection of this gentleman when he came there on that morning.

Mr. CLARKE—I do not wish for anything he has written as a separate independent document, but if he has a record made at the time by him which will give him full recollection of the conversation I am willing to take it.

The ATTORNEY-GENERAL—He cannot pick out little bits; either the document must be read or not.

Mr. JUSTICE WILLS—We had best leave it as it is, I think. Mr. Clarke has the means of cross-examination.

Examination continued—Was anything said about the question of the necessity for an inquest?—Yes. I said (this was while Mr. Doggett was there, I think), "I cannot give a certificate; there must be a post-mortem." Mrs. Bartlett's reply to that was, "Must there be an inquest?" I said, "There must be a post-mortem." A little later on I said, "Really, this is a case that I ought to report to the coroner, but I have no suspicion of foul play, I will have a post-mortem made, and then, if the pathological cause of death is found, a certificate will be given in due course. I will not make the post-mortem myself; I will have a pathologist."

Do you recollect saying anything about what might be found on examination to be the cause of death?—Yes. Mrs. Bartlett asked, "What is he dead of?" I replied, "I don't know; I found no cause of death. It is probably due to the rupture of some small vessel, some aneurism—something that may have been possibly overlooked in my examination. I can hardly think that the death was from syncope." Whether it was a rupture of some blood vessel or some aneurism would be a matter capable of proof or disproof by a post-mortem examination, and that is why I mentioned a pathologist, and not a medical jurist. I suggested Dr. Green, who is a noted pathologist and a man of eminence in his profession; he is physician at the Charing Cross Hospital and at Brompton.

I should have mentioned earlier that when I was attending the deceased, Dr. Dudley was called in on one occasion—either on the 19th or the 20th. On one of my visits, after talking with

198

Evidence for Prosecution.

Dr. Alfred Leach

the patient and saying he was doing well, and so on, some conversation ensued which I do not quite remember. I think it was in reference to his business, the partner wanting him back or something of that kind. Mrs. Bartlett broke in with, as near as I can recollect, these words, " Doctor, will you excuse what I am about to say ? Mr. Bartlett is very contented with your treatment, but his friends have on more than one occasion requested him to let them send a doctor of their own choosing." She added, " Mr. Bartlett's friends are no friends to me." Mr. Bartlett then broke in, " We intend in future, doctor, to manage our own affairs, and not to be interfered with by my friends and relations. I am sorry to say that they are not kind to my wife." I said, " By all means have a consultation, as many as you like." He replied, " No, I will not have a consultation in the ordinary sense of the term; I will not see any one they send, but I will see any gentleman you choose to bring to see me once. I am getting better than I was. I will not submit to any other treatment, but I will see any gentleman once. I do this for the protection of my wife." Either before or after that Mrs. Bartlett had said, " Doctor, Mr. Bartlett's friends will accuse me of poisoning him if he does not get out soon—if he gets worse—if he does not get better."

By Mr. JUSTICE WILLS—Did she say that ?—She said that, I think; the conversation was a joint one; I have tried to pick out who it was that said the different things.

By the FOREMAN—The deceased heard it ?—Oh, yes, we were together.

Examination continued—Extraordinary as Mrs. Bartlett's statements were, they made little effect on me, as I hear many strange things, and I thought it referred to the mercurialism I had found on my first visits. I called in Dr. Dudley. He approved of my treatment, and prescribed a fresh tonic and a combination of the drugs that hitherto I had given him separately.

To go back to 1st January, I asked Mrs. Bartlett whether any time had elapsed between her finding her husband dead and calling the servant and Mrs. Doggett, and she said that as soon as she found she could not rouse him she ran up for the servant and sent her to me. She told me that she was sitting beside her husband's foot in the easy chair, where, in fact, she always slept. She had her left arm round his foot. She said she woke and heard him snoring, and that it was a peculiar kind of snore. But, as it was not unusual for him to snore, she dropped asleep again. She evidently tried to describe to me the stertorous breathing. Then, later on, she woke up with the cramp in her arm and saw him lying on his face in an uncomfortable position. When she said that she had her arm round his foot I came to the conclusion that she meant outside the bedclothes. When she woke and found him lying on his face she rose from her chair and went towards his

Adelaide Bartlett.

Dr. Alfred Leach

head to turn him into a better position. She was alarmed at his condition, and tried to rouse him. She found him cold. She applied brandy—I do not know whether she said she poured any down his throat, but I understood she rubbed some on his chest (probably that was an inference, because it agreed with what I discovered myself), and sent for me. She told me she sent up to the servant's room.

I do not think you need follow that——

By Mr. CLARKE—I think we must have the whole of the conversation?—I think it has a little bearing on the loss of time. She went up to the servant's room and told her to dress and come for me. The servant then went down to the kitchen, Mrs. Bartlett said, and Mrs. Bartlett chafed at the delay. Of the rest I am rather doubtful. She called Mrs. Doggett.

Mr. CLARKE—This is evidently nothing.

Examination continued—I do not think she explained to me how she was able to change her husband's position from lying on his face into this position. When she told me that she found him lying downwards on his face I did not understand that his whole body was turned.

All you mean to convey is that his head was twisted round?—Yes, and his shoulders. I imagine that was the impression conveyed to me and left on my mind.

On that same 1st January do you recollect asking Mrs. Bartlett about poison?—Yes, we discussed all the poisons I could think of that were rapid in their action, digitalis and prussic acid. I asked her if it was possible that he could have any digitalis or any of the alkaloids in his possession. I knew that he was a friend of some wholesale chemists, and she said, " No, he could have had no poison without my knowing it; he could have got no poison without my knowledge." I asked her, " What is this chlorodyne doing here? "—for I had never seen it before. " Oh," she said, " Edwin used to rinse his mouth with it at night." I said, " Rinse his mouth! Then he must have swallowed some." She said, " No, he only rubbed his gums." I asked whether he ever went into the bedroom at all, and she said, " No." I said, " If he rinsed out his mouth and spat out the chlorodyne, we must find some of it in the room." I looked under the bed into the most natural receptacle into which he would spit. She said, " No, I think not; he never put much into his mouth; he only rubbed his gums." Chlorodyne is a substance that smells strongly. I did not perceive any smell of chlorodyne. The smell of chlorodyne that has stood for some time is extremely like that of pure chloroform. It contains one in eight of pure chloroform.

Do you suggest, supposing he had used chlorodyne in the way Mrs. Bartlett described for his gums, that accidentally swallowing some would cause death?—It would depend on how much he swallowed. Drugs had a peculiar action on the man. It is

Evidence for Prosecution.

Dr. Alfred Leach

known that as little as a drachm of chlorodyne has killed. I thought it might possibly be so in this case, but I have since quite given up that idea, of course.

Why?—Because of the result of the analysis proving the absence of the other ingredients of chlorodyne, one of which is prussic acid, but the more stable ones, alkaloids.

You do not believe at all it was death from chlorodyne?—No, and I am sorry I entertained that belief at one time.

Were you aware on that evening, 1st January, that there was in Mrs. Bartlett's possession any quantity of chloroform?—I knew nothing of that till twenty-six days afterwards. It then came upon me as a surprise.

Did Mrs. Bartlett on that occasion in any way refer to chloroform?—On some occasion Mrs. Bartlett asked me, "Could he have died of chloroform?" I cannot fix the date when the reference was made to chloroform, but I do not think anything was said about it on 1st January. I cannot remember about that, because there was nothing to make the mention of chloroform more remarkable to me than the mention of digitalis or any of the others.

The post-mortem examination took place on 2nd January. Dr. Green was the principal, and Dr. Murray, Dr. Dudley, Dr. Cheyne and I assisted in various capacities. I think Dr. Dudley was there as an onlooker, and I was there from the natural interest I took in the case. Being there, I was asked to take the notes, which I willingly did. My notes were written at the time, and they are as accurate as I could make them. The notes I wrote at the time are as follows :—Examination 38 hours p.m. Body well nourished——

Does that mean the examination took place thirty-eight hours after death?—It took place at half-past two on 2nd January, and Mr. Bartlett was supposed to have died early on the morning of 1st January. "Rigor mortis present. On abdomen much cutaneous fat, deep yellow colour, no appearance of subcutaneous hæmorrhage or external injury. Heart, on opening pericardium, nothing abnormal. Heart, on removal, normal in size; muscular tissue a little flabby; valves free from disease; tiny patch of atheroma at root of aorta." Atheroma means the degeneration of one of the coats of the blood vessels, and the aorta is one of the large blood vessels. "The p.m. staining of lining membrane of the cavities and large vessels abnormally deep; blood in cavities dark and quite fluid. Aorta, with exception of a few small patches of degeneration, is normal. Lungs and pleura normal; liver normal. Spleen normal; kidneys normal. Œsophagus (the gullet) lower part abnormally vascular and irregularly denuded of its epithelium "—that is, its scaly lining. "Pharynx, upper part of œsophagus and trachea present nothing abnormal. Stomach, after being ligatured at both ends, removed; contents

Adelaide Bartlett.

Dr. Alfred Leach

placed in a clean stoppered bottle." The word " clean " was put in afterwards. " Nearly an ounce of contents, consisting of brownish grumous liquid varying in consistence, the more solid portions paler in colour, and look something like thick mucus; smells strong, pungent ethereal odour resembling a combination of chloroform and garlic. Cardiac end of stomach—the mucous membrane is of a dusky pink colour, which to the naked eye looks uniform, but under a lens there is a distinct punctiform and capillary hyperæmia." That means the end of the stomach nearest the spleen; the mucous membrane there is of a dusky pink. To the naked eye the colour looked of uniform distribution, but under a lens it indicated that the minutest blood vessels, the capillaries, were congested with blood—not inflamed, congested. " The surface of membrane at this part of stomach is covered with an abnormal amount of thick, tenacious mucus or lymph. At the most dependent part of the stomach there is a patch about the size of a five-shilling piece, where the mucous membrane presents a rough, irregular appearance as though it were partially destroyed. Here the membrane is more easily removed by the finger nail than elsewhere. In other parts of the cardiac end of the stomach the mucous membrane is not easily removable. Pyloric end of stomach is of a pale greenish colour, covered with a tenacious mucus, but otherwise normal. Head—on removing the calvarium, the dura mater is found abnormally adherent." By that I mean that on removing the skullcap some difficulty was experienced in tearing it from the membraneous envelope of the brain. " With the exception of rather more p.m. staining than usual, the surface of brain presents nothing abnormal. A careful examination of the brain throughout fails to reveal anything abnormal. Intestines—on removing, the contents of the small intestine were allowed to run into a glass jar. They present the same peculiar odour as those of stomach, only in less marked degree and less pungent. On opening bowels, nothing abnormal in the mucous membrane is discoverable. Some small pieces of what appear to be mango-chutney found in intestines throughout their whole length. One or two pieces of the same were observed in the stomach. Large intestine contains much fæcal matter, also containing considerable amount of half-digested mango. Lower jaw, incisor surface necrosed."

Now, let me ask you, does that examination or does it not disclose a healthy state of all the vital organs?—Yes.

There is a reference there to something abnormal in the condition of the stomach?—Yes, but I take it you do not include that among the vital organs.

Was there anything abnormal or unusual in any other part of the physical system of this man?—From the notes I have read I gather that the only abnormalisms present, except those of the stomach, are fluidity in the blood, with a dissolving out of the

202

Evidence for Prosecution.

Dr. Alfred Leach

colouring matter staining the tissues; and what I should scarcely perhaps allude to is a certain amount of adhesion present in the dura mater. There was nothing at all suggestive of the cause of death, excepting in the stomach, and the blood acted upon through the contents of the stomach. The contents of the intestines were put into a bottle, but I did not take any active part in the post-mortem, and I did not see the sealing process. All the bottles that could be found in the back room, which all belonged to the deceased—all the bottles and jars containing the results of the post-mortem were carried by my directions into the front room. The undertaker did it, I think, it being understood that the front room was going to be locked. I could not say whether the front room was locked and the key handed to Mr. Wood, the solicitor.

By Mr. JUSTICE WILLS—The post-mortem took place in the back room, the bedroom.

Examination continued—Did you notice anything about the tongue of the dead man?—Yes, a very, very white condition of the whole tongue, but this had passed off before the post-mortem was made.

Was it so peculiar a condition as to present itself to your mind as something striking?—Yes, but I only learnt to interpret it some days afterwards by reason of an experiment I made upon myself.

What was that?—Swallowing chloroform. I took $3\frac{1}{2}$ drachms into my mouth, and, to the best of my belief, swallowed 20 or 30 drops of it; I then ejected the remainder, and was surprised when I looked in the looking-glass to find my tongue was very white. The interpretation of what I had then seen in the dead body came to me. I may add that this condition of my own tongue passed off in a few hours. I have no experience at all, from any previous post-mortem examination, of the effect of chloroform taken into the stomach. I do not remember to have seen Mrs. Matthews on 1st January, and I don't think I saw Mr. Dyson then. After the post-mortem examination on 2nd January the other doctors made me their spokesman. To the best of my recollection, I said, in the presence of Mrs. Bartlett, "These gentlemen wish me to state that we have very carefully examined the body of the deceased, and we are unable to discover any pathological lethal cause—that is to say, any natural or obvious cause—of death. The contents of the stomach are suspicious, and we have preserved them." That was a correct statement of the result. I just remember now that it was I who went downstairs to summon the relatives from the smoking-room, and there, in the presence of Mrs. Bartlett and the others, I said something to the effect that the contents of the stomach had a pungent ethereal odour. I may have said " Dr. Green," or one of the doctors, " suggests chloroform "—I probably did mention chloroform—" but if it is, it is the chlorodyne." I was under that impression then, but that delusion has entirely

Adelaide Bartlett.

Dr. Alfred Leach

disappeared since. On the occasion of the post-mortem on the 2nd no search was made of the drawers in the back room. I still adhere to my statement that Mrs. Bartlett said nothing to me about her having possession of chloroform until 26th January. On the occasion when I made the reference to the chloroform, when announcing the result of the post-mortem, Mrs. Bartlett made no answer, so far as I can remember.

Mrs. Bartlett called on me on Wednesday, 6th January. I informed her then that I wished to be put in possession of any facts surrounding the death of the deceased which would enable me, on the following day, to lay some clear statement before the inquest which had been fixed for the 7th. I likewise asked her to repeat the hurried account she had given on the morning of my visit to the corpse. I am not quite sure but that she brought to me on that occasion notes of how the time had elapsed between her husband's return from the dentist and my appearance at four o'clock in the morning. I asked her to jot down a memorandum of how the time had passed while the events were still fresh in her memory. I think it was on this occasion she read it to me. I said I thought that it was satisfactory, but I did not take a note of it, because I did not wish to burden my mind with things that had been observed by another person, and which I thought she would like to give in evidence herself. I thought she would make the statement giving the evidence herself. She was not at any time examined before the coroner. I have some very brief notes here of her visits. May I refer to them?

Mr. CLARKE—I do not object to the notes of the conversation being referred to, provided they were written at the time the conversation is described, and used as assistance to memory.

By Mr. JUSTICE WILLS—I am not speaking of the detailed thing that I drew up afterwards. These notes were not made at the time; I do not know when they were made, but I see that they are on Police Court paper. I have no notes of importance regarding 6th January.

Examination continued—Was any reference made to the impossibility of his swallowing chloroform on that occasion?—I think all the conversation about the impossibility had taken place much earlier. No doubt on this occasion chlorodyne was again referred to, because, unfortunately, I continued to harp upon that subject. She reiterated the same statement, that he could not have swallowed it. I saw Mrs. Bartlett on 6th, 14th, 18th, and 26th January. By the 26th I had heard the statement as to the result which the analysis had shown. Mrs. Bartlett called on me on the 26th, after I had heard the statement, and she was with me for an hour or more. I began the conversation by saying, " Mrs. Bartlett, I think I have some good news for you." I knew she was much worried, and I thought it was good news. I said, " The report now is that the Government analyst is going to give acetate of

Evidence for Prosecution.

Dr. Alfred Leach

lead as the cause of death, which is nonsense, for there was no lead in the stomach. Likewise the report says that he is going to return a verdict of chloroform as the cause of death, which is very improbable. At any rate, either one or the other—that should set your mind at rest; but had it been one of the secret poisons given in small amounts, and which could be administered without the patient knowing it, you would have most certainly been very seriously accused of having poisoned him by some people." She then very much surprised me by saying, " I am afraid, doctor, it is too true. I wish anything but chloroform had been found." Naturally that led me to ask the question, " Why, what do you mean? " or something of that sort, and she then proceeded to a long statement.

Mr. CLARKE—If you have a note of that statement I have no objection to your reading it.

By Mr. JUSTICE WILLS—The statement is dated 6th February, and I have it here.

Mr. CLARKE—I make no objection to Dr. Leach reading the note which he made of that statement.

The ATTORNEY-GENERAL—I am entirely in your lordship's hands about it. Of course, it is not a case in which any admission will do.

Mr. JUSTICE WILLS—No; to my mind it is quite outside what is usually admitted as contemporaneous record. Mr. Clarke is in this position of advantage: if there is anything in the conversation he can bring it out in cross-examination, if he thinks it of advantage; but I do not think it would be right to have it read as part of the examination-in-chief.

Examination continued—Mrs. Bartlett began by giving, as I understand her story, a preface containing a sketch of her married life. That sketch was simply this, that, being married young, she had been induced to enter into a marriage compact, scarcely understanding the meaning of its terms; and this marriage compact was, that the marital relations of the pair were, in deference to certain peculiar views held by her husband, to be of an entirely platonic nature; sexual intercourse was not to occur.

By Mr. JUSTICE WILLS—The terms of this compact were adhered to, with a solitary exception when a breach of the terms was permitted in consequence of her fondness for children and her anxiety to become a mother. After her confinement the former terms—that is to say, those of a platonic nature—were resumed, she being indifferent on the matter. Her husband was kind to her. They were affectionate, although the wife on one occasion objected to the use of the term " affection." That is only a quibble in words. Her husband was affectionate, and each strove in every way to fulfil each other's wishes, and succeeded in living upon most amicable terms, the happiness of which was on one occasion disturbed by her husband's father. She then entered

205

Adelaide Bartlett.

Dr. Alfred Leach

into some family details, which really have quite slipped my memory.

Examination continued—By " family details " I mean the conduct of her husband's father, but I do not remember them, and if I made any attempt to give them I should be giving more what I have heard since. Her husband's brother was not referred to. She told me she had consented to her husband's father living with them, but he made her life miserable by his constant insults; and when she appealed to her husband to resent those insults he, in his mild way, did not act upon her suggestion with the zeal that she thought the occasion demanded. She consequently left her husband's house and hid herself from him—I think, in the house of her aunt—I forget for how long; and she only consented to return upon an ample apology being made. That was the end of it. This was the only break in their conjugal happiness. She then said that her position had not been an easy one : it might be almost called cruel, for her husband, though meaning no cruelty, put her in a very difficult position for a woman to maintain. No female friends or relations were ever invited to the house, but he had always liked to surround her with male acquaintances. She said, " He thought me clever; he wished to make me more clever; and the more attention and admiration I gained from these male acquaintances the more delighted did he appear. Their attention to me gave him pleasure, or seemed to give him pleasure." Now we come to the latter end of his life. During the last few months of his life the man's nature seemed to be somewhat changed. " We became acquainted with Mr. Dyson. My husband threw us together. He requested us to kiss in his presence, and he seemed to enjoy it." She gave me to understand—in fact, she used these words, " He had given me to Mr. Dyson."

Do you mean then and there, or in the event of his death?— I do not know and I did not ask. Now, her husband having fully effected the transfer—I mean still in the platonic sense——

The transfer to Mr. Dyson?—Yes—constantly developing symptoms of wishing to, I cannot say resume, but wishing to assume those marital rights which he had never before claimed, you understand my meaning?

You mean desiring to have sexual intercourse with his wife?— Yes; she put it in as delicate a manner as she could, and that is the meaning. This she said she resented in those words. She said, " Edwin, you know you have given me to Mr. Dyson; it is not right that you should do now what during all the married years of our life you have not done," and he agreed that it was not right. She said it was a duty to her womanhood and to the man to whom she was practically affianced, at his wish, and he agreed that she was right. Now, as he got better, while I was treating him, these manifestations of his became very urgent, and she thought for means the more thoroughly to emphasise her appeal to

Evidence for Prosecution.

Dr. Alfred Leach

him or to prevent his putting his impulses into effect. One of the means, unfortunately, was the possessing herself of a quantity of chloroform.

She said so, did she?—She said so. Now, I had no idea till I heard it in Court how long she had had that in her possession, but she said that " the presence of that chloroform in my drawer troubled my mind." She said that her object was to sprinkle some of the chloroform upon a handkerchief and wave it in his face every time it was necessary, thinking that thereby he would go peacefully to sleep. I told her the danger she would have run if she had put that into practice—the danger of their being chloroformed by the bottle being upset—and I informed her that her plan would have been ineffectual. I said to her, " Trying to put chloroform upon your handkerchief and waving it in the face of your husband, he would have resisted it, a struggle would have ensued, the bottle would have capsized and chloroformed the pair of you. It is not the first time that chloroform has been upset in a bed, and the stopper come out." She said, " I never kept a secret from Edwin, and the presence of that chloroform in my drawer troubled my mind." The words were " in my possession " or " in my drawer," but I think she said " in my drawer." She went on, " And I was also troubled with some scruples as to whether putting my plan into practice would have been right, whether I should be doing a right or a wrong thing; and on the last day of the year, when he was in bed, I brought the chloroform to him, and gave it to him." She said she gave the bottle to him, and informed him of her intention, but she gave me no details of the conversation with him. I asked her, " Was not your husband very cross with you, or alarmed, or what was his demeanour? " She replied, " No, he was not cross; we talked amicably and seriously, and he turned round on his side, and pretended to go to sleep, or to sulk," or something of that kind. In answer to a question from me, she told me that she had looked at the chloroform. I believe she told me that it was in a large round bottle, or that it was in a large bottle labelled " Chloroform," and corked, not tied down with leather or anything of that sort, and not full. He looked at the chloroform, and put it by the side where he was sitting or lying, on the mantelpiece at the corner. The next thing she told me was that she fell asleep, sitting in the chair where she always slept, I may add that she had slept there ever since I had attended the patient, notwithstanding my remonstrances. She went to sleep with her arm round his foot. Then she awoke and heard him snoring, and woke again and found he was dead. She had given me that part of the story on the morning of the death. I asked her, " Did you look at the bottle? "—the chloroform. " Was there much gone from it? " She said, " I do not know whether much was gone from it or not." I did not ask her when she got the chloroform, but I asked her

Adelaide Bartlett.

Dr. Alfred Leach

who got it for her. She did not answer, and I saw it was a question to which no answer would be given. She just said, " Some one got it for me," and I asked no more questions; but later on there was no secret about it.

The mantelpiece was not far from the head of the bed. There was no chloroform bottle on the mantelpiece on the morning of 1st January. There was nothing on the mantelpiece but what I have already described. I asked Mrs. Bartlett on 26th January what she had done with the bottle on 1st January, and she said that she took it from the mantelpiece and put it away in her drawer about breakfast time. I am quite clear that it was not on the mantelpiece on 1st January, because both Mr. Doggett and I searched the room in her presence. Mrs. Bartlett never left the room while we were searching it.

Did you ask her on 26th January how it came that she had not mentioned it to you on 1st January when she saw you searching the room?—I do not think I did, for it seemed obvious to me.

Did she volunteer any explanation of it?—No, she did not say specially.

Specially or otherwise?—Well, generally that she wanted to know what he was dead of. She told me that the bottle remained in her drawer until Wednesday, the 6th, when she took her things away, and she said she took the bottle of chloroform with her, emptied it out of the carriage window, and threw the bottle away into some water—I think she said from the train. She did not tell me why she did that, nor did I ask any reason. She told me when she first suspected the real cause of her husband's death, probably she told me that day, but I quite forget what she said.

Cross-examined by Mr. CLARKE—I understand prior to the 10th of December you had no knowledge of Mr. Bartlett or his wife?—No knowledge of their existence.

And, so far as you know, you were called in because the place where you practise is conveniently near where they lived?—It faces their street.

On 10th December till the last of his life had you plenty of opportunities of seeing Mr. and Mrs. Bartlett together?—Twenty or twenty-one.

I believe there were some days upon which you visited him twice or even thrice?—Yes.

And there was at least one visit when you spent several hours there?—Yes.

So far as you could see and judge, during the whole of the time was Mrs. Bartlett tending her husband with anxious affection?—So far as I could see and judge, decidedly.

Could you have thought or wished for a more devoted nurse for him?—No; what I should have wished for was one with a little better memory, that is all.

I think her memory was the only thing in your mind as to

Evidence for Prosecution.

Dr. Alfred Leach

her defects as a nurse, and that was supplied by her keeping a written record?—Yes; she used to pin it on the mantelpiece.

Did she tend him night and day?—Yes; she was most affectionate—in fact, I could not wish for a better nurse. It is only right that I should say that emphatically.

I believe he himself spoke with gratitude of the way she was devoting herself to him?—I do not remember.

Do you remember her speaking of herself breaking down and being tired?—No.

Did you notice it yourself?—Yes.

And comment upon it to him?—In his presence.

You were told that, night after night, during his illness she had sat and slept sitting at the foot of his bed?—Yes.

Never getting for herself one night of restful sleep?—Well, she said she slept comfortably in the chair; she never went to bed.

Do you remember how long it was after your first visit that you noticed it was telling on her?—No; I think very soon after my first visit I asked her to go to bed.

And she refused?—She refused. I asked her on several occasions to go to bed; each time she had some excuse.

And would not do it?—And would not do it.

It was obvious to you that she needed rest and was suffering in strength, was it not?—It was.

Did she tell you on any occasion what would happen if she did go to bed—whether her husband would sleep or be restless?—Yes; that would be about the middle of the third week of my attendance—about the beginning of the last week of December. I said, " Now, Mrs. Bartlett, there is no excuse for you not going to bed." She said, " What is the use of my going to bed, doctor? He will walk about the room like a ghost. He will not sleep unless I sit and hold his toe." The drollness of the expression fixed itself upon my mind.

On 10th December, when she came to you, I think she told you something about the case—when she came to call you in?—Yes, the first time; she gave me a sketch of the case I was going to visit.

Do you remember, in outline, what it was?—No, I am sorry to say, I have tried to, and cannot remember what she said, but I remember my reply.

What was your reply?—" This appears to be a very peculiar case; I will come as soon as I can."

You cannot remember your inquiry, but she gave you, as far as she could, a true account of the condition of her husband, did she?—She did not give me a full one, or I should have remembered it.

When you first went to see him, had she preserved his motions for you to see?—Yes; and she continued to do so regularly, motions and vomit also.

Adelaide Bartlett.

Dr. Alfred Leach

I may just dispose of that in one sentence—she kept motions and vomit for you during the illness, and I think on one occasion, if not more, the urine was sent to you to analyse?—Yes.

On more than one occasion?—It was only analysed once, but it was frequently sent to me. I did not trouble to analyse it again, because I knew his kidneys were sound, but everything was preserved for me.

10th December was the first day you saw him. Did you see him more than once that day?—You will have to supply me with the list, I think.

Have you a copy of your account?—I have not.

That may assist you (handing one to the witness)?—Yes, it will—two visits on the 10th.

On 10th December there were two visits, were there?—Yes; this list has the visits marked which I paid, but some which I paid I never entered.

That day you did not see him three times; you only charged for two visits?—I think I saw him twice that day.

On that occasion did you find extreme nervousness and great prostration?—Yes, nervous prostration; the man's muscular system was good enough.

I quite understand; the physical state of the man, as far as you could test it, was not seriously wrong?—Not seriously impaired —he was suffering.

He was suffering, was he not, from diarrhœa?—Yes, there was more than diarrhœa, it was melæna—diarrhœa with black motions.

And the black motions contained indications of hæmorrhage from the bowels, did they not?—Yes.

He complained, I think, of pains in the abdomen?—Yes; in the left side, I should rather say.

Will you put your hand on the place?—Just above here (putting his hand above his hip), and there was a peculiar dullness on percussion.

Which indicated what, to your mind?—Which percussion led me to try, and at the post-mortem I tried, to find something to account for it, but I could not.

You have no doubt that there was a dullness?—No; and it passed off after three or four days of treatment.

Did he tell you that he had been overworked in business? Do you remember that?—Yes.

He said he had been overworked in business, and did you advise him to see nobody connected with business until he got better?—Yes—I did not say until he got better; it was part of my prescription, I said, to see nobody connected with his business.

Did he complain of sickness?—Oh, yes, and vomited.

On that day?—Yes; when I first saw him he had vomited, and he continued to vomit for about a couple of days, I think.

With pain in the sides, and with diarrhœa and hæmorrhage

210

Evidence for Prosecution.

Dr. Alfred Leach

from the bowels, his physical condition was not very satisfactory, was it?—No; he was in a very bad state.

You have described his condition then as one of nervous exhaustion and depression?—That likewise was present.

Was his breath particularly fœtid?—Very.

And the pulse was poor, and small, and slight?—Yes, it was.

There was something else which specially attracted your attention, was not there—the condition of his mouth?—Yes. He had a blue line round the edges of his gums; his gums were red and spongy; and there was some small amount of salivation—an extra large flow of saliva.

And that condition of his mouth suggested to you that he had taken mercury, did it not?—It did, at once.

And you asked him the question, whether he had taken mercury?—I first examined him carefully for any signs of the reason for taking mercury—in other words, for syphilis.

And you found no signs?—I found no signs.

And with regard to asking him the question about his gums?

By Mr. JUSTICE WILLS—You must have seen something very much more than what would be accounted for by an overdose of blue pill?—I have considered that question very carefully, both at the time and since, and, if permitted, I will submit to you a reasoned opinion upon it.

It seems to me very inconsistent.

Cross-examination continued—Having regard to the indications in the mouth, I think you waited till Mrs. Bartlett left the room?—I do not think I did on that occasion. I think it was on the second visit I asked him the question privately.

After a quarter of an hour, did he say, " Well, doctor, what is the matter with me? "—Yes; either he or Mrs. Bartlett.

And you said, " Mercurial poisoning "?—Yes, I said it sharply, thinking to take him unawares and make him admit it —not admit it then, but to show him that there was no hiding away secrets from me.

And then he said, " How could it come about? " and you said, " From taking mercury "?—Yes.

Then, I think, he answered, " I have not taken any "?—Yes.

And you said, " Think it over "?—Yes.

You did not accept the answers?—No.

Your experience is that sometimes the answer is not to be relied upon?—Not to be relied upon—especially when a third party is present.

And when the third party, Mrs. Bartlett, had left the room, you asked him whether he had not been taking medicines?—Yes.

He told you so?—He told me so.

And then, I believe, you did not press the question, but you had in your mind the idea that he had been in the hands of some quack or practitioner who had given him mercury for real or

211

Adelaide Bartlett.

Dr. Alfred Leach

supposed syphilis?—It flashed through my mind, but I could not disturb him after his answer. He had not had syphilis. I thought he had had syphiliphobia.

You have made notes?—Yes.

Is this your account: " When Mrs. Bartlett was out of the room, I asked him if he could account for it—had he not been taking medicines. He assured me he had not. I did not then press the question further, because I thought he must have been in the hands of quacks for a real or supposed secret disease, and was ashamed to own it "?—Yes, perhaps that is so.

Was that the account you set down on paper?—Yes. I would stand by that more than what I say *vivâ voce*, for when I have a pen in my hand I do not make mistakes.

You, upon that, told him to be careful not to take anything you did not prescribe while you were attending him, did you not? —Yes.

You were anxious that he should not, naturally?—Yes.

By Mr. JUSTICE WILLS—Did you find out what was the origin of that condition?—I think I did.

What was it?—He himself attributed it, and I have no reason to doubt he was right, to having taken a pill of unknown strength and unknown constituents.

Cross-examination continued—Keep that matter entirely apart. " December 11th. This morning, or the evening of yesterday, he told me he had found a clue to the mercury. A few days previously he took a pill. In a moment of abstraction, not feeling well at the time, he picked a pill out of a drawer full of sample pills, and had no idea what pill it was. For want of a better explanation I accepted this one, and reasoned thus—' This man years ago was badly used by some dentists, who put him in a plate of false teeth without drawing his stumps. The latter rotted, and he had to discard the plate. A fresh plate was made, and some teeth that should have been drawn were filed off. These rotted also, and he gave up plate No. 2. He could not clean his teeth, and his mouth became foul, and sulphides were naturally among the products of decomposition. Having got a dose of mercury into the system, the sulphides seized upon all that circulated through the margin of the gums, and formed a deposit in their edges of black sulphide of mercury.' The general mercurial symptoms I accounted for by supposing him to have an idiosyncrasy for the drug. I communicated this argument to him and his wife, and it seemed acceptable to both." That accurately reports?—That accurately reports.

Now, his final condition began to improve from the very first —that is, the bowel and the physical symptoms?—Yes.

But the spirits did not improve?—No.

And he continued, I believe, to complain of sleeplessness?— Oh, yes.

Evidence for Prosecution.

Dr. Alfred Leach

Now, on the 12th again you certainly saw him twice; was that so?—Yes.

And I think that in the evening, after the chemist's shop had closed, you saw him and made another draught for him?—I think after my second visit I let his messenger come home with me and I made up a draught for him.

Was that a bromide?—A bromide draught? Yes.

Now, the 13th was Sunday. I want to note this day. Your lordship may remember a former witness has mentioned the 13th. On the 13th, Sunday, I think you visited him three times?—I did.

And on that day for the first time you found it necessary to inject morphia?—Yes. I should like to refer to my notes to know the exact reason of that if you please.

Yes, look at any note you have. If you look at your document, you will find it mentioned?—Yes. I was doubtful whether it was given him for dental purposes, but evidently it was given him to procure some sleep.

You had already given him some fair doses of narcotics and bromide?—Yes, I have no doubt I had, or I should not have resorted to morphia.

But it was a peculiarity in him that it made him very restless in large doses?—Yes; large doses of bromide he declared were stimulants, and they were the very reverse.

Now, about the 14th, I think, the blue line began to give way—the blue line round the teeth began to disappear?—Yes, it did.

" The blue line now began to give way to a grey sloughing margin, and I brought in a surgeon-dentist in consultation, and his view favoured mercury and not tartar "?—Yes.

On the 14th you visited him twice, and on the 15th twice, and again injected morphia?—On the 15th twice, and on the 15th I did again in the night visit inject morphia.

On the 15th the sleeplessness was getting worse. That was the time his sleeplessness was getting bad?—Yes. That was the time, I have no doubt; his teeth were beginning to pain him then.

His sleeplessness was caused, not by the former cause, but his teeth were getting painful?—Yes.

Now, on the 16th we find there were two visits, and he complained of pain in the tongue, did he not?—In the lower lip, I think.

You gave him a tonic, nux vomica and gentian and peppermint, to produce appetite, and allay the pain in the tongue, and to allay flatulence?—I do not remember pain in the tongue.

Was the pain in his tongue caused by his teeth?—It did in the lips, yes—the under surface of the tongue.

" On the 16th he had two teeth taken out, two central incisor roots, and it was determined to extract the loose roots "?—They were extracted.

Adelaide Bartlett.

Dr. Alfred Leach

"And they were all very much decayed and horrible"?—That fairly describes them, and loose.

Decayed, and was there a foul fungoid growth at the roots?—Not on the 17th.

What do you call horrible?—They were in such a bad state of decay.

And the gums round them—were the gums bad?—Yes, the gums were still bad, and in front, near the incisor teeth, the grey slough, which succeeded the blue line, had sloughed off, leaving a jagged margin.

On the 19th, I think, when he got rid of those teeth or roots, you began to talk to him about getting out of doors?—Quite as early as that.

At all events, whether you pressed him or not, he refused?—Yes; he said it would kill him. He really was so obstinate about going out of doors that he almost at one time made me believe that I had overlooked something serious in him. He was so reasonable on some points that I could scarcely have put it down to sheer folly.

But you recommended going out of doors, and Dr. Dudley recommended it also?—That was Dr. Dudley's chief advice—to get out.

And it was of no use?—No, he passively resisted.

And did he tell you that he liked to lie still and feel happy?—Yes, he did.

I am not going back to the detail of what you have given in your evidence-in-chief, but a couple of days before the 19th he talked to you about the family wanting to send another doctor, did he not?—Yes. Dr. Dudley came on the 19th, and it was on the 18th he told me that.

You were told that his family wanted to send down a doctor, were you?—Yes; I was told what I stated to the Attorney-General.

He would know that, but he was content to get an independent opinion at one visit, and would leave you to choose somebody to come?—Yes, that was it.

And you chose whom?—I chose Dr. Dudley, because he lived near, and he was a hospital physician, and he seemed a most appropriate person to call in.

Now, on that occasion when the conversation took place, did you say that you had almost done with him, and that he only required an outing to be well, and that he ought to go to the south coast?—I think you are running two statements into one.

I do not want to do that, but the actual words can be referred to. Let me read your account: "18th December. During my visit Mrs. Bartlett said, ' Doctor, I have something very unpleasant to say.' "—Excuse me, it was pointed out to me by the Treasury; it was "I hope you won't be offended."

" ' His relations, who are never contented with anything I

214

Evidence for Prosecution.

Dr. Alfred Leach

do, want to send him a physician of their own choosing.' I answered at once, ' Well, let them send him one; I have almost done with him. He only requires an outing to be quite well, and then he ought to go to the south coast ' ''?—Yes, that is the quarter —that is correct.

You turned to Mr. Bartlett for an explanation of that statement, and he sat up in bed and said, '' Yes, that is all true. I am sorry to say my friends are not friends to my wife ''?—It is not in my entry, but certainly he said, '' I am determined to manage our own affairs.''

Did not he, after that, say, '' We are determined to manage our own affairs, and not to trouble about other people ''?—I do not know; it is there.

Now, on that very day did you supply a sleeping draught?— Which day, please?

The 18th?—Not that I know of.

I think you will find chloral hydrate, hydrochlorate of morphia, syrup of red poppy?—On the 18th?

Yes?—I prescribed it on the 19th.

Very well; it was the 19th, I understand. On the 19th was he in a decidedly depressed mental condition?—On the 19th, yes— pretty much as usual.

Would you let me read from your deposition: '' I do not remember any difference on the day I agreed with Dr. Dudley that the deceased was suffering from sub-acute gastritis,'' which remained, only it nearly had disappeared?—Yes.

A '' depressed mental condition; according to his own account, he had been suffering from great sleeplessness for a considerable time ''?—Yes.

Then on the next day, the 20th, you increased the dose of chloral hydrate, I think?—Yes, I did.

And that sleeplessness—you attributed that as partly due to the teeth, I think, because on the 21st the lower incisors were removed?—Yes; principally the teeth were at fault then.

What?—Yes; the teeth were principally at fault, so that we have very little left to complain of.

Now, the gums—the teeth were removed—the gums were getting sloughy round those teeth?—Yes, they were.

Now, at that time did Mrs. Bartlett tell you before her husband '' He still talked about dying, and he will still talk about dying ''?—It was about that time probably; I am not sure but that she said it more than once.

You said that, in your view, he had little to recover from; but did you promise then, on his agreeing to go to Torquay after Christmas, to take him down and put him under the care of a medical man down there, Dr. Dalby?—Yes; I said I would accompany him, and I mentioned Dr. Dalby because I thought it would

215

Adelaide Bartlett.

give him confidence that he would be looked after. He required no looking after practically.

Now, was it about that time you spoke of Mrs. Bartlett being so fatigued?—I cannot remember.

You wanted him to go to Torquay alone?—Oh, yes.

That was for some reason, was not it?—No, pardon me; I wanted to get him away and send him to Torquay alone. That was one reason why I offered to accompany him. He was practically a hysterical patient about that time, and his wife petted him very much. What would have done him good would have been to have sent him a sea trip, with no one to nurse him, and hold his toe, and that sort of nonsense.

If he had been obliged to take care of himself he would have been all right, you think?—Yes, that was it. I wanted to get him to Torquay by himself. He wanted dental care, but from a medical point of view he was out of hand.

That was the state of things, you say, between the 21st and 23rd, but on the 23rd you prescribed this placebo?—The 24th.

On the 24th you prescribed the placebo. We quite understood that was a thing which would do him neither harm nor good, except so far as he imagined it was going to?—That is just it, and I did not tell his wife the secret of it.

Mr. JUSTICE WILLS—That is 38,413.

Cross-examination continued—Yes, that innocent placebo—was the amount which you prescribed 10 drops?—10 drops were to be given in wine and repeated, if necessary, an hour later, if the pain was severe, and I think I said he was to be careful not to take a third dose.

He had been getting better physically up to that time?—Yes.

On the 26th something appeared that upset the whole thing?—Was that the worm?

Yes, the worm?—Oh, yes; that threw everything back again.

I beg your pardon, doctor, I have assisted you to a wrong date; the 25th, was it not?—On the 23rd I saw a lumbricoid worm —yes, he passed it on the 23rd.

That was what threw him back?—Yes, he was in such a condition——

Such a condition what?—About it, that I put off the treatment for a couple of days, partly to see if any more passed, and partly to let him gather up pluck and spirit.

Do you mean he was so much depressed and shocked?—Yes, he was so much depressed by it; he thought certainly he had something wrong with him then, and that he had proved then that there was something wrong with him.

By Mr. JUSTICE WILLS—The date was not the 25th, was it; the placebo was 38,413, and the worm was 38,420?—Vermifuge course two days after the lumbricoid was seen.

Cross-examination continued—You say he was shocked and

Evidence for Prosecution.

Dr. Alfred Leach

upset by it, and you say he thought there was certainly now more mischief about him than you had found out?—Yes.

And he told you on that day or a day or two afterwards that he felt worms wriggling up his throat?—Yes, the next day, I think, and kept to it.

It was a delusion, I suppose?—I do not know. Two or three days ago I saw a worm that did wriggle up a patient's throat and was vomited.

Then he may have felt that?—Yes, he may have, but I think in his case it was a mistake, because I asked the doctors to search for a lumbricoid in the post-mortem, and his motions were watched from that day to the day of his death for a lumbricoid.

He felt worms wriggling up him?—No; he always described them, in my presence, as in his throat.

That would be the imagination of a very nervous man upset by this having happened?—Yes.

Would not that be so?—What do I commit myself to by answering this?

Only for a suggestion which I make to you. Supposing he was to describe himself as feeling worms wriggling about him, from his legs upwards, that would be the delusion of a nervous man upset and shaken by what had happened to him?—A nervous man? What I say is that I am not inclined to set down every man as nervous who says that, because worms might be there.

Worms could not really be there?—I do not know; I have no basis to form an opinion on.

You are entitled to guard yourself in that way. I understand what you say about his nerves and depressed condition at that time is not necessarily connected with this imagination about worms?—Yes, that is so.

Now, you say that the appearance of that worm had thrown everything back?—Yes.

And he was in a more depressed troubled condition after that time, was he not?—Yes, for a day or two.

Well, did a very curious matter take place within the next day or two after that with regard to mesmerism or magnetism?—I cannot fix the date of it from memory.

Well, somewhat earlier in your attendances at Claverton Street had he mentioned to you the subject of mesmerism?—I cannot say when he did, but I think I have notes of it somewhere. I think the Treasury have them. I think I must have parted with my original copy. Oh, I have it here; probably on the 26th. It was on the 26th.

It was on the 26th, was it?—Yes.

Was it on the 26th that he told you, or was it on the night of the 26th you think he said it happened?—Are we talking of the same subject?

On my word, I do not know. What I am putting to you is

Adelaide Bartlett.

Dr. Alfred Leach

that he gave you an account of something that happened one night with regard to his standing up for two hours?—Yes.

Did you understand his doing that had happened on the night of the 26th, or was it on the night of the 26th he told you?—No; I think it must have happened a couple of days earlier than the 26th, or a couple of days later, because he told it me one morning when I went in and asked what kind of a night he had passed.

There had been a previous conversation between you about mesmerism?—He told me an extraordinary tale on the night of the 26th.

An extraordinary rigmarole?—Yes.

About the possibility of being under somebody's influence from a distance?—Yes; he thought he and his wife had both been mesmerised by a friend.

You say, on going in one morning he made a statement of something that had happened in the night?—Yes, a very peculiar one; shall I relate it?

Do, please?—I said, " Well, Mr. Bartlett, how have you slept?" He said, " I could not sleep; I was nervous and restless when I saw my wife asleep in the easy-chair, so I got up and went and stood over her like this " (holding up his hands)—he was in a very excited state then—" for two hours, and I felt the vital force being drawn from her to me. I felt it going into me through my finger tips, and after that I laid down and slept." And his wife said, " That is a nice story. Imagine him standing for two hours and doing anything."

So that Mrs. Bartlett treated it as a mere delusion on his part?—Yes. I imagined he had stood for two minutes and felt the vital force, as he imagined it.

You did not imagine he had stood over her for two hours extracting the vital force from her?—I did not imagine he would stay two hours doing anything. I was of Mrs. Bartlett's opinion on that matter.

The Court adjourned.

Fourth Day—Thursday, 15th April, 1886.

Dr. ALFRED LEACH, recalled, and further cross-examined by Mr. CLARKE—You told us yesterday that you had found that the sedatives did not produce their expected effect upon him?—That is so.

Did you find the same thing happen with respect to purgatives?—Yes.

On the 26th you subjected him to somewhat persistently severe treatment in order to open the bowels, I think?—Very.

There were two draughts then; there were two globules containing croton oil?—Yes; those he called stimulants.

I was going to ask you as to that. With regard to croton-oil pills, those ought to have been very effectual for their purpose?—Yes; and very rapid too.

But he attributed to them precisely an opposite effect?—Yes.

He said he felt stimulated by them?—Yes; he said they were warming and pleasant—to his stomach comforting.

Then you got him his hot tea and coffee with the intention of inducing those remedies to act?—Yes.

And that tea and coffee did not have the desired effect?—No; nothing had.

I believe you applied galvanism to the abdomen?—Yes.

And that failed?—That failed.

And you practically gave it up in despair?—I did. I may mention that he was not suffering from constipation previously; it was not constipation that I was treating him for, but the vermifuge (worm powder) that had to be driven out of the digestive organs. He had swallowed the worm powder, and I naturally had to give purgatives to clear that out.

What would have been the effect of the worm powder if it had remained there, and no purgatives had been administered?—It would have made him very miserable; he would have seen everything green; he would have suffered from buzzing in the ears, and all sorts of troubles, which I did not wish to subject him to.

By Mr. JUSTICE WILLS—Did he have all these troubles?—No, he did not; he should have had them; I know that from personal experience.

Cross-examination continued—You expected him to have them?—Yes. I have tried the same drug upon myself, and always try to avoid letting any patient experience what I experienced on that occasion.

As a matter of fact, do you know whether it was carried off

Adelaide Bartlett.

Dr. Alfred Leach

from his bowels—for two or three days, at all events?—I don't remember—yes, it must have been.

Do you remember?—Yes, I recollect now. He did not suffer from constipation afterwards.

You have told us that the stools were preserved for you?—Yes.

On what day after that did you see a motion?—I saw a motion the next morning when I called—a small one, I grant.

Not satisfactory?—No.

Now, on the 30th I think it was that you said you would not visit him any more?—The day before I said I would not visit him on the 30th; the 30th was Wednesday, I believe.

You said on the 29th that you would not come on the 30th; is that so?—If the 30th was Wednesday, that is so.

Mr. Justice Wills—Yes, it was the 30th.

Cross-examination continued—Then you told him on the Tuesday that you would not visit him again?—Yes, I did.

He was apparently distressed at that, was he not?—Yes, he was.

What did he say about it?—I don't remember.

Except that you saw he was distressed apparently at your saying that?—Yes, he was. I know it was not the first time I had threatened. Nothing specially fixed that in my memory.

The idea had always distressed him of your not continuing to attend him?—Yes, it had; and Mrs. Bartlett said, " You had better come, doctor," on previous occasions. That was why I visited him so often as I did during some portion of the time. She said, " You had better come, doctor; he will be anxious," or something of that sort.

Had he crying fits about this time?—I saw none.

But you heard of them and spoke to him about them?—Oh, yes.

When you spoke to him about his crying, did he tell you that he could not help it?—I don't remember; he made some reply of a queer nature, I know.

By Mr. Justice Wills—I suppose that is just exactly what hysterical and nervous patients do?—Oh, yes; it was a reply quite fitting the case.

Cross-examination continued—I am only reminding you, Dr. Leach—I am quite sure you wish to tell us all about it. Was this what you said before the coroner : " I was told by Mrs. Bartlett on several occasions that the deceased had had one of his crying fits "?—Yes.

And on speaking to him, he said that was so?—Yes.

" Mrs. Bartlett said, ' Edwin sits in his armchair and cries an hour at a time; and when I ask him about it, he says it was because he was so happy ' "?—Yes.

Evidence for Prosecution.

Dr. Alfred Leach

" If that was true, I should have put it down to male hysteria " ?—Yes.

" When I asked him why he cried, he said he could not help it " ?—That is most probably true, because the facts were better in my mind then.   Mrs. Bartlett's reply I remember distinctly. She said, " He cries because he says he is so happy."   That I distinctly remember, even now.

That struck you as being odd, I suppose ?—It could not fail to.

But that was said in his presence ?—Oh, yes.

Was he a man who used to discuss medical matters at all ? Did he dwell upon his condition and talk to you about it, and so on ?—No ; he was not a talkative man.

Not talkative ?—No.   The only time that I saw him what might be called talkative was the time that he told me about his being mesmerised ; then he fired up with quite unwonted eloquence.

Now, during the last two or three days of his life the jaw symptoms became alarming, did they not ?—Yes.

I think it was on the 29th, the 30th, and the 31st that his jaw symptoms became alarming.   I am reading from your depositions : " It was on the 29th, the 30th, and the 31st that the jaw symptoms became alarming " ?—Yes, that is so.

That pointed to necrosis ?—It did, of a superficial kind.

If you please, but alarming ?—Yes.   I don't use that word in its worst sense.

Mr. Justice Wills—I wanted to know what was meant by that, because it is a vague word.

Cross-examination continued—You have said to-day they were alarming ?—They were alarming ; they alarmed me.

When you say that, you do not use the word in its worst sense ; necrosis may often be a very terrible matter indeed.   As a matter of medical science, when you find that necrosis has set in, it is very difficult to set a limit to its mischief, is it not ?—It depends upon the constitution of the patient.   This necrosis being due to local causes, I had no great fear as to its ultimate result.

That is, not a result as affecting his life, you mean ?—As affecting his life ; that is what I wish particularly to explain.

That is the limit, then ?—Yes.

But, short of that, you were alarmed as to the consequences that might follow ?—Yes.

Just let me ask you, as a matter of medical science again, what is the principal cause of necrosis—the most common cause of necrosis ?—Injury to the bone or periosteum.

But injury how caused ?—By traumatic or chemical causes.

Shall I suggest to you the ordinary causes of necrosis ?—Pray do so.

Well, necrosis may follow a blow ?—That is a traumatic cause.

It may follow on a fever ?—Yes, indirectly.

Adelaide Bartlett.

Dr. Alfred Leach

Of course, in a particular form, it follows on phosphorus poisoning?—Yes.

What is called a lucifer-match necrosis?—Yes; caries begins the process then.

I said in a " particular form "; but the most ordinary cause by far of necrosis is mercury, is it not?—No; syphilis.

Syphilis is the most common, is it?—The most common; I don't exclude mercury, mind.

As a matter of fact, there have been a good many cases where necrosis has followed upon taking mercury even in small doses where syphilis has not been present at all?—I have no doubt that is so.

You have told us that when you first saw Mr. Bartlett you told him that he was suffering from mercurial poisoning?—Yes.

Don't you connect necrosis with mercury?—There was no necrosis then.

But when necrosis did appear?—Yes, indirectly.

By Mr. JUSTICE WILLS—Will you explain what you mean by that?—Explain it in its immediate cause?

Explain what you mean by connecting it indirectly. Do you think the one had anything to do with the other?—Decidedly.

In what way do you think they were both due, to syphilis or what?—No, my lord. I take it to be that mercury was one of the causes in the chain of events that led up to necrosis.

In one sense, of course it would be. A thing that has happened before in the course of a man's life is part of the chain of events that leads up to his present condition. Do you think that one extra dose of some mercurial poison would lead to necrosis of his jaw—an extra dose of some pill which contained mercury? Do you think that caused the necrosis, or had any serious operation in producing the necrosis, of his jaw?—I thank your lordship for putting it to me so. I can answer " Yes " to that.

Mr. JUSTICE WILLS—I beg your pardon, Mr. Clarke, but I wanted to understand this vague expression, for this does not help me a bit.

Cross-examination continued—I am obliged to your lordship for putting it. Now, Dr. Leach, on the afternoon of the 31st, I think you privately arranged with Mrs. Bartlett about his going to the dentist's?—Yes.

Was that in order to spare him the dread of looking forward to that visit?—Yes.

I think when you left on that evening you arranged to come and see him again on the following day?—Yes, after he left me that evening.

He understood that you would come and see him on the following morning?—On the following day.

So that in the ordinary course of things you would have been there on the 1st of January?—Yes.

222

Evidence for Prosecution.

Dr. Alfred Leach

By Mr. JUSTICE WILLS—Did he leave you at the dentist's door, or did you go back with them to Claverton Street?—He and his wife left me at the dentist's door, and they went back to Claverton Street in a hansom.

Cross-examination continued—Now, I am not going over again the account which you gave us yesterday as the account which Mrs. Bartlett gave you of that particular evening. I understand that, before you gave your evidence before the coroner the first time you gave it, you asked her to put you in a position to give evidence.

By Mr. JUSTICE WILLS—Before we have that, I should like to ask about a thing to which reference has been made once or twice, but about which no question has been asked. It was said that, when they were driving to the dentist's together, the deceased referred to the very happy life which they had had, and said he should like to be married again. Was that in your presence?—That was in my presence.

Was it on that evening?—On the evening of the 31st.

Was it upon the way to the dentist's?—On the way to the dentist's.

Mr. JUSTICE WILLS—It has been referred to by somebody, but never proved.

Mr. CLARKE—It was in the opening, my lord.

By Mr. JUSTICE WILLS—That was on the way, was it?—Yes, in Denbigh Street.

Tell us what happened?—As we were approaching the corner of Denbigh Street and Charlwood Street, the conversation ran upon the subject of recent marriages in the locality. Mrs. Bartlett said to me, " This morning Edwin and I, doctor, were talking about the number of our friends who are getting married, and we were saying we wished almost that we were unmarried that we might have the pleasure of marrying each other again." I turned to the deceased, and said, " That is very flattering to you, Mr. Bartlett, after so many years' experience of yours," and his reply was not quite clear, for he was muffled up, his mouth was covered with wraps. On the way to the dentist's he said, " Yes, we suit one another very well; we agree in our views," or " in our ways," I am not sure which he said, and then the conversation dropped before we arrived at the dentist's.

Cross-examination continued—Although you had very kindly tried to spare him the hour's dread, he did know then that he was on the way to the dentist's to have the operation performed?—Oh, yes; I returned to Claverton Street to take him to the dentist's myself, and I found that he was already dressed.

And was it your impression that his wife was lively and cheerful, trying to keep up his spirits on the way?—Oh, yes, she always did that; you are quite right, on leaving the house she tried to cheer him in every way.

I will take you to the morning when you went there, and the

223

Adelaide Bartlett.

Dr. Alfred Leach

death that happened.　　Was Mrs. Bartlett apparently very much distressed?—Yes.

She burst out crying, I think, in speaking of her husband to you?—Let me say what actually did occur.

By all means; that is what I want?—Directly I entered the room she said, coming up to me, " Is he really dead? " and then it was that I made the formal examination, really thinking in my mind at the time, " How can I best put it to this poor woman; how can I best really break the news to her? " and I turned round and said, " Yes, Mrs. Bartlett, I am afraid he is," or something to that effect, and then she burst out crying bitterly.

I won't go through the whole story, because you have told us; then she said, " What can he be dead of? " ?—Yes, a little later, that was to say, she was crying, and when the crying was over, we began to talk about the possible cause of death, and she said, " What is he dead of, doctor? " or " What can he be dead of? " I am not sure of the words, and my answer was, " I don't know."

Well, then I think you asked if he could have got prussic acid?—Yes, that was the most rapid poison that suggested itself to my mind.

You asked that?—I asked that.

And she said, " Oh, no " ?—She said, " He could have got at no poison without my knowledge "; and then, soon after that reply, I suggested to her digitalis and other alkaloids that he had got, anything which his friend Squires had had, or anything that he had had by him; all those things were said.

And she negatived everything?—She negatived everything.

Did she appear anxious to find out and get at any suggestion as to the death?—So far as I could judge, most emphatically yes.

Her conduct was perfectly natural—the natural conduct of a loving wife who had just sustained that shock?—You are asking me to judge of things rather beyond my ken. I have no hesitation in giving my opinion for what it is worth on the matter.

Well, did her conduct appear to you perfectly natural?—It may be after-events had biassed my mind; she seemed not only grieved, but very much alarmed, very much scared—that is the impression on my mind now; of course, I did not think it then, but I do now.

Not only grieved, but did she appear startled by the suddenness of the thing?—I don't know.

Was something said about pills?—Yes, yes; when speaking of poisons, of course I mentioned morphia and opium amongst others, and she said, " There are the two opium pills which he had had by him some time; he asked me to give him one last night, but I am very glad I did not."　　I went to the cupboard and saw the pills.

You had prescribed opium pills?—Yes.

And she said she was very glad she didn't give him one?—Yes.

Evidence for Prosecution.

Dr. Alfred Leach

And then you went to the cupboard and saw that the pills were there ?—That they were there.

Then we hear that you said, " There must be a post-mortem examination," and she said, " Must there be an inquest ? "—Yes.

Did she wish to have a post-mortem examination made as quickly as possible ?—She certainly did. She chafed at the delay till next day. When I told her that Dr. Green could not come that afternoon, she said, " Can't he be persuaded to come ? "

Persuaded to come in order that he might make the post-mortem examination on that very day ?—On that very day.

And did she say this to you, " Spare no expense; get any assistance you want; we are interested in knowing the cause of the death " ?—I think she said, " We are all interested "; the other words she did certainly say. It was on the strength of that permission that, when Dr. Green telegraphed to me, or wrote to me (I am not sure which), saying, " I will come and look on, if you will do the post-mortem "—it was on the strength of that permission that I replied to him by telegraph, " No; bring an assistant with you; I will take no part in it." I have the telegram here. I can tell you the exact words.

I don't think the exact words matter, but it was on the strength of her saying that to you, " Spare no expense; get any assistance you want "———?—That I felt justified at once in telling Dr. Green to bring with him whatever gentleman he chose.

Did she speak of the death as a mystery that she wanted to have cleared up ?—Yes. Dr. Green, in replying that he could not perform the post-mortem on that day, suggested that I should get some one else, and said, " Please act independently." Then I telegraphed to him, " Can you fix this for to-morrow morning ? Remuneration adequate." Then he said, " To-morrow. Your house, 2.15."

I am very much obliged to you; then she pressed that the examination should take place at once ?—She did.

And if Dr. Green had been able to come that afternoon it would have taken place that afternoon ?—Yes.

And it was your waiting till the next day, not thinking it necessary to employ any one else ?—Yes; I wanted to employ Dr. Green, for I thought there might be some peculiar pathological question involved here.

And Dr. Green is an eminent pathologist ?—An eminent pathologist.

There was one occasion upon which she made a statement to you as to what took place with a view of your giving evidence before the coroner; that was the first time, I think, that you gave evidence ?—Yes.

Now a good deal later, on 26th January, she made another communication to you with regard to her having had the chloroform in her possession ?—Yes.

Q

Adelaide Bartlett.

Dr. Alfred Leach

Was that a communication which you considered at the time was spoken in confidence to you?—Yes.

I think, when you were before the coroner, you were somewhat reluctant to give it in evidence, on the ground that it had been spoken in confidence to you?—Pray don't take me over what I did that afternoon before the coroner. I went before the coroner not thinking I should give that evidence, thinking that she was going into the box and would give it herself, and that I should never be called upon. I felt utterly incompetent to give the narrative straight off without thinking it over, and I equivocated by saying I was so confused that I did not know what to answer; but as soon as I got out of the Court I wrote it.

Pray understand, Dr. Leach, I am not disputing or going to challenge in the least degree the accuracy of what you said. The point is this: I think you said that you considered what was said was said in confidence, and then, when it was very properly pointed out that you were bound to repeat it, you did so?—Yes, it was so, in confidence; in that sense decidedly.

You did consider it was in that sense?—Yes.

Then in the statement she then made there was one word which I wish to refer to. I think you said that she told you, after she had explained the matter to her husband why she had got possession of the chloroform, and when she had given him the bottle, he seemed grieved, and turned over?—Yes, those were her words so far as I remember; in fact, it was; yes, I am sure of it.

You said this: " She gave the bottle into his hand, they talked affectionately about their relations to one another for a short time, and he seemed much grieved "?—Well, the " grieved " was hers, the " much " would be mine.

I am reading from your depositions, Dr. Leach. And you were desired to say what she told you?—Yes.

Did she then say that, at the time of the death—the idea of his having swallowed the chloroform did not enter her head at that time?—She certainly did not say that it did not enter her head; if that is in my depositions——

I am reading: " She said, ' Is he really dead? ' She further said (it was on the 26th) that the idea of his having swallowed the chloroform did not enter her head "?—Have you finished the sentence, may I ask?

I will begin the whole: " She got up to turn him into a more comfortable position, and was greatly alarmed at his condition. She rubbed his chest and applied brandy, but, becoming frightened, she sent a servant for me. On my arrival, her words were, ' Is he really dead? ' She further stated to me on the 26th that the idea of his having swallowed the chloroform did not enter her head at the time, and that she did not remove the bottle from the mantel-piece where he last placed it for hours, or some time after I had seen the body. When she first mentioned the chloroform, Mrs.

226

Evidence for Prosecution.

Dr. Alfred Leach

Bartlett told me that it was labelled ' Chloroform,' and that it was a large bottle. She continued, that about breakfast time she placed the bottle in a drawer in the next room, where it remained nearly a week. She said that her first real suspicions as to the cause of death were aroused when she heard it stated that the contents of the stomach smelled of chloroform (that statement was made after the post-mortem), but, hearing me say that that smell might be due to the deceased having swallowed some chlorodyne he had in his possession, she refrained from making any suggestions that would necessarily throw grave suspicions upon herself '' ?—Yes; and she told that to me more than two or three times. I have not read that evidence since I gave it before the coroner. That statement was written a little rapidly; if I had to write it now, I should say to-day that it did not seriously enter into her head, and her first suspicions in that case were these. I did not mean to say that she did not say that the idea did not flash across her mind, but that she had failed to entertain it.

That evidence was given at a time very much nearer to the conversation than the time of which we are now speaking; it was much sooner after the conversation this evidence was given, was it not?—Yes; this is a part of the depositions which I wrote and gave to the coroner.

It is a part of the coroner's note, and you signed it on Monday, 8th February—the conversation took place on 26th January, and you wrote it out on 4th February?—Yes; please remember, too much stress must not be put upon any word or sentence, because, by direction of the coroner, I went home and wrote it out very plainly, and could not say accurately every word I said.

Mr. JUSTICE WILLS—Probably that was all for the best; if you did not think so much of the literary effect, and would tell us what happened, it would be better for everybody.

Mr. CLARKE—That was on 4th February, and we are now at 16th April.

The WITNESS—My lord, pardon me if I say that it is not the literary effect, but the accuracy, I strive to attain.

Mr. JUSTICE WILLS—We do not strive to get any phenomenal accuracy. Just tell us what happened.

Cross-examination continued—It was when the circumstance was well known that chloroform was found you said it was not chloroform, but the chlorodyne, he had swallowed?—Yes.

And when you suggested that he had swallowed chlorodyne, she combated that idea?—She certainly did.

And pointéd out that the chlorodyne he used was simply to rub the gums?—Yes.

She would not accept the suggestion that it was chlorodyne?—No, she refuted it.

Now, after the post-mortem examination had revealed the necessity of further inquiry into the contents of the stomach, she

Adelaide Bartlett.

was told that she must not remain in the rooms, I think?—I don't know—I don't remember any one telling her so. I thought she said she would not remain.

It was an understood thing, at all events, that she was going? —Yes.

Did she take, or ask to take, anything with her?—Pray divide that question.

Did she give you her keys?—Yes; in answer to your question, she did take something, but she did not ask to take anything.

What was it she took?—Her hat, I think.

She took her hat, but it happened thus—she handed you her keys and asked you to go to the drawer and get her hat out?— Yes, because the hat was in the room where the corpse was lying.

You took the keys and fetched the drawer, I think?—Yes, I brought the whole drawer.

And she took her hat from it?—Yes.

Her cloak was given her by Mr. Bartlett, was it not?—I don't remember.

You put the drawer with its contents back into its place and locked it, did you?—Yes; and brought the keys back to her.

Did she ask you then to keep the keys?—She did; and I suggested that Mr. Wood should take them.

You suggested that Mr. Wood, her solicitor, should take them?—Yes; and I looked round to my colleagues, the doctors, to get a suggestion from them.

You did keep them?—I did accept them, and took them home.

By Mr. JUSTICE WILLS—Mr. Wood took them, did he?—No. I did accept them, and took them home. There has been some slight misunderstanding about those keys, and I wish it to be plainly understood that those are the circumstances under which I took them.

Cross-examination continued—Really, I think you are afraid some one is blaming you; I assure you I am not?—Well, these things go into the papers and are misunderstood by the public.

Mr. JUSTICE WILLS—I am very reluctant to say anything, but if you would think less about your own share in the matter, and more about the solemn character of the matter we are engaged in, it would assist us. This perpetual self-consciousness detracts from the value of what you have to say.

The WITNESS—I take your instructions, my lord, and will follow them.

Cross-examination continued—There is one question I have to ask you as to a part of the communication she made to you on the 26th. I am obliged to read to you a longish passage in order to found the question. It is at page 23 of the coroner's depositions. " She proceeded to a statement, the exact words of which I will not pretend to remember." I want you kindly to listen to this passage, and I will tell you

228

Evidence for Prosecution.

beforehand the question I am going to ask you, that you may follow it in your mind as I read it. You say this: " I was personally cognisant of those facts up to this point; they had been partly told me, partly implied, and partly from observation, the rest was nearly all news "?—Yes.

Now I will read the passage which precedes that statement: " She proceeded to a statement, the exact words of which I will not pretend to remember, but from which I gathered the following: —Mr. Bartlett, deceased, was a man with one or two strange ideas. Among them was that a man should have two wives, one for love, and the other, as he expressed it, for use. At the age of sixteen years she was selected by him in the former capacity, viz., as a life companion for whom no carnal feeling should be entertained. The marriage compact was that they should live together as loving friends, and not know each other sexually. This rule was faithfully observed for about six years of their married life, and then broken at the earnest and repeated entreaty of the wife that she should be permitted to be really a wife and become a mother. A single act of coition occurred, and the result was a child that died at its birth. From that moment, now about six years, she grew, so far as child-bearing was concerned, disheartened. Her entreaties ceased, and the two lived together, but their relations were not those of matrimony. The deceased made no secret of his views on marriage. He spoke freely of them to his relations, and the doctor who delivered Mrs. Bartlett was given to understand that the child was the result of a single coitus. The deceased lived on terms of great affection with his wife, and with two exceptions they had no differences, and they only quarrelled once, but the terms of their cohabitation remained ultra-platonic. He encouraged her to pursue studies of various kinds, and this she did to please him, for he desired her to be very learned in all subjects. He affected, too, to admire her (physically), and he liked to surround her with male acquaintances, and enjoy their attentions to her. The position was a trying one for a woman to comport herself in, not to say cruel. Mrs. Bartlett's words to me were: ' I was a consenting party to this marriage contract, and felt bound by it, and never complained, although, when I agreed to the terms it proposed, I did not understand what they meant.' She was married at sixteen or thereabouts. I was personally [*i.e.*, the witness] cognisant of these facts up to this point. They had been partly told me, partly implied, and partly from observation "? —Pardon me, for one thing, if you please (*referring to his notes*), " I personally was to some extent cognisant."

I am reading from your deposition, Dr. Leach: " I was personally cognisant of these facts "?—Then it is a mistake in the depositions. I think the Treasury once possessed the exact copy.

Pray do not think of the Treasury?—I was not cognisant of those facts except at a certain part.

229

Adelaide Bartlett.

Dr. Alfred Leach

I have thought over beforehand with great fairness what I am now going to ask you. Tell me how far you did know these facts from personal cognisance, and how far from observation?— I beg your pardon, I am a little confused this morning. I am sorry I am such a bad witness. In this way: Mrs. Bartlett had consulted me two or three times since her husband's death, and I had become aware of facts during that consultation that somewhat paved the way to my accepting what she told me on the 26th.

You had become aware of facts with regard to herself?—Yes; which came to me from her lips.

Came to you as a medical man advising her as to herself?— Exactly so. I therefore put it there. The statement did not altogether surprise me. It was not altogether new.

All the matters which you had observed and which came to your knowledge with regard to her prepared you for it to some extent, I understand you?—Exactly.

And at all events justified you in accepting that statement as a correct one?—Yes; that contributed to it—her marrying her husband, and several things which I do not remember, all prepared me to accept a statement which, coming from other parties, would have seemed almost too extraordinary for credence.

Do you mean that certain things took place in her presence? —Yes.

By Mr. JUSTICE WILLS—Do try and recollect; we know nothing about these matters, and we must depend upon you as to what you really mean?—My lord, I wish I could particularise.

This was a very extraordinary communication, and a most important thing?—I am aware of it.

And we are entitled to have, and we must have—I shall have it before it is done with—the grounds upon which you made that statement. Do not understand me as indicating anything to disturb you at all. All I mean is this: that we take nothing for granted in a Court of justice, and we cannot accept the *ipse dixit* of anybody; and we must really know what is meant by this vague statement. It must come some time or other. It may as well come now as come afterwards at my intervention. This is the natural time to know what is meant by those somewhat vague words?—If I may be permitted, I will look for the statement and tell you, as I know it, how this very inconsistent fact suggested itself to me.

Cross-examination continued—I told you beforehand what this statement was likely to be. Mr. Bartlett was a man of very strange ideas?—That goes without saying.

By Mr. JUSTICE WILLS—No, nothing goes without saying here. Please to take that as an axiom. What were the one or two strange ideas?—The one or two which Mrs. Bartlett now alluded to were those on matrimony—relating to matrimony.

230

Evidence for Prosecution.

Dr. Alfred Leach

What were they? What have you heard from him?—Nothing about matrimony, but very vague ideas about mesmerism and vital force, and things too insignificant to make a note of, which conveyed to my mind the impression that my patient was one of the most extraordinary men I ever had to deal with—though a very pleasant and nice man.

Cross-examination continued—Let me, before you go any further, ask you this. You say that he was one of the most extraordinary men you ever had to deal with. Had the extraordinary communication about mesmerism been such that you actually suspected him of insanity?—At one time I did, and I tried to find the key to it.

By Mr. JUSTICE WILLS—With regard to this matter about two wives, one for use and one for companionship—that did not come from him?—Not in the least. I never heard him allude to it.

That came from her?—Naturally; not for the first time.

Not for the first time. Are you personally cognisant of that fact?—Permit me, my lord; I said, in my written statement, I was personally to some extent cognisant.

Cross-examination continued—You are not bound to read that written statement?—Yes, I think I am.

Mr. JUSTICE WILLS—Mr. Poland, have you got that written statement?

Mr. POLAND—Yes. I think it was put in, my lord. (*To witness*)—Just look at that—is that the one?—That is the one—" I was married at sixteen, or thereabouts."

By Mr. JUSTICE WILLS—This does contain the phrase, " I was to some extent perfectly cognisant of the fact, Mr. Bartlett, the deceased, was a man of strange ideas "; and that is struck through with a pencil—" which I can corroborate." Did you strike that through?—I think it was struck through by myself at the coroner's table. I think I am right in saying that.

Mr. CLARKE—I must ask your lordship to let me look at it.

Cross-examination continued—You say that, with regard to the relations of marriage, nothing was said by Mr. Bartlett?—No.

Had not that been mentioned in his presence at any time?—No.

Are you sure?—I have said no.

You are not angry with me for asking you whether you are sure?—No; but your suggestion does not bring back anything to my mind. I am as sure as I can be at this distance of time.

Just let me suggest something to you. You told me, yesterday, that Mrs. Bartlett was breaking down, or her husband thought she was breaking down, and her husband thought she was suffering from the strain of watching?—Yes.

231

Adelaide Bartlett.

Dr. Alfred Leach

Did you ever suggest that they should both go to bed in the back room?—I did.

When?—I do not remember.

What was the answer? What did Mr. Bartlett say?—I do not remember. I remember what you have mentioned up to now, but I do not remember his answer.

He did not do it?—He did not do it; oh, no.

Did he give you any reason?—No.

Is not it the fact he did not do that, although you suggested it? Was not that one of the things in your mind that supported that statement?—Yes; the fact that I knew he had always slept on a camp-bedstead, and I had a strong impression of having been reminded by that that they did not always occupy the same bed even before they came to Claverton Street, but the impression is so vague that I cannot say more.

You cannot say more, but you have the impression that you have heard it before?—Yes, and I think in his presence. The words mix up with me, somehow.

Now, did not the recollection of this thing come to your mind as supporting the statement that Mrs. Bartlett was making to you?—I have no doubt it did; all that I knew about the deceased and his wife—everything that passed, came in review through my mind at the time, and enabled me to accept that statement.

Now, will you kindly go on, just looking down the passage?—" He had two wives—one for companionship, and the other for use."

Are you sure you had not heard that about two wives?—I think I should have remembered it—certainly, if it had been in those words.

Very well. Will you just look down over the account?—" At the age of sixteen she was selected by him in the former capacity." I knew she had been married very young before.

By Mr. JUSTICE WILLS—It is not so much being married very young, as that she had been selected for companionship. It is very remarkable?—That I was not cognisant of. I had no time to stop and think when I was writing that. " For whom no carnal feeling should be entertained." I think I could say something upon that, but I hardly know how to say it. Having observed as narrowly as I did, I did not fail to observe the deceased's manner towards other people—his manner towards his wife. The picture of it came back into my mind while she was telling me this; and, although I remember signs of—great signs of—affection, signs of kindness and interest, and everything else, I cannot say that there was anything—I certainly can say there was nothing—in his demeanour to her to make me doubt that. That is as far as I can go. That weighed with me at the time. Nothing in his behaviour to her led me to doubt that—I can believe that

232

Evidence for Prosecution.

Dr. Alfred Leach

what I witnessed during my attendance on my patient was the affection of brother and sister. I can believe that. I don't say it was.

Cross-examination continued—At all events, your mind had received that impression which to that extent supported that statement?—Yes. " The marriage compact was that they should live together as loving friends, and not know each other sexually."

Just run your eye down it?—I have nothing to say to that. " That rule was faithfully observed for about six years." I had heard that.

From whom?—I had heard the child was born.

You had heard her first pregnancy was six years before?—Yes, for I had at some time or other heard that a child had been born some years previously. It was while he was alive; but I see what you mean. I hesitate very much to speak of a professional consultation, to go into the details of it, but this was quite true. The first professional consultation that I had with Mrs. Bartlett led to questions that certainly support this statement, that her first pregnancy, her only pregnancy, had occurred about six years ago.

By Mr. Justice Wills—Is this what you mean, that what she first communicated to you was consistent with her having had a child about six years ago?—Yes.

Do you mean that (I must define the extent of what you mean, you know)—professional delicacy is out of the question in an inquiry of this kind, and you must put it aside. I don't want to go into details unnecessarily, but I want to know what you mean by the expression you have used. It may mean a great deal, or it may mean nothing?—I mean this : that in the course of a consultation with her, I learnt from her that she had only been pregnant once, and that some years previously. That consultation would be on 14th January; I see by my prescription that it was.

Your extreme delicacy, excuse my saying it, I think is misplaced. There is nothing to shock the ears of anybody in that?—No; it was hesitation to reveal professional secrets.

Cross-examination continued—I have a question to ask you on that. At the consultation on 14th January the conversation in which she mentioned that to you was independent of this case or any question with regard to his death?—Quite. I fancy little was said on that day about her husband.

I need not go into detail, but the statement was made when you were consulting with her by herself?—Yes; a purely medical consultation that was.

Now, just cast your eye over the next two or three lines, and see if it is necessary to read them?—Yes, I certainly know she was fond of children. " Earnest entreaties that she should become a mother." I know she was fond of children; that I had heard before.

Adelaide Bartlett.

Dr. Alfred Leach

That you had heard during her husband's lifetime?—Yes; children and dogs. I had heard her say how fond she was of both.

She told you about that in his presence?—Yes. "And the child born died at its birth." That was new. "From that moment, now about six years ago, she grew, as far as child-bearing was concerned, disheartened, her entreaties ceased, and the two lived together, but their relations were not those of matrimony." I see nothing to comment on there.

Was that new—that their relations were not those of matrimony?—Yes. I have explained in what sense it was new to me. "The deceased made no secret of his views on marriage." That was new to me, although I have not put it in this statement. She told me something about the trouble the deceased had with one of his relatives (his aunt, I think) for having mentioned in her house his views on matrimony. "He spoke freely of them to his relations, and the doctor who delivered Mrs. Bartlett was given to understand that the child was the result of a single coitus." I knew a doctor had attended Mrs. Bartlett at one time.

Did you hear the name of Dr. Woodward as the doctor who was called in?—No, I did not; not to my recollection. I thought it was Dr. Barraclough. That may be the name of the doctor that Mr. Bartlett, senior, mentioned to me once.

As having attended Mr. Bartlett?—I don't know.

That is immaterial?—" The deceased lived on terms of great affection with his wife." That I have told before. "And, with two exceptions, they had no differences." That I am quite prepared to accept. "And they only quarrelled once; but the terms of their cohabitation remained ultra-platonic. He encouraged her to pursue studies of various kinds, and this she did to please him." That I was quite prepared to accept. I had seen how she tried in every way to please him, and some facts had come before me of her studies—what they were I don't remember at the present moment.

Had you heard anything of her going in for examination?—I am not sure. I think I did. Yes, it is very probable I did; I cannot call it to mind with certainty. "For he desired her to be very learned on all subjects." Yes, it is less words than looks that I am thinking of now when reading this: "he desired her to be very learned on all subjects." I remember distinctly on one occasion, when in the presence of the deceased—I think it was the first time I saw Dyson there. I can see the deceased sitting with a look of being lost in admiration at his wife, while she was discussing some subject or other with Dyson, and I am not sure but that I took part in the conversation, although I was chiefly interested in watching my patient; he sat, never uttering a word, but watching them talking. It was some rather remote subject they were talking about.

Evidence for Prosecution.

Dr. Alfred Leach

He was admiring her?—Yes, admiration that fitted in with this sentence. " He affected, too, to admire her physically." That I don't know. " And he liked to surround her with male acquaintances." That sentence explained a good deal that had puzzled me about Dyson.

Had you seen Mr. Dyson there from time to time?—Yes. It had occurred to me: " This minister is about here a good deal." That certainly had occurred to me.

And had you noticed the husband seemed quite to take it as a matter of course?—Oh, yes, he was as welcome to one as to the other, I saw; and the deceased had spoken to me of Mr. Dyson in terms of the highest admiration and affection, so far as he would be likely to talk on the subject of affection. Oh, yes, they were very proud of Mr. Dyson, I know. They had his photograph in the room.

When you say they were, you mean Mr. and Mrs. Bartlett?— Yes; I think it was he who once remarked to me how very highly educated Mr. Dyson was; and they spoke in terms of great affection too. " The position was a very trying one for a woman to comport herself in."

I think that passage is only a repetition of what you have stated before?—I hope I have made clear how much I knew before —how much I was able to accept.

At all events, you have gone through?—The sentence, " I was personally cognisant," was put in to mark the beginning of absolutely new facts.

Now, I think we have got the whole statement of what you really had noticed. Now, I think there is only one other question I want to ask you on a matter of fact. From the bed on which Mr. Bartlett lay, one could reach the mantelpiece or something on the mantelpiece without getting up?—One could.

You could not, I believe, reach it if lying down flat?—No.

But by rising on the left arm it would be easy to reach it?— It would.

Were bottles kept—medicine bottles, I mean—kept on the mantelpiece?—Not as a rule; they were chiefly kept in the bedroom. I mentioned once to Mrs. Bartlett. " Why don't you keep his medicines near him?" and she said, " I like to make this room as little like an invalid's room as possible," so that there were really no bottles on the mantelpiece.

Now, just a few questions on a different subject, Dr. Leach. In your experience, you have not seen a case of death from poisoning by liquid chloroform at any time?—No.

And, so far as you know, that is extremely rare, isn't it?— Yes; it certainly is among the rare causes of death from poison. It has occurred, of course; it is rare.

Have you seen a case of death from inhalation?—Yes; at least it was supposed to be.

Adelaide Bartlett.

Dr. Alfred Leach

Have you yourself administered chloroform from time to time? —Yes; about two hundred times.

It is an operation that requires to be very carefully and skilfully done, I think?—It is an anxious one.

As a matter of fact, the use of chloroform as an agent for producing anæsthesia has been a little lessened of late years, has it not, and chloric ether used instead?—You mean ether, not chloric ether. Chloric ether is merely chloroform and spirit; in fact, it is the old name of the old London Pharmacopœia. There is no chloric ether nowadays.

You mean to say no chloric ether is used?—There is a confusion of terms. Do you mean chloroform or chloroform mixed with spirit? That certainly is not used for inhalation.

Take ether, then? Has ether been substituted for chloroform? —Yes.

Do you know why?—Because it is less dangerous in most conditions.

And not only that it is less dangerous; but that some things incidental to chloroform are not so often found with ether; vomiting, for instance?—Yes; quite so.

By Mr. JUSTICE WILLS—You mean vomiting is constantly found with inhalation of chloroform?—The patient usually vomits afterwards, and even during the administration.

Cross-examination continued—In many cases the vomiting begins almost immediately, does it not?—It depends; there is a class of cases in which it does.

Of course, it depends very much on the condition of the stomach?—Oh, yes; if food has been given previously.

I was going to say, if you had made up your mind to administer chloroform to a patient, you would take care with regard to diet six hours or so before?—At least four, and that must only be beef tea or some liquid easily got rid of—easily digested, I mean to say.

If you had any indigestible substance in the stomach, such, for instance, as a substantial quantity of mango-chutney it would almost certainly produce vomiting?—It might.

It would, would it not?—I should not like to say it would.

I should not like you to prophesy, certainly, but you would expect it to?—Yes; it is a very likely suggestion.

Have you ever administered chloroform to an adult in sleeping?—No.

Did you ever hear of such a thing being done?—In the *Pall Mall Gazette* only.

Which you do not accept as a medical authority?—I think not. I am not saying it could not be done.

I do not want to take the answer as meaning more than you desire it to mean. You, at all events, have never done it?—No.

Evidence for Prosecution.

Dr. Alfred Leach

And you have never heard an authentic case of its being done?—No.

Are you familiar with post-mortem indications of death from inhalations of chloroform?—No. I am glad to say I am not, if you mean from personal experience.

As a matter of personal experience or——?—As a matter of general knowledge, I am.

As to what the post-mortem appearances would be?—It would depend upon the quantity; if, as in that case, where 15 drops killed by inhalation, you came to make a post-mortem examination, there you would find no signs whatever either in the eyes or nose or anything, because it is sudden inanition of the heart's functions, and death.

That is to say, if death occurred from so small a quantity, it is rather death from some disturbance of the heart's functions than the entrance of chloroform into the stomach?—Yes; the mixture of air and chloroform—the mixture of too strong a percentage of chloroform in the lungs.

In administering chloroform you have to be very careful as to the mixture of chloroform vapour with the air?—Very; you must not go above 4 per cent.

Not above 4 per cent?—Not if you can help it; it is dangerous if you do.

I had not finished. In cases of death from such a small quantity of chloroform, there is no indication of it whatever?—For the reason I suggested to you.

The death is sudden?—In cases where the patient has died after chloroform, and narcosis is thoroughly produced, you will find the smell of chloroform in the lungs, in all probability. It would depend, of course, on the length of time.

We are dealing with the case, I mean, of a real inhalation of chloroform?—Yes, we are dealing with chloroform narcosis; in popular language, until the man is chloroformed.

Yes, there would be the smell of chloroform in the lungs; what else?—There would be probably, not necessarily, some amount of congestion of the lungs. The same as regards the brain. In cases of death from an excessive amount of chloroform, there would be fluidity of the blood and staining of the brain membranes, and the brain itself smelling of chloroform. You will find, in the three instances I have noticed, very nearly the same effects as you would find in a case of poisoning by liquid chloroform, except that there would be more to be seen about the lungs.

There would be more to be seen about the lungs?—Yes.

And, although I do not want to confuse my lord's notes, I do want to draw a scientific distinction between death from liquid chloroform and that from inhalation—in death from swallowing liquid chloroform, you would find some of the same effects on the

237

Adelaide Bartlett.

Dr. Alfred Leach

lungs and some smell in the brain?—Not the same effect on the lungs, but the effect on the brain would be the same, I think; there might be less congestion.

As regards the smell?—I think it would.

Now, about the condition of the heart when a man had died from inhalation of chloroform or died from swallowing chloroform?—There need not necessarily be anything peculiar about the heart, but, as a matter of fact, you generally find that those who have died from inhaling chloroform have died from it because their heart was fatty—fatty degeneration, I mean.

As regards the post-mortem appearances, has not it been found, in the larger proportion of cases of this kind, that there has been engorgement of the right side of the heart?—Yes, if he died from asphyxia.

If he died from asphyxia through an overdose of chloroform by inhalation, you say you would have found the right side of the heart engorged with blood?—Yes, and the lungs too.

Now, it is just as well I should use your own popular expression, "chloroformed." Suppose a person to have been chloroformed, and shortly after to die, you would expect to find some post-mortem indications, only in a smaller degree than if death had actually happened from asphyxia?—As I understand your question, I do not think so.

Assuming that shortly before death a person had been chloroformed in the ordinary sense of the term?—Yes, and then recovered.

No, when chloroformed, say shortly before death, then recovery of sensation had never taken place, you would expect to find the post-mortem indicative of what you have spoken?—Yes, not necessarily engorgement unless the mode of death were asphyxia.

I beg your pardon; I think I was careful to keep that limitation in view?—Yes.

Now, is there one other indication to be found in the post-mortem examination—one other indication of the recent inhalation of chloroform?—To be found at the post-mortem room, or in the laboratory?

In the post-mortem examination, how about the urine?—I do not know.

Now, put aside the question of the heart for the reason which I quite understood with regard to death from asphyxia. With regard to other matters, there was no congestion of the lungs or smell in the lungs?—I did not make the post-mortem examination.

I am much obliged to you; you were making notes, but you were taking your observations from the skilled pathologist whose observations were recorded in those notes?—Yes.

238

Evidence for Prosecution.

Dr. Alfred Leach

Re-examined by Mr. POLAND—Was there anything in the notes dictated to you by Dr. Green to lead you to the conclusion that death had taken place from chloroform?—Not at the time—no.

Was there anything in the post-mortem examination itself up to the time, or since, to lead you to the conclusion that death took place from chloroform?—Only in conjunction with the analysis.

But I mean independently of that, from the post-mortem appearances alone, was there anything to lead you to the conclusion that death had taken place from chloroform?—Not sufficient to lead one to the conclusion, but suggestive of it.

What was suggestive of it?—Well, the smell in the stomach.

I am speaking of the post-mortem appearances of the different parts of the body?—They would have been overlooked; they would have been of small importance except as regards the smell.

Yes, in the notes I read; just turn to them, please?—Yes, I have the post-mortem notes here. Well, the fluidity of the blood, the staining of the tissues, all agree with chloroform poisoning as with many other poisonings.

By Mr. CLARKE—As with many other poisonings?—Yes.

Re-examination continued—Yes, only those two signs?—I must stop there.

You must stop there?—Yes; you exclude the stomach, I think.

Yes, I exclude the stomach. Nothing whatever in the appearance of the brain. Just look, please?—I was thinking of that just now; it is so slight, it seems merely a waste of time to allude to it.

By Mr. CLARKE—I shall be glad if my friend will read the exact words?—" With the exception of rather more post-mortem staining than usual, the brain presents nothing abnormal " (reading the passage). Those are Dr. Green's words. I could not feel justified in mentioning that as one of the indications.

Re-examination continued—Now, have you known any other case of death through swallowing liquid chloroform?—No, never.

When you told my learned friend, Mr. Clarke, you thought the effect on taking liquid chloroform would be the same as when the chloroform were taken by inhalation; that is only your own opinion?—Yes.

Mr. CLARKE—Dr. Leach is an experienced doctor. My friend seems to resent my taking his opinion. He is not entitled to tell the witness " that is only your opinion," because he is a scientific witness in the box. I quite assume that where Dr. Leach did not give us the result of his individual experience he gave us the result of medical science.

Mr. POLAND—It is all he knows about it, I take it for granted.

By Mr. JUSTICE WILLS—As far as your reading and knowledge enable you to form an opinion, that is your opinion?—Yes.

Adelaide Bartlett.

Dr. Alfred Leach

Re-examination continued—You have made no actual experiments?—No.

No experiments with animals or persons to ascertain whether the opinion you form is correct or not?—No.

And until this case, had you ever read of a death from liquid chloroform?—Oh, yes.

Very rare, is it not?—Yes, rare.

And have you at all studied the subject since?—Yes, I have; I have read up cases from back numbers of the *Lancet*.

Tell me with regard to the vomiting. If chloroform is inhaled, is the vomiting a rare thing?—No, a very common thing.

And does that generally arise from its being administered too soon after a meal?—Yes, generally—well, that was not quite—I have not expressed exactly my meaning there. If it be administered too soon after a meal, you are pretty sure to get vomiting, but I won't accuse the hospital authorities of giving a meal too soon before in every case where sickness occurs.

I mean, as far as your own experience goes, what would be likely to cause vomiting would be the administration of chloroform too soon after a meal?—Yes, that would be one very potent cause.

Not the only one. And the usual time is, how long after a meal?—Four hours will do if the meal consists of what is called the " chloroform breakfast."

Do you mean by that, a light breakfast?—Beef tea.

Beef tea only?—It depends; in some places they give beef tea only.

But in a case of an ordinary meal, would it depend on what the meal was?—Yes, and on the digestive power of the patient.

You say beef tea, and then four hours afterwards would be the right way of giving it by inhalation?—Yes.

That would be calculated, of course, to avoid the vomiting?—Yes.

Now, will taking liquid chloroform produce vomiting?—As a rule, where a large quantity is taken it seems to produce vomiting.

Large quantities?—I mean such quantities as 4 ounces. I have a case now in my mind where a lady walked down Sloane Street swallowing 4 ounces. She vomited afterwards.

Have you known any case of vomiting from liquid chloroform from a less quantity, or is that the only case known of?—I am in touch with this case, but I cannot call to mind reading any other. I should think 2 ounces would be enough to cause vomiting, but I am guessing now—I do not know.

Have you at all formed an opinion as to how much liquid chloroform would be a fatal dose?—Yes; I should say the smallest fatal dose known for an adult would be 6 drachms.

Evidence for Prosecution.

Dr. Alfred Leach

By Mr. JUSTICE WILLS—That is three-quarters of an ounce?—Yes.

Re-examination continued—Now, I do not know whether you have formed any strong opinion whether chloroform could be given by inhalation while a person is asleep?—I have heard Dr. Stevenson in evidence give that, and I accept fully anything he says.

I understand from that, you see no difficulty in that being done?—No; with skill.

Mr. CLARKE—With skill? This does not arise out of my cross-examination in the least.

Mr. JUSTICE WILLS—I do not think it does, and, after all, it only goes to the character of another witness. It only comes to that which is not evidence, according to our usual laws—his opinion of the character of another.

Mr. CLARKE—We shall have to deal presently with Dr. Stevenson. I leave it to him. The question is a more remote and recondite part of this subject. I do not like to have put on me answers which are not provoked by my cross-examination.

Re-examination continued—I ask you your own opinion, apart from Dr. Stevenson's. According to your own opinion, is there any difficulty in giving chloroform to a patient by inhalation while he is asleep?—Yes, there is difficulty, but it could be done; it would require skill—that is what I wish to say.

Chloroform, of course, in that way—its inhalation in the ordinary way?—Yes.

Now, one or two other matters I wish to trouble you about. The prisoner, Mrs. Bartlett, first consulted you, as a medical man, on 14th January?—On 14th January. Yes.

And it was on that occasion she told you she had only been pregnant once?—I think so.

Was it also on that occasion she told you she was very fond of children?—No.

That was a previous occasion.

Mr. JUSTICE WILLS—I do not think he mentioned that.

Re-examination continued—That is so, is it?—Yes, on a previous occasion.

Was there anything, when she consulted you as a patient, that she said at all about her relations with her husband—her relations as a wife with her husband?—No. I see the bearing of your question, but I say no to that.

By Mr. JUSTICE WILLS—If you will kindly not trouble yourself with the bearing of the question?—I do not wish to be misunderstood.

Re-examination continued—As a matter of fact, when she consulted you as a medical man, did she tell you anything about her relations with her husband—I mean her sexual relations with her husband?—Yes, she alluded to that.

R

Adelaide Bartlett.

Dr. Alfred Leach

When?—On 14th January.

What did she tell you about them?—I forget the allusion. On this occasion it was in this way—it was not about her husband in particular—it was on the general subject of sexual intercourse and her internal conditions; it was in connection with that she consulted me, and then it was that I learned the fact of her having been pregnant once.

Did she say anything with respect to her not having been pregnant since?—I assume so.

Did she? I want to know what she said—what she told you about her sexual relations, if anything, with her husband?—I have told you all I know. I do not remember.

I mean at any time. I am not alluding to the 14th January?—Then we come to the 26th. Then she did.

What did she then say?—What I have told you.

Only what you have already detailed?—Yes. I think I have put all I know—certainly I have put all that is important—before the Court.

Now, you said that Mr. Bartlett—you never heard anything from him at all that his married life was other than the ordinary state?—No; I heard nothing about his married life from him.

Tell me what you mean by telling us that they seemed like brother and sister. What do you mean by that?—It is a very difficult question to answer. I can say no more than that they appeared to me—I have neither the power of description nor the facts to go upon.

On the 31st, when going to the dentist's, they spoke about their happy married life, and said that they would like to be married again, to be happy again?—Yes; it was in no way inconsistent. That is what I observed.

You observed the affectionate terms they were on—that she sat up and nursed his foot?—Yes.

Then what did you mean?—I was prepared to say, in that affection I had observed there was nothing sexual.

Why?—I do not really—if you will help me, I will——

I cannot suggest anything more than on one occasion from his speaking to you, because you suggested that they should both go to bed in the back room, and they did not. Is there anything beyond that?—Yes; there was the general bearing of the parties.

What general bearing? I want you to describe it?—I might as well try and describe the general expression of countenances. I am sure his lordship sees it.

By Mr. Justice Wills—I have not this delicate discrimination. I am a plain man, and it seems to me a very unusual state of relationship between husband and wife; and it seems to me that if I came to that conclusion with regard to people I knew, I should probably have some reason to give for it. I cannot say

242

Evidence for Prosecution.

Dr. Alfred Leach

more. If you cannot tell us, you cannot tell us?—It is not delicacy, my lord, it is inability to express more than I have said.

Have you seen any other people of whom you have fancied the
same thing?—No.

It is an unusual thing in married life, is it not?—I should
say a very unusual thing, and I do not say it did not strike me
at the time it was so. I have merely described that, from what
I remember of their relations from one to another, it is quite
possible that may have been so.

Re-examination continued—What may have been so?—That
there was nothing sexual in the relations I witnessed.

By Mr. JUSTICE WILLS—Did you ever know, from your experience, a man for year after year sleeping in the same bed
with his wife, and nothing occurring between them?—I have heard
of things very much like it.

I understand he was a great deal away from his wife?—You
mean on business?

Yes; he had long business hours, and I understand he was
away frequently?—You do not mean away at nights? Do you
mean away travelling?

I know he was away in the daytime, and I assumed, and still
assume, he was sometimes away at nights. That is so in the
majority of cases, I believe. The husband goes to business and
has long hours, and is sometimes away at nights. Is there any
reason for supposing that they do not forgather with their wives
in the usual sense?—No; but I am not talking of a normal man.
I am talking of the deceased.

Mr. POLAND—Very well.

By Mr. JUSTICE WILLS—What was there? I cannot appreciate
it. I have been watching most carefully to see what were the
facts, and the one fact I have gathered is that he talked in an odd
way about mesmerism, and you suspected at once his sanity. Is
there anything else; because it is the only thing you have mentioned at present?—I wish I could put the picture before your
mind that I have in mine.

Re-examination continued—I will not trouble you further. I
only wanted, if you really could, to say anything definite that you
observed that led you to make the observation that they were more
like brother and sister. There is nothing more. I will not
trouble you further if you say there is nothing more; if you can
think of anything else, say it?—There is not one thing that comes
forward more prominently than another. I can only sum up by
saying that their general bearing to one another was asexual——

Forgive my saying that is somewhat vague. You say there is
not one thing. Give us two or three things?—I am afraid I shall
fail.

Then never mind. Now, about the mesmerism. Have you

243

Adelaide Bartlett.

Dr. Alfred Leach

studied mesmerism yourself?—I have observed its effects some-times; I cannot say I have made a study of it.

Do you know, with regard to mesmerism, that it is supposed that the vital force goes out from one person to another?—No; I do not know.

Do you not know that it is supposed something proceeds from one person to another which is called the vital force?—I call it nothing.

I am talking now of whether, in books on mesmerism——?—I have read none, to begin with.

You do not know what the mesmerists suppose themselves able to do?—Yes; I know that, for I have had my attention directed to them orally to a very small amount.

Have you ever read a book on mesmerism?—Depotés I have looked at.

Have you read any books on magnetism?—I have not even read " Braid on Magnetism."

Have you heard of odic force?—Yes.

Odic force is supposed to go from one person to another without touching in the act of mesmerism?—Yes, I believe it is.

There was nothing strange in this man supposing that this force proceeded from his wife to him? It is not a symptom of insanity, is it?—Oh, no; I do not say he was insane.

What do you mean by saying, at one time you suspected him of insanity? Was it on the mesmeric ground?—Chiefly. There are two mesmeric incidents. You have alluded to one. I did not suspect him; I had to find the key to my patient's char-acter. Shall I read the notes of the occasion?

Yes; if you think it will assist us, do by all means?—I do not think it will take longer than my trying to say it off. " Memo-randum of conversation with Mr. Bartlett, deceased, and Mrs. Bartlett; held about ten p.m., most probably on the 26th December, 1885." That was the night that I was administering purgatives to get the worm powder away.

By Mr. JUSTICE WILLS—Most probably the 26th. I suppose this was made at a time when you had forgotten the occasion?—This was made on the 9th of February, and " most probably " I should be prepared to scratch out now. It was that night, I am sure. " Having occasion to sit some hours with my patient, we conversed, and by accident the word ' mesmerism ' was men-tioned. Deceased became all alert at once, and asked me if I could mesmerise. I told him I had never tried, and did not mean to, giving as my reason my opinion that no medical man should seek to become a mesmerist. But he again asked me to make the experiment on him, and I declined. He said, ' Do you understand much about mesmerism? ' I told him I had frequently watched the effects of skilled mesmerists and had applied scientific tests,

244

Evidence for Prosecution.

Dr. Alfred Leach

and was interested enough in it to give some study for the psychological problems involved. He said, ' Can you tell me whether I am under mesmeric control ' (I think he used some such word) ' at the present moment? ' Smiling, I said, ' Do you think you are? ' He answered, ' Yes, I do,' and proceeded to explain : ' Last summer, a friend, who could mesmerise, visited us, and I asked him on several occasions to mesmerise me, but he always refused. Now, why do you think he refused? ' I told Mr. Bartlett I could not guess. ' Well,' said Mr. B., ' I think he must have done it then, or on some subsequent occasion.' Then Mrs. Bartlett broke in, ' Oh, Edwin, how absurd you are! He does get such strange ideas into his head nowadays, doctor.' He continued, without interrogation, ' I think he mesmerised me through my wife. Is that a possibility? ' I said I did not know, but that the subject was very amusing; would he tell me some more about it, especially the symptoms that led him to a so extraordinary belief? With some pressing I got this reply : ' Well, I am doing such absurd things— things against my common sense; in fact, both my wife and I are doing so.' ' What kind of absurd things are you both doing? ' I asked. His only reply was that they were doing things that were unusual and contrary to common sense. During this conversation he had emerged from his usual reserve, and was speaking with an unaccustomed vigour and excitement, and I was growing anxious about his night's rest; but thinking I had perhaps to do with one of the phases of insanity, and was on the point of getting a key to his peculiar nervous temperament, I decided to push my inquiry. ' Mr. Bartlett,' I said, ' if my brother medicos were to hear us, they would think Mrs. Bartlett the only sane person among us three, but I do not despise ideas because they are contrary to my every-day experience; pray tell me more about yours, especially about the nature of the things your mysterious friend makes you do.' '' Vulgarly, I tried to draw him. '' Here Mrs. Bartlett interposed remarks calculated to turn the conversation. She said it was all ridiculous nonsense he was talking. But, persisting in trying to find my key, I obtained her permission to continue the conversation *au grand sérieux*. ' Do you ever hear voices telling you to do this or that, Mr. Bartlett? ' ' Oh, no,' he said; and I regarded his reply as one of considerable importance. ' Do you ever converse with your magician when he is not near you? ' Again he said, decidedly, ' No '; giving his reply in a manner to relieve my mind, in a medical sense, of some anxiety. But he persisted that he was under a mesmeric influence, and asked if I knew of no method for discovering the truth of the matter, and I promised him that, if he would fully describe to me his feelings and the ground for his suppositions, I, in return, would consult a very high authority in mesmeric phenomena concerning the case. I said, ' How long did the influence last—I mean, how long did

Adelaide Bartlett.

Dr. Alfred Leach

you continue to do strange things?' He replied, 'I am still doing them.' I said, 'But what are they?' He answered, hesitating, 'Well, perhaps I should not be here if it were not for the influence' (I think he used the word). 'Where would you be?' He said, 'Elsewhere; perhaps at the seaside, perhaps abroad.' Then a suspicion flashed across my mind, and I said, 'Does your mesmeric friend control you in your city purchases—make you spend your money differently to your ordinary notions? Has he ever implanted you with a fixed idea to sign any cheque or draft, or indorse anything?' To all these questions he replied in a manner to indicate that I was very wide of the mark, and persisted that he only felt impelled to do 'queer things,' saying, 'I am acting in a way different to what I should do if I were not mesmerised, and that is all.' Then the idea struck me that he might really be in terror of somebody who had acquired ascendancy over him, so I asked, 'Do you feel a sinking or depression when you hear him coming; or do you shudder when he approaches?' 'No, not at all; I like him.' Then, despairing of making head or tail out of my patient's mental condition, I put my last query : 'Do you feel positive that your supposed friend is really a friend, and not trying to work out his own ends through his influence with you—mesmeric, or otherwise?' He said he was sure this was not the case. I appealed to Mrs. B. for her opinion, and she said, 'Edwin and he are the best of friends, and he is a true friend to both of us.' I repeated the question to her in private, and received the same reply. As a sequel, to keep faith with my patient, I put the case, at his request, to a distinguished student of things mystical, and asked the latter if he believed it to be within the bounds of infinite possibility that any dominant idea could be made possess a man in Mr. Bartlett's state, and, if not, how could I best conjure him into his right senses again. At a subsequent visit, I assured Mr. Bartlett that his delusions had been very carefully thought over ; and that they were delusions, I proved to him in argument. He was convinced then, and a few days later assured me that he was thoroughly of my opinion. I may add that I remember these events so accurately by reason of my being permitted to discuss them at the time with my occult acquaintance.''

Re-examination continued—I suppose an '' occult acquaintance '' there? I suppose you know some people think they are very much under the influence of others?—In the asylums, or out of them?

Out of them?—Under the influence of others, yes.

Only one other question—Do you know in mesmerism some mesmerists claim to be able to influence people although they are not present?—Yes.

Miles away?—Yes.

That is a common belief amongst some mesmerists?—Yes.

Evidence for Prosecution.

Dr. Alfred Leach

Only two or three other matters—When you were first called into Claverton Street, did you think that Mr. and Mrs. Bartlett had been recently married?—I did; all this petting, &c., led me to that conclusion.

By Mr. JUSTICE WILLS—You could hardly have supposed then there was anything like brother and sister in their relations, could you?—I have distinctly said I did not at that time suppose it, but even going back now to my recollection of that day on which I saw them, and thought they were recently married, I still do not hesitate to say that after all it is quite possible that it was an asexual relation.

Re-examination continued—Did you, after visiting Mr. Bartlett, see Mr. Bartlett and Mrs. Bartlett remain on the same terms?—Yes, the whole time.

And with the exception of the mesmerism, was there a single delusion about Mr. Bartlett that you saw?—Yes; there was that thinking he had a worm in his throat.

Any other?—No doubt I could remember some.

Any more?—Pray let me think a moment.

Before you pass from that, worms do come up the throat, I think you said?—Yes.

And he had a worm?—Yes.

That may or may not have been a delusion; any other?—I can call none to mind.

When you were examined before the coroner, did you say he had no hallucinations?—He had no hallucinations.

You say that now?—I say that now.

By Mr. JUSTICE WILLS—May I just ask what is the distinction between a hallucination and a delusion?—Do you ask it from me, my lord?

Yes?—A hallucination is defined as being a deception of the senses; a delusion, one of the intellect. That is like a college examination on oath.

I do not know what you mean by your distinction between hallucination and delusion; hallucination is deception of the senses?—Of the senses.

Delusion, of the intellect?—Yes.

Is it a hallucination when a man sees a thing look green which is not really green?—That is the act of a drug.

Hallucination is the case of a man seeing a ghost?—Yes.

Like a man that has delirium tremens?—Yes.

Re-examination continued—I won't trouble you further. The necrosis you referred to, you said there was no immediate danger from that?—No, none that I could see.

Alarming from the after-consequences?—Yes.

I suppose, in treating your patient, you did not alarm him in any way about this necrosis?—No.

By Mr. JUSTICE WILLS—Did you say anything to Mrs. Bart-

Adelaide Bartlett.

Dr. Alfred Leach

lett about the necrosis—the consequences?—Yes. I said evidently under that fungoid growth there was necrosis setting in, and we must have dental advice about it at once, because it was spreading to the canine tooth that was taken out the last day he went.

And did you say anything as to the extent of the probable mischief—did you say anything to alarm or to comfort her when you used that term? Tell us, so far as you can, exactly what you told her?—I told her he must have it taken out if the dentist advised it; because she had rather wished him to have no more teeth out.

Did you say anything to indicate danger to his life from this? —Oh, there was not ever any danger.

Can you give us anything more? Can you give us anything more as to what you said to her about it? Did you say anything more than he must have the tooth out if the dentist advised it? Did you say anything about what necrosis might end in?—No; that word " alarming " has given rise to some misunderstanding. I used it for brevity's sake, without due consideration to accuracy, I am afraid.

Now, in all your conversations with her from first to last, did you ever encourage the idea that he could not recover?—Oh, on the contrary. I always told her it was nonsense for him to say he would not.

How often did you see Mr. Dyson there?—I cannot remember, my lord. I should think perhaps three times.

You say it had struck you he was a good deal about the place? —It had struck me he was on very intimate terms when there, and that they spoke of him a good deal when he was absent.

Did you ever hear him called by his Christian name?—I heard an individual frequently mentioned as " Georgius Rex," and I have no doubt—I have reason to know—that was the name under which they always alluded to him. For a time I did not know who this Georgius Rex could be, but I know now. In fact, I knew before the deceased died.

I mean, when he was present, how was he addressed?—Oh, as Mr. Dyson.

That was when you were there?—That was when I was there; yes.

Did you ever hear him call Mr. Bartlett " Edwin," or Mr. Bartlett call him " George "?—No, and I think it would have struck me if I had.

You never heard him called by his Christian name by either of them?—Not in his presence.

And I suppose you never heard him call either of them by their Christian names?—No.

One more question. When you went into the room on 1st January, did you notice anything about the fire?—I did.

What was it?—I noticed that the fire was not a large one. I

Evidence for Prosecution.

Dr. Alfred Leach

looked at it with a view of estimating the temperature in which the corpse had been lying, and my chief recollection of the fire was that it was one that would not, to any extent, have influenced the temperature of the room, and it was, to the best of my recollection—and I have thought seriously over the matter—there were ashes or cinders, and it may have been piled on each side of it, and a large piece on the top, but there my observation finished.

There was nothing that called any sort of special attention to it?—No, none whatever.

By the FOREMAN—I should like to ask one question. I think you said you saw a glass with brandy in it?—Yes.

You smelt it?—Yes.

If chloroform had been in it, would you have detected it?—I am not quite sure.

Did you detect any?—No; I am not quite sure whether it could be detected. I think brandy dissolves very little chloroform. Had there been a large quantity I should have seen it, though I am not quite sure whether I should have smelt it. I have such an objection to the smell of brandy.

By a JUROR—I think you said death had occurred three hours previous?—I estimated it at three hours. It is the nearest I can arrive at, and I have no doubt that is an accurate time.

Did the fire look as if it had been freshly made up?—I do not pretend to know what a fire looks like freshly made up—freshly stirred, I suppose, you mean; and, as the question only occurred some time after I saw that fire, I am utterly unable to say. It did not strike me as such, I may say that.

By the FOREMAN—I suppose if any chloroform had been poured down his throat you would have noticed some signs of it afterwards? —No, because chloroform passing over mucous membrane leaves very little trace.

There would be no inflammation?—No.

By Mr. CLARKE—If chloroform were spilt on the face in the process of administration, would it not produce a sore place?— If left some time it would blister; it may produce a little chafing of the epithelium.

By Mr. JUSTICE WILLS—How long would that last?—I cannot say.

A few minutes?—I cannot say.

By Mr. CLARKE—It turns to a sore place?—You have to leave it for some time before it does. A chloroform blister is a very difficult thing to raise.

[It was here observed that two of the jury had left the box during the last two or three questions. On their return]

Mr. JUSTICE WILLS—Gentlemen, while two of your number were absent, a question was asked. Mr. Clarke will repeat that question now.

249

Adelaide Bartlett.

Dr. Alfred Leach

By Mr. CLARKE—With regard to the fact of spilling chloroform on the skin, if chloroform be accidentally spilt in the process of administration, does it not produce a sore on the skin? I am now using the commonest word?—Not if accidentally spilt—you mean sprinkled—it does not. On the lips of the person it will; but, as a rule, to produce a sore with chloroform, you must hold it in contact, and if left for some time it will raise a large blister, and would cause a wound.

By Mr. JUSTICE WILLS—On the skin?—Not on the skin of anything but a child.

By Mr. CLARKE—Are you sure? The ordinary best way of administering chloroform is to roll up a handkerchief and put it in a glass, and then sprinkle chloroform on it, is it not?—That is so, certainly; but I prefer an ordinary cloth, with my hand underneath it.

That other way I say is recommended?—Yes.

Now, in holding the chloroform, if the chloroform be spilt from the glass on to the skin, do you mean to say no soreness is produced?—Not once spilling; it would have to be repeatedly spilt.

There are a great many chloroformists who habitually practise the administration of chloroform—I mean that chloroform is habitually employed in the practice of administration, and do not they smear their lips with grease?—Yes; I do myself.

What for?—To save any chafing; and it might produce a sore, but I have never seen it.

That is why you use the grease?—I do not always use it.

When you do use it, that is the reason?—Yes, one of the reasons; and before he went off I should not like to touch his lips, so I use it in a subjective sense.

If chloroform is put on the skin and not covered up, it evaporates. Does it leave any mark?—It leaves a certain mark which you can see in a certain light.

You say that you could perceive it in a certain light?—Yes. It is not obvious; you have to look for it.

And even then how soon does it go off?—I do not know. When I have made any experiments upon myself, I have forgotten to see the end of them.

If chloroform is kept confined touching the skin?—Then it would make a little blister.

If covered up and kept upon the skin, then you say it would make a little blister?—Yes.

By the FOREMAN—You say a small bottle was inverted in a glass?—Yes.

Did you examine that bottle?—No, I did not.

You did not smell it?—No; I was accustomed to see a glass of Condy's fluid, and I took it to be that.

By Mr. JUSTICE WILLS—The small bottle you recognised as
250

Evidence for Prosecution.

Dr. Alfred Leach

containing Condy's fluid, you say?—A small tumbler containing the fluid. It always stood by his side. It had contained a draught which I had sent on the 18th.

By Mr. CLARKE—You said just now you recognised the bottle by the label?—No; there was no label.

By a JUROR—You were asked how would it look if chloroform was poured into the mouth. Would it affect the gums?—Oh, yes, it would make the gums feel very painful.

Would it leave any trace so that you could detect it afterwards?—If it was left there some time, it would; it would cause a blister, or make a sore even, if found in the stomach.

Did you find any trace?—No; the mouth was examined, and there was no trace, but the post-mortem examination will tell you more accurately than I can.

Dr. JOHN GARDNER DUDLEY, examined by Mr. POLAND—I am a doctor of medicine of the University of Cambridge and member of the College of Physicians, London. I practise at 71 Belgrave Road. Dr. Leach called me in to see Mr. Bartlett at Claverton Street on 19th December. I was with him for twenty-five or thirty minutes, and in conjunction with Dr. Leach examined him. Dr. Leach had already communicated to me what he was suffering from, and then I tried to find out for myself what his ailments were. I found his gums to be spongy and inflamed. I did not find any lime on the margin of the gums. He had a very depressed appearance, and he seemed wanting in energy. He was lying in an easy posture, apparently free from pain. He told me that he required rest, that he had been overworked—mentally and bodily; that he was very sleepless; that he had not slept well for a considerable time, and scarcely at all the last few nights. I examined him to find out whether he was suffering from any disease, but I found no signs whatever. The organs all seemed to be quite healthy. After I had examined him I told him that he was a sound man, that he ought to sit up and go out for a walk or a drive daily. I do not think he made any reply. I prescribed a sedative and a tonic for him. I do not think there is anything else that is necessary for me to mention with regard to my examination of him. I only saw him on that one occasion. I afterwards heard of his death.

By Mr. JUSTICE WILLS—Mrs. Bartlett was present throughout the interview, and she replied to several questions that I put to her. She took a part in the conversation generally.

Examination continued—I think I asked her some questions with regard to his previous health and his habits. Her answers were all favourable, that his habits were temperate, and that his general health had been previously good. On 2nd January I attended the post-mortem. There was nothing from the appearance of the various organs to account for death from any natural

251

Adelaide Bartlett.

cause. In the stomach there was an erosion, a patch where the mucous membrane was destroyed in the most dependent part of the stomach—on the dependent part of the stomach, the portion that was lowest near the spinal column. That would be occasioned by some noxious agent remaining in contact with it—an irritant.

Would liquid chloroform account for it?—Yes, very likely. The blood was very fluid.

If death had been caused by chloroform would that cause the blood to be fluid?—Yes, it would. When the stomach itself was opened I smelt it. It smelt very strongly of chloroform, or a combination of chloroform and garlic. The whole contents of the stomach were placed in a clean glass-stoppered bottle in my presence and sealed with my seal. I smelt the contents of the intestines, and I found that they had the same smell, but in a less degree. A quantity of the contents of the intestines—about an ounce—were put into another jar and sealed. The stomach itself was also put into another jar and sealed up. There was also placed in a bottle and sealed some chutney which was found at the post-mortem. After those four bottles had been sealed up they were put in the front room, the post-mortem having been made in the back room. After the post-mortem we deputed Dr. Leach to announce the result to Mrs. Bartlett. There were present at the time Mr. Bartlett, senior, Mr. Wood, the solicitor, and Mr. Dyson. The announcement was made in the front room, and it was to the effect that we found no natural cause of death; but that there were suspicious appearances in the stomach and with regard to the appearance of the stomach itself; and that it would be necessary to make the coroner acquainted with the facts. I do not remember that there was anything said by any one to that.

Cross-examined by Mr. CLARKE—When you went to see him on the 19th I think he presented a depressed appearance?—He did so.

He seemed disinclined to change his posture, or even to raise his eyelids?—Yes.

And he looked at you through his half-closed lids?—He did.

He told you he had been overworked, mentally and bodily, I think?—He did.

And that for some time he had suffered from sleeplessness?—Yes.

Did his wife seem very nervous and anxious about him?—She seemed very attentive to him.

And very anxious about it?—Yes.

You were an absolute stranger to them both?—I was.

Dr. MONTAGUE MURRAY, examined by Mr. WRIGHT—I hold the degree of M.D. of London, and I am assistant physician at Charing Cross Hospital. On 2nd January last I, along with Dr. Green, attended at the post-mortem examination on the body of Mr.

Evidence for Prosecution.

Dr. Murray

Bartlett at 85 Claverton Street. Dr. Leach, Dr. Cheyne, and Dr. Dudley were also present. We began about half-past two. I did the operative work, while Dr. Green watched the operations and dictated the notes which were taken down by Dr. Leach. We all, to some extent, checked the operations as they were described; if there was any doubt we discussed them as we went on. The general condition of the body showed that it was exceedingly well nourished. The heart was the first we came to; it was normal in size and was healthy, although the muscular tissue was perhaps a trifle flabby. The lining membrane was deeply stained, and the blood in the heart was fluid.

Were any of these conditions abnormal, considering the long time which had elapsed since the death?—Yes, the fluid condition of the blood and the excessive staining of the lining membrane were not quite what one would have expected from health. Apart from the contents of the stomach and the condition of the stomach, there was nothing whatever in the state of the organs to account for death. I took out the stomach and intestines. I have heard Dr. Dudley's evidence, and I concur in his account of the way in which the proceedings took place. There was a small amount, above an ounce of a dark fluid in the stomach, with a few small lumps of solid matter, and it smelt very strongly of chloroform. The intestines smelt slightly of chloroform; the smell was much more disguised, because other things were mixed with it. There was an inflammatory blush over the whole of the cardiac end of the stomach and the whole of what is described as the most dependent part, in area about an inch and a half in diameter. The mucous membrane was rather softer than the other parts and a little roughened and irregular.

By Mr. JUSTICE WILLS—The patch was about an inch and a half in diameter in the dependent part of the stomach, the part lowest down when the person is lying on his back.

Examination continued—That condition of things suggested the action of a mild irritant poison.

Where death results from causes other than poison, would that be a natural place to expect the ulceration or inflammatory condition of that kind?—No; when ulceration occurs it usually occurs near the other end of the stomach, and at the upper rather than at the lower part, but not invariably so. That would probably be the part of the stomach through which its fluid contents would naturally gravitate if the person were lying on his back. If a man were lying on his face I should not expect it to gravitate to the same part. The inflammatory blush must have taken place while life continued.

By Mr. JUSTICE WILLS—Do you confine your evidence to the inflammatory blush, or does it extend over the thinning of a portion of the tissues?—I should not be certain about the thinning of the portion of the tissues.

253

Adelaide Bartlett.

The other, you think, must have been produced while in life?—Yes.

Examination continued—There was softening of the tissues at the place I have mentioned; at the most dependent part. The mucous membrane was a little softer than natural; it could have been stripped off with the finger more easily.

Must that necessarily have been something that happened ante-mortem, or subsequent to the death—the softening of the tissues?—I think the signs, taken altogether, must have happened before, but I am not prepared to say that any one of the others could not have been.

By Mr. JUSTICE WILLS—I do not quite follow you. You say something about being taken all together?—Leaving out the inflammatory blush, the others, the softening and slight thinning, I do not think they were post-mortem, but I do not feel quite sure. I think they were more likely ante-mortem than post-mortem.

Examination continued—Supposing that the appearances which I saw were the result of swallowing chloroform, I am not able to form any opinion as to what period of time must have elapsed between the swallowing and the death and to give time for these appearances to be caused. I could not give the limit of the smallest time, but an hour would certainly be sufficient, I think, between the swallowing and the death, to produce the condition of the stomach. I cannot tell how much less would do it. I saw the stomach as recently as last night, when Dr. Stevenson showed it to me. I do not think I have anything to add as the result of what I saw last night. I examined the gullet also last night. I have not mentioned that the lower part of the gullet was just in the same condition as the adjoining part of the stomach—the part of the gullet next the stomach; that had an inflammatory blush just in the same way, and was a little roughened; I suppose the lower 3 inches or so of the gullet.

By Mr. JUSTICE WILLS—That was the portion of the gullet which comes nearest to the stomach, which opens into it.

Examination continued—At the post-mortem I examined the lower jaw, and found a patch where it was becoming necrosed. There was nothing serious or dangerous about that.

Cross-examined by Mr. CLARKE—This is new matter. With regard to your examination of the gullet, I understand that was made quite recently?—I made the examination of the two at the post-mortem, and I saw them together again last night.

You say yesterday you saw the gullet?—Yes.

All that indicated was that the irritant, whatever it was, had been taken through the gullet?—Precisely.

Of course, there are possible ways in which an irritant poison may be introduced into the stomach, but the condition of the

Evidence for Prosecution.

Dr. Murray

gullet shows that it was taken down the throat in the passing to this spot. You have been speaking of the redness; that would show that at the time the liquid passed down the throat the body was in a recumbent position. Would that indicate that, or might the body have been erect at the time?—It might have been erect at the time it was taken. I should say it would show that after it was taken for the greater portion of the time that life lasted the body must have been in a recumbent position.

Are there not extraordinary varieties with regard to the cause of death by liquid chloroform, both as to the quantity producing death and also as to the survival after the dose?—I believe so, but I have no special knowledge myself upon that subject.

By the FOREMAN—Suppose that the person was insensible—I suppose it would take some time, and it would have to be done very gradually to administer chloroform down the throat?—To pour it down the throat.

It would take some little time to do it; you could not do it suddenly if the person was insensible?—Different methods might be employed; there might be a tube employed.

But suppose that, with the tube, the head might be held back to pour it down the throat quietly?—I could not say the time it would take.

But it would have to be done gradually if the person was insensible?—A portion might be poured down gradually.

If poured down gradually, it would very likely leave some mark on the tongue or throat?—No, not necessarily; it need not last so long as that.

Then you do not think that it would leave more marks in that way than if a person took it up and drank it up quickly?—No.

By Mr. JUSTICE WILLS—You speak of a short time; unfortunately, to my mind that conveys no notion. How long do you suppose the operation of pouring down anything which would be a fatal dose of chloroform must necessarily take, supposing a person to be asleep?—It would depend somewhat upon the degree of insensibility. I could not say definitely how long it would take.

Cross-examination continued—But would it be minutes or hours?—Oh, certainly not more than minutes; not more than two or three minutes.

Mr. CLARKE—Would your lordship kindly ask, or allow me to ask, the witness whether, so far as he knows, or so far as his reading goes, such a case has ever happened of liquid chloroform being poured down the throat of an insensible person?—I have no knowledge of such a case.

Have you ever heard of such a case?—No.

By the ATTORNEY-GENERAL—Probably, my lord, it would be proper to ask upon that, do you see any difficulty in its being poured down the throat of a person in a state of insensibility? Is

Adelaide Bartlett.

Dr. Murray

there any difficulty in performing that operation?—If the insensibility was profound, there would be no difficulty that I can see. It might be poured down.

But I mean, would there be any physical difficulty in doing it if the person down whose throat it was sought to pour it was in a state of insensibility?—I know of none.

By Mr. JUSTICE WILLS—If the insensibility was very profound, there would be a difficulty in swallowing, would there not? Swallowing is rather a muscular action?—Certainly. They would have to take some mechanical means to get it down, because the parts would collapse.

That is to say, that there would have to be a tube?—Certainly.

But I think you must exclude that supposition. Supposing there was no tube, what would you say then?—Then the greater part would remain in the mouth, and some trickle down.

Trickle down the gullet, do you mean, or do you mean outside?—Inside.

Down the gullet?—Yes.

That is to say, in the case of profound insensibility. Now, suppose insensibility was not so profound (I do not know whether I use the right expression) as to paralyse the muscular action of the throat—there is muscular action necessary in swallowing, is there not?—Then the insensibility would prevent the swallowing.

Might there be an insensibility so profound that the person operated upon might swallow without resistance, and yet so little profound that the muscular action would not be paralysed?—Yes.

Does that answer your own view that the touch of the liquid would excite the involuntary act of swallowing? Does it apply to such a case as that—to such a condition as that?—I think so.

Then it would be swallowing, and not trickling, in that case? —Yes.

Cross-examination continued—By what test would a medical man be able to ascertain that the particular stage had been reached where reflex action of the muscles continued, but yet there was insensibility which would prevent the burning, and so on?—Oh, by the presence of reflex in other parts.

How would he test it?—He would test it by touching the eye, and there would be a closure of the eyelid. That would show that reflexes were present.

Would you mind touching your own eyelid—just show how the medical man would touch the eyelid?—He would separate the eyelids, and just touch the conjunctiva, the white membrane of the eye. Then the lids would immediately contract, supposing reflex was not carried farther.

If, on touching, the eyelids contracted, he would then know that there was some reflex action existing which might render the act of swallowing instinctive?—Yes.

256

Evidence for Prosecution.

Dr. Murray

How would he know there was insensibility to pain?—By the relaxation of the muscles, and by the abolition of the reflex— I mean sufficient abolition to perform the operation.

You say the medical man would judge that there was insensibility to pain from the laxity of the muscles?—Yes.

Through the relaxation of the muscles and also from the abolition, I think is the word you used?—Yes.

Of the reflex action?—Yes.

I am very anxious not to repeat your words for fear of any mistake.

Mr. JUSTICE WILLS—That is quite right, but it is a thing that seems to introduce a new condition, and a very important one in connection with that which is proceeding now.

Cross-examination continued—Then the physician intending to do anything to the patient which would involve pain, and with a view to which the insensibility was to be produced, would not do it until he found the reflex action had stopped?—That would depend to some extent upon the nature of the operation. In some operations more profound insensibility has to be produced than in others.

I think I follow you. Your mind has now come to the producing of insensibility by chloroform. There are some cases in which chloroform is used in which it is not desired to produce complete anæsthesia?—Yes.

There are some cases where it is desired to use it to deaden the pain; it is not desired to obtain a condition which is one of absolute insensibility?—Certainly.

Then, in those cases the physician would judge whether the exact moment had come at which there was sufficient diminution of sensibility to enable the patient to bear the pain, and yet not sufficient diminution absolutely to destroy reflex action?—Do you mind repeating your question?

I have put before you the class of cases in which it is not desired to produce complete anæsthesia; only to deaden the pain. In those cases the physician has to exercise his judgment as to whether the moment has come in which there is sufficient insensibility to produce anæsthesia, yet not the entire abolition of the reflex action?—Certainly.

But supposing anæsthesia is carried to a point which prevents any pain, then the reflex action has disappeared?—Some reflexes disappear before others; they do not all disappear at the same time.

But supposing the anæsthesia to be carried to the extent of destroying the sense of pain, has not the reflex action then entirely disappeared? If you have a doubt, I am afraid it cannot be a very easy question, doctor?—Well, it is a question one is familiar with—the loss of certain reflexes. I was thinking

Adelaide Bartlett.

whether there might not be others. You see, one judges practically by this conjunctiva reflex. One knows practically if that is gone, the patient will not feel pain; and you judge also by the muscular relaxation.

I think I follow you. You say the physician judges by that test?—Yes; I am not prepared to say that at that moment there is no reflex which can be obtained.

But you are not prepared to say that there is?—I am not prepared to give an opinion.

By Mr. JUSTICE WILLS—Just tell me this. In operations where chloroform is administered, is it ever necessary to give brandy, or anything of that sort, while the operation is going on?—Yes; but it is not given by the mouth easily under that condition.

By injection?—Yes.

TOM RALPH, examined by Mr. POLAND—I am an officer in the Metropolitan Police Force, and I am the coroner's officer in this case. Mr. Braxton Hicks was the coroner who held the inquest on 4th January. In consequence of what he told me I went to 85 Claverton Street about half-past nine at night. I went into the front room, and I there found four glass vessels, jars, or bottles, which were covered over with brown paper, and had string tied round them, and were sealed with the initials of Dr. Dudley—J. G. D. At the same time I took possession of thirty-six medicine bottles. Some of them were in the front room; they were not corked. I corked them and sealed them up. I placed the jars and the medicine bottles in two separate hampers and took them to the mortuary at 20 Millbank Street, and placed them in a large safe, under cover, in the back yard. There was no lock to the place, but I put a piece of tape across it and sealed it up. On 9th January I went there and found the tape in the same condition. I had been to Claverton Street on the 9th. Mr. Doggett, junior, gave me a tumbler, which appeared to contain Condy's fluid. There was a small glass bottle inverted in the tumbler, which was open, without any cork in it. As I was moving it into the glass jar that I had taken with me it broke, so that the whole of the broken tumbler and its contents went into the glass jar. I fastened it up, sealed it with Mr. Doggett's seal, and took it to the mortuary, and put it with the other things. The little bottle that was inverted remained in the glass jar along with the contents of the tumbler and the broken pieces. I fastened up the mortuary again. On the 11th I took all the things to Dr. Stevenson at Guy's Hospital, and he gave me a receipt for them. After giving these things to Dr. Stevenson I went to Claverton Street again, and met Inspector Marshall there by appointment. Mr. Wood, the solicitor, was there, but

258

Evidence for Prosecution.

Tom Ralph

not Mrs. Bartlett. I examined seven boxes on the floor in the front room, and in one of the boxes I found two glass bottles. One of these was like a scent bottle, with a silver top on it, and there seemed to be some white powder in it. The other bottle was similar. I also found in another box a small wooden box containing white powder. I sealed those three things up and handed them to Dr. Stevenson on the 16th. I found a tin box in the front room containing a man's suit of light clothing, which I examined. In the right-hand trousers pocket I found four or five of what are popularly called French letters. I did not take possession of them. I left the clothes with the things in the pocket in the box. I also found in one of the boxes the letter that has been produced here addressed, " Dear Edwin," and signed " George." I suppose it was in Mrs. Bartlett's box— they were all there together. The other boxes contained some gentlemen's clothes and some ladies' clothes. I saw on a table in the front room the book Squire's " Companion " in the same state as it is now in, " Companion to the British Pharmacopœia," comparing the strength of various preparations, and so on. I did not go with Marshall to Wandsworth Common.

Dr. DUDLEY, recalled and further examined by the ATTORNEY-GENERAL—The contents of the stomach were put into an open unstoppered bottle, which we could find no cork to, and they remained in that bottle for about half an hour, when we got another bottle from a chemist's, which had a glass stopper. We transferred the contents from the unstoppered open bottle into the other one. Chloroform is very volatile.

Dr. THOMAS STEVENSON, examined by the ATTORNEY-GENERAL —I am a doctor of medicine in practice as a consulting physician and am Professor of Medical Jurisprudence at Guy's Hospital. I am one of the analysts usually employed by the Home Office. I have written on the subject of medical jurisprudence. I recollect receiving from the last witness, Ralph, a number of bottles and packages. I think he has described them by enumeration with substantial correctness. There were eight packages on 11th January, and on the 16th there was one sealed package containing three enclosures. No. 1, on the 11th, was a paper package containing the lower jaw of an adult, with the tongue and the soft parts adjacent to the tongue and jaw. No. 2 was a glass jar containing a thick semi-fluid mass measuring a quarter of a pint, apparently the contents of the small bowel. No. 3 was a jar containing a human stomach, that of an adult. No. 4 was a bottle containing mango-chutney. No. 5 was a 4-ounce glass-stoppered bottle containing half an ounce or a tablespoonful of thick fluid, apparently the contents of a stomach. The im-

Adelaide Bartlett.

Dr. Stevenson

portant ones are No. 2, the contents of the smaller bowel; No. 3, the stomach; and No. 5, the bottle containing the tablespoonful of semi-fluid matter. No. 6 was the glass jar, sealed, containing some Condy's fluid, a broken tumbler, and 1½-ounce medicine bottle; No. 7 was a brandy bottle, sealed, containing some fluid. No. 8 was a hamper, sealed, containing altogether some thirty-six bottles of various kinds used for medicinal purposes. On the 16th I received one package containing a small toilet powder box, with toilet powder, and a pepper castor, which are not material to go into. No 3 contained some santonine, a medicine given for worms.

I commenced my analysis on 12th January. I began by opening the stoppered bottle No. 5, which contained a tablespoonful of thick semi-fluid matter from the stomach—I could see it was most likely to be that before I opened it. The characteristic smell of the contents was that of chloroform. I described it as strong, very strong. There was also a slight garlicky odour, of which I discovered the cause, namely, the mango relish. Although I opened it with a view to beginning my analysis, I did not in fact begin my analysis until the 13th. I smelt it, and then stopped. It was slightly acid. I afterwards proceeded to test its component parts by analysis, and I found the presence of chloroform, of which I estimated the quantity to be 11¼ grains. I produce here the same quantity, which I have weighed and placed in a tube. Eleven and a quarter grains are equivalent to between 8 and 9 minims. Approximately that represented about 5 per cent. of the entire quantity that I analysed. Besides the chloroform there was a trace, a very small trace, of alcohol. I tested it for possible traces of any other poison besides chloroform—prussic acid, morphia; I found no other trace of any alkaloid. The fluid did not contain any chloral.

Chloral, I believe, decomposes in the stomach, does it not?— If the contents be made alkaline by the use of carbonate of soda it will become chloroform in the stomach.

Did you find there chloral, or, if it had decomposed, any other substance?—Nothing except chloroform. If it had been decomposed by the alkali, it would form acid, of which I found none.

Was there any trace of chlorodyne?—No, chlorodyne being composed of chloroform and other ingredients. I satisfied myself that the other matter was chloroform. My analysis extended over several days.

No. 2, the contents of the smaller bowel, was the next thing in order that I took. It was a fluid mass in a bottle, about a quarter of a pint. It was only loosely stoppered—a glass bottle, the stopper of which had been tied by means of brown paper. Chloroform is a very volatile substance, and, if it were in a vessel which was not hermetically sealed, it would gradually evaporate.

Evidence for Prosecution.

Dr. Stevenson

The result of my examination as to the contents of No. 2 was that there were traces of chloroform, to the extents of about 3/10ths of a grain. I also tested the chutney and part of the contents of the intestines, and I found them to be free from any poisonous matter. Were you able to perceive any special smell from that or not? —No special smell of chloroform. The stomach had already been cut open. It was in a good state of preservation. It was inflamed. The cardiac or first end of the stomach next the gullet, the centre of that patch of inflammation, showed over an area of about an inch and a half in diameter—that would be about the size of a crown or half-crown piece—a more intense effect of inflammation; that is to say, the epitheliæ or lining membrane was detached and softened, giving a certain amount of roughness to the inner surface of the stomach towards the cardiac end. I will describe it more particularly presently. That appearance of inflammation extended to the gullet; round this patch of which I have spoken the redness of inflammation extended to a patch almost as large as my two hands, and extended into the gullet. That spot indicated where the greatest amount of inflammation was to be seen; it extended 3 inches up the gullet. I would describe that inflammation as acute and recent, referring to the time at which it had commenced. I should say that it had commenced and run its course within a few hours of death. I should like to say, with regard to the patch in the stomach, that it has been fairly and accurately described. It was about the part to which liquid would flow when a person was lying on his back. It was the usual spot at which we find it after swallowing irritant poison.

Was or was not that a state of things which might have been occasioned by swallowing chloroform?—It might have been produced by swallowing chloroform. I found no other cause for it. So far as I could ascertain, the presence of chloroform was an adequate cause, and there was no other cause ascertained or ascertainable. I tested the contents of the stomach for traces of every poison that could suggest itself to me, and I found none. I found a trace of copper in the gums, in No. 1. It is usual to find traces of copper in a healthy subject. From one-half of the gum and the whole of the soft parts, approximately, the amount of copper and lead altogether was not more than 1/80th of a grain. I do not think that is a matter at all of any consequence worth dwelling upon. The presence of lead and copper is to be accounted for by a vast number of vegetables, bread, the use of copper utensils, &c. Lead is less commonly found; it comes from leadened pipes containing drinking water and things of that kind. The traces were quite minute, and they would not account for the death of a person. No. 6 was a glass jar, which had some decomposed Condy's fluid, but I found nothing in that. In the tumbler in No. 7 I found a little sulphate of magnesia or Epsom salts. The

Adelaide Bartlett.

Dr. Stevenson

hamper contained thirty-six bottles. There were poisons, but medicinal doses only, not poisonous doses.

You have already said that chloroform is very volatile. Is it cumulative?—No. An ordinary dose of chloroform taken will disappear from the system very quickly. The effect I arrived at from the analysis was the presence of chloroform in the contents of the stomach. I made no analysis of the blood of the deceased man, nor did I analyse the stomach itself for chloroform. From my analysis I would judge that the man must have swallowed a large dose of chloroform, enough to produce a very serious inflammation of the stomach, and such a quantity would, I believe, be sufficient to cause death. I did not find anything to suggest any other cause than chloroform. When chloroform is swallowed—I have experimented on animals—at first it sometimes produces a state of intoxication, but not always. It then produces insensibility, stertorous breathing, or hard snoring, with muscular relaxation, paralysis, and death. It suspends the operation of the heart —paralyses the heart. It passes into the blood, and, of course, from thence into every region of the system, and it produces a liquid condition of the blood after death, which remains fluid for a long time. If the contents of the stomach were put into an open jar, and remained some time before being put into a stoppered bottle, some of the chloroform would evaporate and some would remain, some might settle down at the bottom and be unobserved. I tested that on these very contents of the stomach; I found they lost their smell in the course of an hour very gradually by exposure. I know that in this case the deceased died on 1st January, and the post-mortem was at two o'clock in the afternoon of the 2nd. My analysis began on the 13th. I would not expect there to be an evaporation of chloroform from the bottle in the interval, but there was a disappearance of the chloroform from the stomach while the body was lying before the post-mortem, by a process which we call diffusion.

According to your experience, have you any reason to suppose there would be indications of chloroform having been taken in the brain?—When swallowed I do not think there would be—there might or might not. I have frequently examined bodies where there has been no obvious smell of chloroform in the brain and no unusual appearances in the heart—in fact, nothing to indicate that death had occurred from inhalation of chloroform. I would not necessarily expect to find it in the brain. My observation is that oftener than not you find nothing in the brain to indicate the cause of death—I mean short of analysis of the brain. I have analysed, and have found traces in cases of inhalation.

Does it pass more rapidly into the blood by inhalation than by swallowing?—It would be difficult to answer that question.

Evidence for Prosecution.

Dr. Stevenson

Inhalation is the most rapid means of introducing gaseous poisons into the blood, but it would get there by either means.

If swallowed, I understand you to say that you would not expect to find it in the brain?—I should expect to find it by analysis, but no obvious odour; there might or might not be.

If a person accidentally takes a dose of chloroform sufficient to cause death, the person being at the time in the possession of sensibility and faculties, should you, or should you not, expect that person to make any sign? Might he, or might he not, be conscious that he had done something that he was suffering from?—Yes, he would at once perceive the peculiar character of the liquid he had swallowed. It would produce pain and a hot, fiery taste.

I mean, could he take an excessive dose, a fatal dose, of chloroform and suppose he was taking some innocent thing?—No, I do not think he could. It has not the taste of any article of food or drink. I have swallowed it myself, I have had it in my mouth several times, and I have found that it is very hot and very sweet and burning.

Now, there is another matter, please. Is it or is it not, according to your experience, possible to put a liquid down the throat of a person who is insensible, in the sense of being unconscious, but still having the sense of feeling?—Yes, you can put liquids down the throat of a person who is fairly moderately under the influence of inhaled chloroform.

Assuming that the liquid is in some such bottle as I showed you, would there be any difficulty in putting it down the throat of a person in the condition of insensibility?—Not any great difficulty. I have myself put liquid down the throat of a person while I have been chloroforming him by passing it with a teaspoon to the back of the throat.

Would there be any difficulty?—No, not if the man were lying on his back with his mouth open. It could easily be poured down his throat.

Assuming it could be put to the back of the mouth, would its presence not occasion the act of swallowing?—Yes, up to a certain point of sensibility.

What is the point of insensibility to which the sense of swallowing would not respond to the presence of liquid in the gullet?—At the point from what we understand by reflexes had disappeared there would not be swallowing. That simply means that such a stimulant as chloroform at the back part would not excite muscular action, because the nervous centres, which are concerned in swallowing, would be paralysed beyond a certain point. In other words, the swallowing might be effected up to that point, which I have described, of paralysis. When I tried the effect of the introduction of chloroform into the mouth I found a hot, burning, sweet sensation, which passed away after I ejected it. It left a

Adelaide Bartlett.

Dr. Stevenson

little numbness on the tongue, but not to prevent me going about my usual avocations. It also left a blotch—a little redness—which passed off quickly. Since the hearing before the magistrate I have made some experiments as to the effect of chloroform upon animals.

Mr. CLARKE—We ought to have had a note of these experiments upon the animals if they are to be given in evidence.

Mr. JUSTICE WILLS—Yes; I think, if they have not been supplied, they should hardly be gone into.

Examination continued—I repeated an experiment which I made before. The animal I selected was a rabbit. There were two experiments.

By Mr. JUSTICE WILLS—Confine yourself to the one upon which you have spoken before?—That was the one. I must just reflect what I did say before the magistrate. What the point was —it was in cross-examination—it was a question as to whether chloroform passed into the blood from the stomach; and I took a rabbit, and by means of a tube I introduced a quarter of a fluid ounce or two large spoonfuls of chloroform into the stomach. I observed the symptoms. And then, at the end of three hours—the animal had been upwards of two hours in a dying state—it was nearly dead, but the blood was still circulating. I then cut the throat of the rabbit, and collected the blood which flowed. I analysed the blood to see whether it contained chloroform, and I found that it did.

Any appreciable quantities or only a trace?—Traces. You never got more than traces in the blood, but it was quite obvious. I also extracted the stomach of the animal, and observed the effects of the chloroform upon the stomach. The effects upon the stomach were acute inflammation, and the mucous membrane was softened and partly removed, so as to give it a roughened appearance— blood diffused into the coats of the stomach. There was chloroform obviously present in the stomach also.

Examination continued—When you were mentioning the effects of the taking of chloroform—the first sensation of intoxication— was that the result of your own experiment and observation?— This animal rolled about as if intoxicated. I have seen persons under the influence of chloroform inhaled, and I have seen one under the influence of chloroform swallowed. It produced vomiting and pain, and the patient was very much alarmed. It is many years ago, and I do not remember that it produced absolute insensibility. It was not a fatal dose. Vomiting is a very frequent accompaniment of chloroform swallowed, but not always. I have seen a great number of persons under the influence of chloroform by inhalation. It is possible to produce a state of insensibility by inhalation during sleep. I have not done that myself, but I know many instances in which it has been done, and I have no doubt whatever that it can be done if the person is

Evidence for Prosecution.

Dr. Stevenson

soundly asleep. Most of the appearances of the stomach to which I have spoken, and which I attribute to the presence and action of chloroform, must have been produced before death. The action is a vital action. They might be produced in an hour before death, or it might be longer. I showed the bottle containing the contents of the stomach and a small quantity that remained to Dr. Tidy. I showed the stomach to Dr. Murray. Assuming that, in the attempt to put chloroform down the throat of a person in a state of insensibility or partial torpor, any of it fell on the chin or breast or throat, I would not usually expect any indications of it; there might be, but it would be unusual for the momentary contact to produce any lasting effect. There might be a temporary redness, which would pass away, as the case which I was illustrating by myself.

Cross-examined by Mr. Clarke—I believe you have for many years given your attention to subjects of this class?—I have.

And you have had a long experience of the administration of chloroform at Guy's Hospital?—I have.

And you have not only had personal experience, but you have given study to the results of the experience of other doctors?—Yes.

And you have edited " The Principles and Practice of Medical Jurisprudence, by Dr. Alfred Swaine Taylor," who is well known as one of the greatest authorities in that branch of medical science? —Yes.

You edited and reproduced and corrected the book he had written, and called it the leading work upon the subject?—I believe so; you are quoting from the book.

So far as your skill and experience have enabled you, have you taken care that it is complete in the subject upon which it deals?—Yes; it is fairly complete, I think.

The last edition under your editorship having appeared as lately as 1883?—Yes.

Now, chloroform has been used in this country as an anæsthetic for almost forty years, I believe?—Possibly.

It was early in 1847 that Dr. Morton used it?—Yes, '47.

And, from the very first, I think, the characteristics of chloroform have been the subject of great interest to the medical profession?—They have.

And by many writers, yourself among them, the result of the administration of chloroform, whether by inhalation or in liquid, and whether accidentally taken or intentionally, have been carefully studied and carefully recorded, have they not?—Yes, as to inhalation. I do not think attention has been drawn to it much till last July as to swallowing it.

Chloroform is a most important agent of medical science, is it not?—Yes.

Adelaide Bartlett.

Dr. Stevenson

And there is a great deal of literature as to chloroform and its application?—Yes; chiefly by inhalation.

Can you refer me to any recorded case, anywhere, of murder by the administration of liquid chloroform?—No.

So far as you can judge, there has never been such a case?—I know of none.

Now, of course, you are familiar with the fact that there have been many murders by poisons well known to medical science—prussic acid and strychnine, and poisons of that class?—Yes.

Has the use of chloroform been somewhat given up of late years, ether being substituted for it?—Yes.

I think there are several reasons for that. I will suggest one or two, and will ask you as a medical authority; chloroform is an anæsthetic of uncertain effect?—I should not say very uncertain.

I did not say " very "?—It will produce insensibility, but the time and amount vary a good deal—the time of insensibility and the amount.

The time, the amount required, and the symptoms involved?—Well, the permanent symptoms are the same.

When you say uncertain with regard to amount and time, of course, they have some relation to each other?—Yes.

But in the case of chloroform, do you sometimes find that a very small dose inhaled proves suddenly fatal?—Yes.

While a very large dose taken into the stomach does not produce death?—Yes.

In the last edition of your book you have given a number of instances, and you have given them substantially on the authority of Dr. Taylor?—You are referring to the book there?

Yes?—I think it was taken almost entirely from previous editions.

Textually?—Yes; I do not think I added any fresh cases.

Though it was published in 1883, is it the fact that no case is quoted since 1870?—I understand not. I think there has only been one fatal case of swallowing chloroform in this country within the last twenty years—I mean recorded. I know of another case which occurred.

Was that at Lewes, or was it the Chichester case?—No. It was a case which happened to some one in this Court—I mean a fatal case which happened in the practice of a gentleman in this Court.

That, of course, was a case of accident?—A case of accident; yes.

Have there not been deaths in this country from the swallowing of chloroform by accident, besides that within the last twenty years?—One I know of, and the one I have spoken of, but I cannot call to mind now any others. There is a paper on that table containing a record of known fatal cases.

Evidence for Prosecution.

Probably it is a proof-sheet of your new edition?—No; my new edition is on the table; but there is a copy of a journal of repute, giving them in chronological order up to last July. The table, you will find, is in chronological order.

Mr. JUSTICE WILLS—Give me the name of the paper, Mr. Clarke.

Mr. CLARKE—It is the *Medical Record* of 11th July. It is an American paper—11th July, 1885.

By Mr. JUSTICE WILLS—That contains a table, you say, of all the known cases of death by swallowing chloroform?—All the known cases up to 1885. I have added a list of some half-dozen more since, my lord.

Cross-examination continued—Have you at all—I am much obliged for this—have you at all, yourself, arranged those in any class? Can you tell me, out of the fifty-six, for instance, how many died?—I can give you the cases of death.

By Mr. JUSTICE WILLS—Those are poisonings, but not necessarily fatal?—No, not necessarily fatal. I can give you the number of fatal cases I know of. I have added a few to the list, but I can give you the number in the list. I think you will see, at the end, it says how many were fatal.

Cross-examination continued—No, it does not say?—I think, out of that list, you will find something like seventeen.

Out of fifty-six?—Yes; about 30 per cent. of all the cases known to me were fatal—31 per cent., twenty cases out of sixty-five.

And this purports to be, and so far as you know is, a diligent collection of the cases occurring in different countries reported in books?—Yes; I have verified some of them, and found them very fairly accurate—very fairly stated.

Without wishing to occupy too much time, and having this in my hand for the first time, I will go through the cases in which death has occurred, and take the number of hours after the administration in which death occurred. Case 3: " Two mouthfuls; death in thirty-six hours." Case 4: " A male child, aged four, took from 1 to 2 drachms—died in three hours." Case 7: " Six ounces; died in forty-eight hours." Case 10: " An ounce and a half; twenty hours." Case 13: " A wineglassful "—that would be about 2 ounces?—About 2½ ounces, probably.

" Died on eighth day "?—Yes.

Case 15: and the reference to that is—A man of twenty-eight " had attempted to disembowel himself; had shot himself in each side of the chest," and so on. It is no use referring to that?—No.

Case 16: " An ounce and a half; twenty-three hours and a half "?—I think that is twenty-six. You see a reference.

You have corrected it to twenty-six?—Yes; I have a note of it as twenty-six.

Case 23: " One ounce; twelve hours "?—Yes.

Adelaide Bartlett.

Dr. Stevenson

There is a note to that. " This was a case of supposed chloroform poisoning; the amount taken was approximated. The coroner's jury were unable to come to a decision as to the immediate cause of death." Case 24: " Five to 9 drachms; death on eighth day " ?—Yes.

Case 25 : " Two ounces." I will read that. " Seen in one hour; a few minutes before his death. In three minutes (estimated time) he could with difficulty be aroused from the stupor into which he was sinking; could not speak, but indicated that he had severe pain in the stomach. In five minutes he was entirely unconscious, lying still, breathing stertorously. Medical assistance arrived too late to be of service. Post-mortem examination showed congestion of lungs, œsophagus, and stomach. Mucous membrane could be pulled off with the finger nail." Case 27: " Two ounces; nineteen hours " ?—Yes.

Case 28 : " Ninety grammes "—what would be 90 grammes?— I think you will find in my note—I say what it is about.

Rather over 2 fluid ounces ?—Yes.

" Twenty-nine hours and a half " ?—Yes.

Case 29 : " One ounce; sixty hours." Case 43 : " An ounce and a half "—that is about twenty-six or twenty-eight hours?—I have made a mistake about the other. In case 16 death took place twenty-three and a half hours after the first dose was taken. In this last case twenty-six hours and a quarter elapsed before death.

This is twenty-six and a quarter?—Yes; I was confounding the two.

Case 48 : " Fifty to 60 grammes; thirty-one hours " ?—Yes.

By Mr. JUSTICE WILLS—That is a little over an ounce and a quarter?—I have got it about an ounce and three-quarters; 50 to 60 grammes would be a little under 2 ounces—about a fluid ounce and a quarter of chloroform.

Cross-examination continued—Case 48 : " Seen in about four hours; deep intoxication; artificial respiration." I think that pretty well indicates that there is very great uncertainty as to what the action would be?—When swallowed.

Mr. JUSTICE WILLS—May I just interpose a question?

Mr. CLARKE—I hope so, my lord.

Mr. JUSTICE WILLS—It is whether these are cases when it was discovered, and means of restoration attempted.

Mr. CLARKE—In some cases it does appear so.

By Mr. JUSTICE WILLS—Because that would make a great difference in the length of life, would it not?—Yes; many of these cases were treated unsuccessfully.

Was the effect of the treatment, although unsuccessful, to prolong life?—Yes, it would be likely. Some of the cases lived a long time, and died from acute inflammation of the stomach, and

Evidence for Prosecution.

not by the direct effect of chloroform—by producing paralysis of the heart.

Mr. CLARKE—Your lordship will not find any rule, for this reason. One case (7) is an adult male who took 6 ounces in the Royal Infirmary in Edinburgh. One may assume that he was seen immediately. He recovered from the immediate effects, but died in forty-eight hours from acute gastritis. I do not think you can get any rule from it. Then case 10, seen in twenty minutes, and the woman died in twenty hours.

Mr. JUSTICE WILLS—That is a very remarkable case. I mean remarkable as it differs from any others. And 25, what was that?

Mr. CLARKE—" Seen in one hour; a few minutes before his death. In three minutes (estimated time) he could with difficulty be aroused from the stupor into which he was sinking; could not speak, but indicated that he had severe pain in the stomach." I should assume in three minutes after taking the dose.

Mr. JUSTICE WILLS—I should think so. If the people around him found out about it, they could not perhaps treat him at once.

Mr. CLARKE—Yes; medical assistance arrived too late to be of service.

Cross-examination continued—Now, you have only had experience in one case of chloroform swallowing?—Only one.

How many years ago was that?—A good many.

Do you mind giving a figure? We won't accuse you of being too old?—No; I suppose it must have been probably twenty-five years ago.

Now, you say the post-mortem symptoms in inhalation and swallowing would be of the same character, in your judgment?—In inhalation there would not be the appearance in the stomach.

I ought to have excepted that, because, of course, swallowing brings a local irritant to act on the stomach?—Yes, and you don't always observe the known great fluidity of the blood, too, after inhalation.

And the condition of the stomach?—The condition of the stomach, and one thing follows the fluidity of the blood—that is, the post-mortem staining of the lining membrane of the heart.

Now, with regard to the condition of the internal coats of the stomach, that would depend a good deal on what the state of the man's health was a short time previous to death?—I do not think the condition I saw would be dependent on the condition previous to death. I mean the post-mortem or pathological appearance.

The post-mortem appearances following on the taking of liquid chloroform by a man who had been recently suffering from acute or sub-acute gastritis would be a little stronger, more obvious than in a man with a perfectly healthy stomach?—I do not think they would if he had recovered from his sub-acute gastritis, as it is termed.

Adelaide Bartlett.

Dr. Stevenson

Supposing there were any return of that, surely it would be affected by the rapidity of the actual irritant?—If there were actual gastritis at the time he took it, it would.

Leaving out the condition of the stomach and blood, may I take it that, in your judgment, the effect produced by the swallowed irritant and observable in post-mortem examination would be the same as that produced by inhalation?—Not always. The appearances after inhalation are very variable.

The post-mortem appearances are not very definite?—No; there is often nothing, unless you know the history of the case, to lead you to suppose that death occurred from chloroform.

But there are some appearances, are there not, where death has followed from inhalation of chloroform?—Some have been frequently observed; yes.

That is to say, so frequently observed that they are indicated and would be looked for?—Yes. One would look, of course, for any indications whatever.

And you would look with still greater care for those that had frequently been observed?—Yes.

If you had no indications at all, of course, you are helpless, but, in trying to find indications, you look for those that other people have frequently observed?—Yes.

Now, in the case of the administration of chloroform by inhalation, death takes place very suddenly sometimes, does it not?—Yes.

Not, if one may say so, from the chloroform having been inhaled and taken into the system, but from some action on the heart which is not quite—I will not say not quite understood, but not—determined?—Yes. A patient would die in a few minutes after a few whiffs occasionally.

But where chloroform has been inhaled by the patient just a short time before death, you would expect, would you not, to find a distinct odour in the ventricles of the brain?—Not always; it has been observed.

Is it not one of the most prominent symptoms recognised?—Not according to my own observations. I am speaking from my own observation.

I do not want to challenge your book by any other; but you know " Guy and Ferrier "?—Yes.

Is that a book of substantial authority?—Yes.

So that, where it did not actually conflict with your own observation, you would attach importance to a statement there?—I certainly should attach importance to any statement made in such a book.

Thank you, that is very fair; I am at page 550 of " Guy and Ferrier," 5th edition. " In many cases the appearances are those of asphyxia. The odour of chloroform is perceptible on opening

270

Evidence for Prosecution.

Dr. Stevenson

the body. It is especially observable in the cerebral ventricles. The heart is frequently collapsed and flabby. In cases of sudden death the heart may be found in a state of fatty degeneration. Sometimes bubbles of gas are observed in the blood. Their exact nature is not determined. The post-mortem appearances are, therefore, neither very definite nor characteristic "?—Yes; that is speaking of asphyxia, or suffocation from the inhalation of chloroform. I have not the book before me, but as you were reading it to me——

I am reading the whole of the passage. " In many cases the appearances are those of asphyxia. The odour of chloroform is perceptible on opening the body. It is especially observable in the cerebral ventricles "?—Yes; I suppose it is a matter of grammatical construction, but I presume it means in cases of asphyxia from chloroform.

I do not take it to mean that, because it says, " In many cases the appearances are those of asphyxia "?—Yes, it ought to be read all together; but what I mean is, asphyxia generally arises from giving too much chloroform—a large quantity given—and there you would expect to find the smell more prominent in such a case than when the patient died from small quantities.

I quite agree it may be a question of quantity, but what I am putting to you is, if you are looking for, and you can find, any post-mortem indications of chloroform having been inhaled, the odour in the cerebral ventricles would be one of the principal ones? —Oh, certainly I should look for it.

You would agree to my proposition, it would be one you would certainly look for?—Yes.

Now, there is another case which rests, perhaps, on the better authority—we won't discuss that, it rests on another authority— that is the question of the engorgement of the right side of the heart. Is that a post-mortem appearance which you would expect to find after the patient had died after inhaling chloroform?—If the death had occurred from asphyxia.

You would expect to find it in smaller degree if the death had occurred, as you just told me it sometimes does, during the administration of chloroform, but owing to some sudden failure of the heart?—No; if the heart was paralysed on the right side, it would not necessarily be engorged.

But if the inhalation be carried to the point of asphyxia, it leaves that result in the heart. Supposing that during the inhalation of chloroform the patient had died from the failure of the heart, you would expect to find some trace in the engorgement of the heart?—If the patient was in a state of asphyxia, and died from engorgement of the heart——

Yes?—Yes; you would find, probably, the right side of the heart engorged.

Adelaide Bartlett.

Dr. Stevenson

Suppose the patient was brought to the verge of asphyxia—a state of insensibility by the administration of chloroform—and then death suddenly should take place, or almost suddenly, from whatever cause, you would expect to find that engorgement of the right side of the heart?—Yes; in all asphyxiated conditions you would expect to find it.

You have yourself made a study of the engorgement of the right side of the heart?—No; I do not know that I have made any special study.

Did you not yourself examine thirty-four cases?—Oh, I dare say.

And you found in twenty-seven cases engorgement of the lungs or of the right side of the heart?—Probably you have got something I have written.

Yes; I have. You know Taylor's book on poisons? It is a very well-known book?—Yes; I had nothing to do with writing that.

No, but a book you are familiar with—oh, you are referred to with regard to the two hundred administrations at Guy's. It is Dr. Snow who is mentioned with regard to the thirty-four cases?—Dr. Snow is a great authority on chloroform.

Is there also intense inflammation of the air passages where there has been inhalation of chloroform?—There may be occasionally, but I have not myself observed that condition. I think intense inflammation of the air passages is certainly not the ordinary result after death from inhalation.

Is this the fact—again I am quoting from "Guy and Ferrier," 5th edition, page 544: "The poisons, alcohol, ether, and chloroform, have the common property of inducing a state of narcotism often preceded by delirious excitement, and followed by indisposition, of which nausea and vomiting are generally the leading symptoms. In large doses, and in the concentrated form, they may destroy life suddenly by shock; but they generally prove fatal by coma, or by paralysis of the heart. They act as irritants to the parts with which they come in contact, producing intense inflammation in the lining membrane of the stomach when swallowed, and in that of the air passages when inhaled. But they do not affect the whole tract of the intestinal canal, as poisons of the irritant class do. All the poisons of this group are more or less volatile, and their vapours, when inhaled, act more powerfully than like quantities of the liquids themselves when swallowed"?—I do not agree to that.

You do not agree?—No, if that were the case, the patient would generally have acute bronchitis after it.

I will read you the whole passage: "The poisons, alcohol, ether, and chloroform, have the common property of inducing a state of narcotism, often preceded by delirious excitement, and fol-

Evidence for Prosecution.

Dr. Stevenson

lowed by indisposition, of which nausea and vomiting are generally the leading symptoms. In large doses, and in the concentrated form, they may destroy life suddenly by shock; but they generally prove fatal by coma, or by paralysis of the heart. They act as irritants to parts with which they come in contact, producing intense inflammation in the lining membrane of the stomach when swallowed, and in that of the air passages when inhaled." Do you agree with that?—I do not, as regards the chloroform.

You did admit to me, just now, that "Guy and Ferrier" was a book of substantial authority?—Yes, I admit the authority; I do not admit the statement.

You have come to a different judgment?—Yes.

Now, is there another result to be found after the inhalation of chloroform? Does it affect the urine?—Yes.

An indication would be found there?—It acts on what is termed copper solution—it reduces copper. A copper solution is the test we apply.

By Mr. JUSTICE WILLS—You apply a test?—By boiling it with a certain solution of copper, and it turns it red.

And did you have any of the urine sent to you for analysis? —No.

Cross-examination continued—Now, you have spoken of the possibility of administering chloroform to persons while in sleep? —Yes.

Did you speak of adults?—Yes.

As a matter of your own practice?—No; I said I had not done it myself.

I am much obliged. Well, when you say you know of cases in which it was done, are you speaking of recorded cases?—Yes.

Of adults?—Yes.

In the case of adults, is it the fact that the attempt to administer chloroform by inhalation, during sleep, wakes the man?— Not almost invariably.

Not almost invariably?—If I might refer to figures and the largest number of experiments made by one individual—Dolbeau— he found that the proportion that woke up either when heavily sleeping or lightly sleeping was three to one, three awoke to one that was chloroformed. I think Quimby experimented on four, and he succeeded in chloroforming them all.

"Quimby and Elliott"?—"Quimby and Elliott."

"Quimby" was the American we have just read?—Yes.

I have not got Dolbeau's book, but I have a reference to Dolbeau, the authority on that matter?—And Hussey. He was coroner for Oxford, I think. He did it thirty-six years ago.

I am asking for recorded matters, of course, that one can look at. Do you know Wynter Blyth's book on poisons?—Yes.

I dare say I may look at that reference to Dolbeau?—The book is there.

Adelaide Bartlett.

Dr. Stevenson

By Mr. JUSTICE WILLS—What book is that?—The " Annales d'Hygiène," a book of great authority, and it appears that Dolbeau's experiments were published in 1874.

Mr. CLARKE—I am rather reluctant to translate it lest I should appear to give it too favourably to myself. May I translate it, and ask you to check me? " Scientifically it is difficult, but often possible, to render persons who are in natural sleep insensible by chloroform. Certain precautions, the employment of a pure spirit and great skill, are among the conditions which may favour the attempt to anæsthetise. It is probable that certain subjects are absolutely refractory—that is to say, it will be impossible to anæsthetise them in spite of all the precautions that may be taken. Other persons, on the contrary, little children by preference, will easily submit to anæsthesia without being aroused from their slumbers by the irritation that the anæsthetic agent produces in the air passages."

(*To Witness*)—With regard to Wynter Blyth, just let me take this. I find a passage on page 136 : " Dolbeau has made some interesting experiments in order to ascertain whether under any circumstances a sleeping person might be anæsthetised. The main result appears to answer the question in the affirmative, at least with certain persons; but even with these, it can only be done by using the greatest skill and care, first allowing the sleeper to breathe very dilute chloroform-vapour, and then gradually exhibiting stronger doses, and taking the cloth or inhaler away on the slightest symptom of approaching wakefulness. In 75 per cent. of the cases, however, the individuals awoke almost immediately on being exposed to the vapour. This cautious and scientific narcosis, then, is not likely to be used by the criminal classes, or if used, to be successful." Will you kindly tell me that other name? What was it?—Quimby, *Boston Medical Journal*.

That is an American book, is it not?—Yes.

I think " Wharton and Stillé " is an American work with which you are acquainted?—Yes.

Do you remember in that the results of experiments are stated with regard to endeavouring to give chloroform to sleeping persons? —I do not remember the statement in that book. Probably there would be one. Is it a recent edition?

I will tell you. 1884?—Probably it would be a reference to Quimby. I have not so recent an edition.

Then I shall be glad to give you the reference. The following testimony is given at page 393 of vol. ii. of Wharton and Stillé's " Medical Jurisprudence," and " is taken from the records of a recent trial (New Bloomfield, Perry County, Pa., 18th January, 1871) for an attempt at robbery by the use of chloroform :—F. F. Maury, M.D., recalled : Chloroform *very very* often produces resistance. It sometimes produces irritation, and sometimes a

Evidence for Prosecution.

Dr. Stevenson

depressing feeling. It produces vomiting. If the stomach is full, nausea and vomiting almost always follow. Sometimes it does not. I experimented with chloroform on six sleeping persons. Out of that number all resisted more or less. Two *men* woke up immediately, and one remarked ' you are trying to give me something.' Unquestionably it requires more chloroform to produce death in a recumbent position than in an upright posture. One man cannot administer chloroform to another "?—I know those experiments—Quimby and others have experimented to try and settle the question, and Dolbeau's experiments were taken up for the same reason, I know.

Dolbeau's, then, are the most recent?—No; Quimby's are more recent. He is referring to a trial—1880.

Stillé is quoting in 1884?—Yes.

Quimby's is an American book?—It is a paper by Quimby, who is, I believe, a person of repute, in the *Boston Medical Journal*,* 17th June, 1880.

You have got the French " Dolbeau," and now you mention " Quimby and Elliott "?—And I have another American authority.

But, so far as English authorities are concerned, can you find me any suggestion in any book that it is possible to administer chloroform to sleeping men without waking them?—Yes.

Where?—Hussey, the *Medical Times and Gazette*, 1880, ii. 251.

The *Medical Times and Gazette*, excuse me saying it, is not a book in the sense I am using. I am speaking of treatises?—Hussey is a perfectly reliable person.

I have no doubt, but you know one can deal with medical treatises, but it is not so easy to find things in the *Medical Times and Gazette*.

By Mr. JUSTICE WILLS—Have you got it there?—No.

Cross-examination continued—This, you tell me, is the only book—an English authority—in which there is a mention of this matter of administering chloroform during sleep—a book of very considerable authority—" Woodman and Tidy "?—I think it is mentioned there.

By Mr. JUSTICE WILLS—I have not appreciated what you say about Hussey?—Hussey said it was done in his presence at Oxford Infirmary as far back as 1850.

The chloroform was administered to a sleeping person?—Yes.

Cross-examination continued—I do not want to trouble you. Have you got a record of that case with you?—No.

---

* The *Boston Medical Journal*, 17th June, 1880, p. 592, contains an editorial note only on Quimby's experiments. Quimby's original paper will be found in the Transactions of the American Medical Association, 1880, p. 519.—ED.

Adelaide Bartlett.

Dr. Stevenson

Was it to an adult or a child?—I think it was to a young man of sixteen or seventeen.

You have given your references?—I have—1880, ii. 251. My assistant will get it for me this afternoon.

I suggest to you the only really known matter with regard to this in English treatises is with respect to children. I am about to read an extract from " Woodman and Tidy." It is the edition of 1877, but I think the world wants a new edition. That is the last—p. 525. " A question of some importance to the medical jurist naturally occurs here, namely, *whether chloroform can be administered for improper purposes.* We know, however, that comparatively the insensibility from chloroform-vapour is only slowly induced. It would be difficult, therefore, to administer chloroform to persons forcibly and against their will, whilst, of course, the stories of immediate anæsthesia produced by it are but idle fables. Still, it might be administered to persons asleep without much difficulty (*Lancet*, 5th October, 1872, p. 514, and 12th October, 1872, p. 549), and this seems the only possible condition under which it could be conveniently used for improper purposes, unless considerable force was employed to prevent the person struggling, which, under ordinary circumstances, would be an almost insurmountable difficulty to its use." I have referred Dr. Stevenson to the two references to the *Lancet* given in " Woodman and Tidy," and I find they referred entirely to the administration of chloroform to children. Do you know Dr. Whitmarsh, of Hounslow?—I think I do.

You remember the name?—Yes.

It is not a question of authority. I was only earmarking the question. There is a note here that it will be interesting to know whether this mode of giving chloroform has been noticed by the profession. I do not know if you know Mr. Dobson, of Clifton, Bristol. Reference is made in Woodman and Tidy's book to his letter. (The learned counsel read a letter from the *Lancet*, 1872, ii. 549, by Mr. Dobson.) " In reply to the letter of Dr. Whitmarsh which appeared in your last impression respecting the administration of chloroform to children during sleep, I beg to say I have been in the habit of so administering chloroform when the opportunity occurred. During the time I was house-surgeon to the Bristol General Hospital, where I had frequently to give chloroform to children to straighten their legs in hip-joint disease and the like, I used to consider myself fortunate if I could catch the child asleep and so give it chloroform without disturbing it; the advantage of such a proceeding being that the child speedily became under the influence of the anæsthetic without that alarm and crying and irregular inspirations which are so common in the administration of chloroform to children. The only precaution which I ever found necessary to prevent them from awaking with the first

276

Evidence for Prosecution.

Dr. Stevenson

inspiration of the chloroform, was that the inhaler should be first held at a moderate distance from the child's face, and gradually approached nearer until the requisite degree of anæsthesia was produced, which would be judged of by the usual signs." Apart from that reference in " Woodman and Tidy," you are not prepared to refer me to any English treatises which discuss the probability of administering chloroform during sleep?—It is mentioned in " Taylor." He refers to Dolbeau—in the book on poisons, I think it is.

He refers to Dolbeau?—Yes; there is a paragraph on it—a sentence, at all events.

Oh, that is Dolbeau?—You will find it in the reference to the " Annales d'Hygiène."

Quite right; he did not give the reference to Dolbeau?—No.

But he gives reference to the book, and he only gives this passage, 3rd edition, p. 648: " These facts show that there is no truth in the statement sometimes made in cases of alleged robbery or rape, that the person assaulted was rendered suddenly insensible and unable to offer resistance. Chloroform-vapour does not produce immediate insensibility unless it also produces complete asphyxia and death. There is, however, one case in which it might be used to aid the perpetration of crime. If the person is already asleep, the application of the vapour might intensify this and render him or her powerless, but the conditions for thus using chloroform criminally can rarely present themselves." He does not give the name of Dolbeau, but that is the reference?—Yes.

Now, I just want to come to another question. Do you say the symptoms produced by the swallowing of chloroform entirely correspond with those that follow on inhalation?—Pretty well, I think. You get symptoms of unconsciousness and paralysis intensified.

I speak of symptoms that follow on swallowing chloroform?—There is then inflammation of the stomach, but the general symptoms are not very greatly different.

But the very first case in Taylor's " Medical Jurisprudence," 3rd edition—you have edited that. I am afraid to ask you if you believe in all the cases. Some of them are of very great authority?—I have certainly modified some of that chapter from what has since come to my knowledge.

The first case, vol. i., p. 404, is: " This liquid when taken in a large dose appears to affect the system like alcohol; but as a *liquid* it cannot be regarded as an active poison. A man swallowed *four ounces* of chloroform. He was able to walk for a considerable distance after taking this dose, but he subsequently fell into a state of coma " ?—Yes; the symptoms when taken into the stomach —the absorption is less rapid than when taken into the lungs. I

Adelaide Bartlett.

Dr. Stevenson

should take it symptoms would take longer to develop themselves, but when they do so they are very profound.

I should expect you to answer me in the affirmative directly. The results of swallowing a dose of chloroform vary immensely in different cases?—Yes.

So far as the inhalation of chloroform is concerned, the symptoms are fairly regular, are they not?—Yes; the stage of excitement——

I will read it to you from " Taylor." Now the passage in which he describes it—and I just ask you if you agree—is at page 649 of " Taylor on Poisons," 3rd edition : " There are considered to be four stages in the administration of the vapour. In the first, the patient becomes excited ; in the second, he talks incoherently, and sensibility is diminished ; in the third, he is unconscious, but the muscles are rigid ; in the fourth, the muscles are completely relaxed, and the patient is perfectly insensible. Danger commences with the third stage." Do you agree with that generally? —Yes.

Now, during the first stage, when the patient is excited, the passage of a quantity of chloroform over the lips and tongue and down the throat would cause severe pain, would it not?—Yes.

And in that first stage, the stage of excitement, that pain would be resented, and would arouse the patient to resistance?—Yes. Are you speaking now of its administration to a person awake? In any case——

Forgive me ; you are right in this sense : I have taken you to the stage of the administration of chloroform to a person sleeping, and he would have awakened?—Yes. I do not agree that that state of excitement would be necessary if a person were asleep. I wish not to commit myself to too general a proposition.

We have got from Dolbeau, as far as his experience went, that three out of four persons awoke?—This experience is——

I have got an American authority, where he attempted it with six persons, and they all awoke?—Yes.

Then I have taken the case given by Mr. Tidy, of the children being dealt with while they were asleep in the hospital, and I have read you the letter in which Mr. Dobson practically agrees with Dolbeau. He says he avoided excitement by giving it during sleep?—Yes.

He did it with great care, beginning with the chloroform far off and bringing it closer. Now, apart from the question of sleeping or waking, supposing the first stage here of excitement to occur, the pain of administering the poison would be felt, and would be resisted. That would be the first thing to wake anybody up?—Yes, it might wake a person up, and it might not.

Probably from the first stage, if you only got a person into the first stage, that of excitement, the pain, whether about the tender

278

Evidence for Prosecution.

Dr. Stevenson

places there in his mouth or lips, would wake him if you put the liquid into the mouth?—Yes, in that stage; I misunderstood you.

Then, in the second, he talks incoherently, and sensibility is diminished, so that sensibility is gradually passing away?—Yes, he is intoxicated.

But still capable of feeling pain?—To a less extent.

In the third he is unconscious, but the muscles are rigid. Now, in the administration of chloroform by inhalation, when you come to that third stage, does not the jaw become rigid?—Very often. There is a great deal of rigidity in the limbs generally.

So that at that stage it would require force to open the mouth? —Probably, yes.

And when that rigidity passes away, the muscles become completely relaxed, and the patient is perfectly insensible?—Yes, ready for operation.

And in that stage there is no capacity for swallowing at all, is there?—Yes.

How? Is not the reflex state abolished?—No; the patient is on the operating table, and would continue to swallow.

When completely anæsthetised?—Yes.

That is a question of degree?—That is altogether a question of degree when the patient would cease to swallow.

Then I understand you, in your judgment——

By Mr. Justice Wills—May I interpose one question? When you speak of their swallowing in that sense, do you mean by the muscles acting, or having stuff simply poured down their throat, as Mr. Murray said?—Any liquid put at the back of the throat; the patient continues to swallow his own saliva for some time.

That is by muscular action?—Yes.

Not like pouring it down a leaden pipe?—No. Blood flows into the back of the throat; it is swallowed unless he is under chloroform very profoundly, when he ceases to swallow, and then he becomes suffocated. There is a stage of inhalation where the patient ceases to swallow.

Cross-examination continued—But in this case, where the operation is performed and the blood gets to the back of the throat, is not one of the dangers that blood will get into the air passages?—Yes; he may get into such a state by inhalation that he cannot swallow.

Now, let me put it again. Do you say there is a particular point in the process of chloroforming at which a medical man—at which the patient would be able to swallow, although he was sufficiently under the influence of chloroform not to suffer from the pain?—I do.

Will you tell me how you would yourself ascertain that time had arrived?—Well, I should not like to pour liquid down the throat if the reflex of the eye had been abolished, as Dr. Murray

279

Adelaide Bartlett.

terms it. I would not like to commit myself to say where would be the point at which the reflex would even be abolished.

I take it from you that is taken as the test?—It is the practical test.

Let me ask you this, is not that the test that the doctor does apply in order to ascertain if the sensation of pain has gone?—Yes.

Is that the assumption, at all events, of a doctor dealing with chloroform; until that reflex action is gone, pain is felt?—He assumes that.

Now, suppose you had to deal with a sleeping man, and it was your object to get down his throat without his knowing it a liquid the administration of which to the lips or throat would cause great pain, do you not agree it would be a very difficult or delicate operation?—I think it would be an operation which would often fail, and might often succeed.

Would you not look on it as a delicate operation?—I should look on it as a delicate operation, because I should be afraid of pouring it down the windpipe.

That is one of the dangers you contemplate?—Yes.

If it got into the windpipe, there would be spasmodic action of the muscles, would there not?—At the stage when you had come to the conclusion that you could do it, when there is insensibility, or partial insensibility, the rejection of the liquid by the windpipe would be probably less active than when the patient was awake.

If the patient got into such a state of insensibility as not to reject it, it would go down his windpipe and burn that?—Probably some of it might go down the windpipe.

It would probably do so?—Probably.

If it did so, it would leave its traces?—I should expect to find traces after death, unless the patient lives for some hours.

Of course, a great many post-mortem appearances are changed if the patient lives for some hours?—Yes.

Not only by the chloroform disappearing, so to speak, but also other changes incidental to a post-mortem condition?—Yes.

And if the post-mortem examination had been performed, as Mrs. Bartlett wished it to be, on the very day on which death took place, there would have been still better opportunity of determining the cause of death?—Yes.

The Court adjourned.

Fifth Day—Friday, 16th April, 1886.

Dr. STEVENSON, recalled, and re-examined by the ATTORNEY-GENERAL—You were asked about chloroform being very volatile? —Yes, it is.

Assuming it to have been taken into the mouth and so to have gone down into the stomach, would you expect, after the lapse of four or five hours, that there would necessarily be any smell of chloroform in the mouth?—No.

Or three or four hours?—No.

Or two or three? I want to get some approximate idea?—If the mouth were open, I should expect the smell might disappear even within half an hour.

Can you tell me this—whether the effect of a dose of chloroform swallowed and taken into the stomach would be greater or less in its effects upon the person taking it if that person was insensible or partially insensible by inhalation first?—I should expect that the effect would be greater.

In the direction of causing paralysis of the action of the heart, for instance?—Yes.

You spoke, I think, of the delicacy that would be used in getting chloroform into the stomach if the person were lying back and insensible or partially insensible?—Yes.

You used that word, I think?—I think I used the word or something very like it.

Do you mean, from a medical point of view, it would require to be delicately done in order to prevent its getting into the windpipe instead of the throat?—What I mean precisely is this, that a person unskilled in the anatomy of the part—in such a case there would be a chance whether it got in the right way, down the gullet, or the wrong way, down the windpipe. Some might go down the windpipe if not, in that sense, delicately done; there would be that danger.

My learned friend read a passage from one work in which he spoke of asphyxia as a consequence of the administration of chloroform.

Mr. CLARKE—No; the passage I read was this: that the post-mortem appearances were similar to the cases of asphyxia.

By the ATTORNEY-GENERAL—Is that your experience?—The post-mortem appearances are sometimes those of asphyxia, because asphyxia is sometimes the cause of death from chloroform.

By Mr. JUSTICE WILLS—I do not know whether I am correct in summarising this. The notion I have from the cross-examination of yesterday is, that chloroform would produce death in one of two ways—in the one, by producing asphyxia, which I suppose

281

Adelaide Bartlett.

would paralyse the muscles of respiration; and in the other cases, by paralysing the muscles of the heart; and the two post-mortem symptoms are not quite the same in the two cases?—No.

If that requires correction, pray give it?—Practically, it is so; but one thing with asphyxia, it is not quite necessary that there should be paralysis of the muscles of respiration—it really means suffocation.

It may arise from that?—Yes, or from paralysis of the heart.

Re-examination continued—So it comes to this, if the particular form which the mischief takes is suffocation, you would expect to see on the post-mortem the signs of suffocation?—Yes.

If the mischief results from paralysis of the heart, you do not expect to see signs of suffocation?—Yes.

It sometimes happens, does it not, that, when persons are voluntarily drinking a liquid, some of it may get down the windpipe or approach the windpipe?—Yes, occasionally; that is a rare incident.

With reference to the passage which my learned friend Mr. Clarke was reading yesterday from this book at page 183, what paper do you call that?—It is a paper by M. Dolbeau.

I will just read one passage more to you; it follows the passage which Mr. Clarke read. You know the passage probably; you will recognise it as I endeavour to translate it: "With regard to crime, it is certain that chloroform administered to persons asleep could facilitate the perpetration of certain crimes and misdemeanours. It is, however, probable that conditions favourable to anæsthesia will rarely be found combined at the time of the attempted criminal acts." Do you agree with that?—I agree that it is possible, and that, in a certain number of cases, the production of sleep would be comparatively easily effected.

By Mr. JUSTICE WILLS—The production of sleep, you say?— The production of insensibility during sleep, I should say.

Re-examination continued—My learned friend Mr. Clarke also asked you whether there may not be found some traces in the urine of a person who has died from an overdose of chloroform, and I understood you to say yes. Would it be visible to the eye, or would it only be detectable upon analysis?—Oh, not visible to the eye. It is a little undetermined whether it is due to the undoubted presence of chloroform or the chloroform producing some other substance in the urine. At all events, the urine would act in a particular way at a particular period.

You had no portion of the urine furnished to you for analysis? —No.

And the appearance of the urine would not suggest any change?—The appearance would not suggest it. I have the book, the *Medical Times*, here now, my lord.

By the FOREMAN—We wish to ask you one or two questions.

Evidence for Prosecution.

Dr. Stevenson

We desire to be perfectly clear upon this point. I think you stated that, in the third stage of chloroformism, the jaws are rigid, or partially so?—In one stage. The stages are purely arbitrary, but in one stage there is rigidity.

Then we take it that an unskilled person with a little time to administer a sufficient quantity of chloroform down the throat —sufficient to cause death—must do it very gradually for fear of choking. It must take some little time; they could not do it suddenly?—I do not think in some cases it would be very difficult to do it quickly. It is simply the very act of swallowing.

Then the chances are, I think, perhaps, that some portion of the chloroform might remain in the mouth for some little time?—I should expect it would be a very short time.

But it must remain there some little time?—Some of it might. If the person were unable to swallow, it would be likely to remain at the back of the throat.

Then it will show some sign of its having been there, in the gums or throat, in the same way as if it lay in the intestines?—Yes, if the patient were unable to swallow. If he were in a condition to swallow it, the swallowing would be effected almost momentarily, just as long as it would take to drink a little water.

You would expect more signs, supposing a person could not swallow, than if he was drinking medicine quickly off. In the latter case you would not expect to see any signs at all, would you?—If a person could not swallow, it would remain at the upper part of the windpipe; and upon the post-mortem I should expect to find the effects of contact there—irritation or inflammation.

If taken suddenly, you would not expect to find either?—I should not expect to find it.

By Mr. JUSTICE WILLS—I just want to ask a question as to the term rigidity. It is a little too vague to convey any definite notion to my mind. It may mean that the jaws were closed like an iron vice, or it may mean something very much less. Will you kindly explain that?—In giving chloroform by inhalation at a certain period, and before the patient is altogether unconscious, there is often considerable general muscular rigidity. The arms would be rigid and the patient would grind his teeth or clench the jaw.

Would that be the same if administered during sleep?—I have never seen it given during sleep. I should not think so from the record of those cases—sleep passing into the period of chloroformism.

How long does the period of rigidity last?—Oh, it may be a few seconds or a minute.

Not very long?—No; if the patient is insensible, the rigidity speedily passes off.

Mr. CLARKE—My lord, the letter to which I have referred

Adelaide Bartlett.

Dr. Stevenson

does itself refer to a quotation in the previous week's number of the *Medical Times*. I am endeavouring to find it, but I will not delay. I dare say Dr. Stevenson will be good enough to try and find it for me.

Mr. JUSTICE WILLS—Mr. Hussey's letter, do you mean?

Mr. CLARKE—Yes, my lord. He referred to the *Medical Times*. In that case it was administered to a boy. It is the 28th of August, 1880, which is the second volume of the work, at page 251. I have just found it, and I will read the letter:—" Administration of Chloroform during Sleep.—About thirty years ago the late Mr. Hester, of this city, asked me to assist him in the operation of removing a small pendulous tumour from the inner side of the thigh in a boy. When we entered the bedroom the boy was in bed asleep. We administered the chloroform at once without awaking him; and, when he was well under the influence of it, we prepared a table," and so on; but the point there is that that was the case of a boy.

By Mr. JUSTICE WILLS—I will just ask one more question. We are told that there was unusual and considerable difficulty in putting the patient under the influence of nitrous oxide. Is there any connection necessarily or probably between difficulty in being put into insensibility by nitrous oxide and being put into insensibility by chloroform?—It is quite a guess. I should think the difficulty in the one case would create a difficulty in the other; but that is a pure matter of inference.

A thing you cannot say much about?—A thing I cannot say much about. I will only say generally, if a person is insensible to one anæsthetic, he would be less sensible to another.

Dr. CHARLES MEYMOTT TIDY, examined by Mr. POLAND—I am a Bachelor of Medicine and Master of Surgery. I am Professor of Chemistry and Forensic Medicine at the London Hospital, and I am one of the official analysts to the Home Office. I am one of the authors of the book " Forensic Medicine and Toxicology," by Woodman and Tidy. I have had considerable experience in matters of that description. I have of my own knowledge known of a death from taking liquid chloroform, in the year 1863. Dr. Lankester was coroner at that time, and he referred the case to me. So far as we know, the fatal dose at that time was an ounce and a half; but I am bound to say the details I have of that case are not very clear, for the case was one of suicide, and the fact of chloroform having been taken was beyond all question. Wineglasses are of different sizes, but I take it a wineglass would hold 2 to 2½ fluid ounces. In the case of a death from taking liquid chloroform, I should expect to find some of the actual chloroform in the stomach. In the case in 1863 there was actual chloroform in the stomach, but the exact quantity was

Evidence for Prosecution.

Dr. Charles M. Tidy

not determined, as there was no necessity to do so. One other case of chloroform came before me, curiously enough in 1863, which I saw also with Dr. Woodman, but that was a case of recovery.*

In my judgment chloroform taken in a liquid form entering the stomach would show signs when it came in contact with the stomach. In the 1863 case, which is the only case I know of my own knowledge, there was considerable inflammatory condition of the stomach. I presume that would be the part of the stomach that the chloroform would come in contact with; but I have no note in this case as to where the inflammation was. I should judge that the chloroform would affect the œsophagus, or gullet, if it were sufficiently long in contact with it, but, if the contact of chloroform with a tissue is of very short duration, I am of opinion that no abnormal appearance might be apparent. I have myself tried that in my own case for experiment. I put a tea-spoonful of pure chloroform in my mouth, and I held it in my mouth for something like five or six seconds; I then spat it out and simply washed my mouth out with a little water. There was a slight redness produced, but it certainly did not last longer than a few minutes at the most, although a certain numbness continued for something like nearly an hour. I am clear, there-fore, that the effect of chloroform on animal tissues will be greatly dependent on the duration of the contact. When liquid chloroform is taken into the stomach it then passes into the blood; the diffusibility, as it is called, of chloroform is very great. If taken in sufficient quantity to cause death, I would expect to find traces of chloroform in the intestines; that would not be by its diffusibility through the membranes, however, but by its actual passage from the stomach into the intestines, and I should expect to find traces there if a sufficient period had elapsed between the taking of the chloroform and the death. Upon the death so caused I would expect to find at the post-mortem examination what is described as fluidity of the blood; one of the peculiar effects of chloroform is its action on the blood including various changes of the blood.

On Saturday, 20th March, Dr. Stevenson showed me some of the contents of the stomach—bottle No. 5. I smelt it, and I think that Dr. Stevenson's description, that the smell was over-poweringly strong of chloroform, is a very right one, and it is exactly as I should describe it myself on that date, 20th March. Suppose chloroform was inhaled, and then chloroform was taken in a liquid state, I should think that the chloroform taken in the liquid state would have a greater effect than if taken by a person who had not previously inhaled it. That is rather a matter of opinion, however.

---

* Vide *Medical Times and Gazette*, 1863, vol. ii., p. 378.—ED.

Adelaide Bartlett.

Dr. Charles M. Tidy

By Mr. JUSTICE WILLS—I think I might almost call it a speculation; I do not think I could put it much higher than that.

Examination continued—Supposing death be caused by a fatal dose of liquid chloroform in a body seen some two or three hours after death, I think it is quite consistent with facts that there should be no smell of chloroform in the mouth at all. Chloroform is very volatile, indeed, and if the mouth were opened after death that would be quite sufficient to account for the smell going off. As regards the effect of chloroform on the skin, supposing chloroform spilt on the face, and not covered up, I should not expect to find any marks left. As a matter of fact, I dropped some chloroform on my own hand last night, and there was no sign left at all; there was a slight redness produced for a short time, but it was very transient. There was certainly no sign of the spot where I dropped it half an hour afterwards, and I think I should be more correct if I said quarter of an hour afterwards. At the present moment I cannot determine at all where the spot was. If one was to drop chloroform on the skin, and then place a pad over it, so as to cover it, then undoubtedly it would produce a burn. In giving chloroform which is inhaled I have noticed a rigidity of the jaw, and I have also noticed some cases where there has been no rigidity of the jaw. The rigidity does not necessarily follow in all cases, although it usually occurs; and, further, the rigidity of the jaw lasts a very variable period. In my judgment partial insensibility could be produced by inhalation of chloroform during sleep.

If a person were rendered partially insensible by the administration of chloroform, in your judgment, could the liquid be administered?—I think so, certainly, at certain stages. I should like to say, with regard to my experiment on the action of administering chloroform during sleep, that I think it is fair to state exactly what I have done in the case. Of course, it is always difficult to do it, for you must get the consent of the person, and it is not an experiment you can often make. In the case of a boy between fifteen and sixteen years of age, who had a dislocation of his arm, it was necessary to give him chloroform in order to reduce it. He went to sleep, and we administered chloroform while he was asleep with great ease. I have tried it in two other cases since, but I failed in both cases. In the one case the person was fairly well asleep, but in the other case the man was just dozing.

Cross-examined by Mr. CLARKE—With regard to the three cases you have given us, you succeeded in the case of the boy and failed in the others, I understand?—Yes; in one the person was not in a good sleep, and I failed.

Those are the only experiments you have had the opportunity of making, and were those both adults?—They were adults.

In the case of the boy, I notice that you said " we " ad-

Evidence for Prosecution.

Dr. Charles M. Tidy

ministered chloroform. Was there a surgeon there with you?—The surgeon was there who was going to reduce it.

Have you had long experience?—You mean of chloroform? Yes?—Yes; very long indeed.

By Mr. JUSTICE WILLS—Then you administered the chloroform?—Yes; I administered the chloroform.

Cross-examination continued—With regard to the 1863 case, that was a suicide, I believe?—Yes.

And so, I believe, being a case of suicide, it was not necessary to make detailed notes?—No; the jury wanted the analysis to be made to detect the chloroform, and I did not go very fully into it.

The great majority of cases reported are cases of suicide, are they not?—Certainly; by a very long way.

By Mr. JUSTICE WILLS—Two by swallowing chloroform, I understand?—Yes, entirely.

Cross-examination continued—The majority of cases of inhalation are accidental, are they not?—Yes; I understand that.

So that, apart from positive evidence of facts, the enormous probability of evidence would be in favour of suicide?—I should say so.

You say that, with regard to rigidity, it lasts for a very short time?—Very; it may only last a few seconds, and it may last longer.

It may last much more—four or five minutes?—I should not like to say no.

I am quite content, Dr. Tidy; I will take your answer. The symptoms from the inhalation of chloroform are very variable, are they not?—Very variable indeed.

A person might be chloroformed—I will use that word—in two minutes, or it may take a considerable time?—Yes; while the quantity required to produce the effects varies also. It is not a question of time only, but of quantity.

In administering chloroform, you are guided by the appearance of the patient with regard to the quantity you are to administer, I suppose?—Manifestly so; it is the real difficulty, in administering chloroform, that you cannot lay down any law which applies to everybody.

Exactly; and therefore in all the stages you must exercise a careful judgment?—Yes.

And that is the reason that there are administrators of chloroform who devote themselves to the practice?—Exactly.

By Mr. JUSTICE WILLS—It goes further, does it not? Sometimes persons whom you would not expect die suddenly under chloroform, do they not?—Yes; and in some cases even when a careful examination has been made, and no signs of heart disease discovered.

287

Adelaide Bartlett.

Dr. Charles M. Tidy

And is the converse sometimes the case, that when you think it *primâ facie* very dangerous, the patient will take any quantity?—That is so.

So that it is singularly uncertain?—Yes, and that is no doubt why ether has been so largely substituted lately, because all authorities have found it more certain in its action, although it has its disadvantages.

Do you know whether the case which you read to Mr. Clarke—the one case which was unhappily fatal, was that a case of suicide? I dare say you know the case?—I know the case perfectly well.

Perhaps it does not say?

Mr. CLARKE—It does not say, my lord. It is this—he was aged twenty-six, and he took 2 ounces.

Mr. JUSTICE WILLS—Dr. Tidy says he rather thinks it was suicide.

The WITNESS—I rather think so.

By Mr. JUSTICE WILLS—Just let me ask you one question. Would it be correct to say that there is a similar uncertainty about the action of swallowing chloroform; or would it be more correct to say that not much is known about it?—There is considerable uncertainty in its action; it depends largely upon whether the man vomits or not—whether the person vomits or not. I am only judging now from the cases I have read.

We know the limits of your experience, but I suppose you have read everything there is?—I think I have read everything there is, as far as I can find it.

I suppose one may say—one must have to correctly summarise it—a good deal less is known about swallowing chloroform than about chloroform inhaled?—Oh, very much less.

By a JUROR—I suppose it would be likely, if you were to drop chloroform on the delicate parts of the mouth, to show marks there, though you would not see them on the skin of the hand?—Certainly.

By Mr. JUSTICE WILLS—There is one other question I want to ask of you—or Dr. Stevenson, perhaps of both. Dr. Leach says that, experimenting upon himself, he produced a mark of whiteness on the tongue when he took chloroform in his mouth. Do you know anything about that?—No; it is contrary to my own experiments, and my own experience. There was no sign of whiteness; it was a thing I looked for very carefully, but it was a delicate blush of redness.

Then you only know from that one experiment?—That is all.

It is not anything that is recorded, is it?—No, I think not.

Re-examined by the ATTORNEY-GENERAL—How long do you think the chloroform was in your mouth?—Five or six seconds.

But nothing has been recorded about that in pathological books?—No; I know nothing about whiteness being produced.

Mr. H. B. Poland.

Evidence for Prosecution.

Mrs Mary Ann Furlong

Mrs. MARY ANN FURLONG, examined by Mr. MALONEY—I am a married woman, residing at 77 Phillip Bridge Road, Merton. I acted as servant to Mrs. Bartlett at Merton Cottage from 6th January to 1st September, 1885. I was living then with my husband near their house, and I went home every afternoon. I usually went to the Bartletts' house about eight o'clock in the morning. I made the beds, sometimes alone and sometimes with Mrs. Bartlett. Mr. and Mrs. Bartlett did not occupy separate beds in that house. I was never with them anywhere else. Mr. Bartlett had a cold bath every morning in his bedroom. He went to business every day. Mr. Dyson came to the house sometimes at the latter part, and I have left them alone together.

By Mr. JUSTICE WILLS—My usual time of leaving was eleven o'clock in the day, but if Mrs. Bartlett had company I would stay and cook the dinner.

Examination continued—I used to see Mr. Bartlett coming home in the evening; he passed my house as he came home.

By Mr. JUSTICE WILLS—Mr. and Mrs. Matthews stayed with the Bartletts for a week. They and Mr. Dyson were the only visitors that they had. So far as I saw, Mr. and Mrs. Bartlett lived on very affectionate terms with one another, and, as far as I could judge, they lived as husband and wife.

HENRY MARSHALL, examined by Mr. POLAND—I am inspector of the Metropolitan Police, and I have had charge of this case. I was present at the inquest on 4th and 11th February. On those occasions both Mr. Dyson and Mrs. Bartlett were present. On the 11th Mr. Dyson was examined as a witness. Mrs. Bartlett was represented by a barrister, Mr. Beal, and by a solicitor, Mr. Wood. On the 4th the coroner said to Mr. Wood, or he said publicly, he should like to know whether Mrs. Bartlett intended to give evidence. There was some reply, but I do not know what it was. She did not give evidence.

Did her counsel say anything in her presence in reference to awaiting the result of the analysis, or did anything of that kind pass?—I am not quite clear about that. I remember more particularly about the 11th. After Mr. Dyson had given evidence Mr. Braxton Hicks, the deputy coroner, said he should like to know whether it was the intention of Mrs. Bartlett to give evidence or not, but she was not tendered as a witness. Upon that, from what was said in the inquest room, I took her into custody in the board room as soon as it was cleared. I was in plain clothes, and I said to her, " I am Inspector Marshall. After what has passed here to-day I must take you into custody for the wilful murder of your husband by administering to him about midnight on the 31st of December last a poisonous dose of chloroform. This is a serious charge, and whatever you say I must caution you that I shall reduce it to writing, and it will be given in evidence at your trial."

Adelaide Bartlett.

Henry Marshall

Mrs. Bartlett said, " I have nothing to say." Her solicitor, Mr. Wood, was present and heard all that passed. She was charged in the ordinary way and taken before the magistrate.

Previous to that date, 11th February, I searched the whole of the railway line from Peckham Rye to Victoria to see if I could find any bottle. I found some bottles, but not the one I expected. I was at Claverton Street on 11th January when the house was searched. I saw " Squire's Companion " among the books, and handed it to the coroner's officer. I also found the letters referred to by the witness Ralph. On 24th February I also searched a number of boxes at Claverton Street. No medicine chest was found; I never could find it either at Claverton Street or at Mrs. Matthews', where Mrs. Bartlett had been staying. I searched Mrs. Bartlett's luggage at the office of her solicitor, and I took possession of a certain number of things—the deceased's nightgown and other things—which were handed to Dr. Stevenson. These I got from Mrs. Bartlett's box. The nightgown was cut down the centre. I showed it, the pillow, and the other things to Dr. Stevenson. There were stains on the nightgown just above the neck. These were seen by Dr. Stevenson. On 15th February I went to Wandsworth Common with Mr. Dyson, and I searched the Common for bottles at the place indicated by him. I found the coloured bottle with " Poison, not to be taken " on it. I should say that I have searched the Common twice since, but I have not been able to find the other bottles. On 18th February I received a warrant from the coroner, upon which I took Mr. Dyson into custody, and took him before the magistrate. The warrant was for both prisoners, and it charged them with murder.

By Mr. JUSTICE WILLS—There was a large box of books which were not taken possession of. They were mostly English books; I do not remember seeing any foreign book. The " Pharmacopœia " is the only one that struck me.

Dr. STEVENSON, recalled and further examined by the ATTORNEY-GENERAL—Last night there were delivered to me and Dr. Tidy jointly a nightdress and a pillow case. There were spots and stains on the nightdress. But I could not detect any substance beyond a little sugary substance. The stains might have been due to any ordinary article of liquid food, such as beef tea, or it might be the result of perspiration. It was not caused by tea, as the tannic character of tea or brandy was absent. It might have been sweet, I think. There was no sign on the pillow case.

Mrs. CAROLINE DOGGETT, recalled and further examined by the ATTORNEY-GENERAL—Mr. and Mrs. Bartlett came to lodge with me in October. The illness began in December, and Dr. Leach was called in on the 10th. The first week that the Bartletts were

Evidence for Prosecution.

Mrs Caroline Doggett

living with me they had only one bedroom and one bed, which they used together. Afterwards a smaller bed was put into the bedroom, which they continued to occupy up to the time of the illness. The small bed was then moved into the drawing-room. I sometimes went to help the servant to make the large bed, and I found the small one remade, but whether Mrs. Bartlett had made it or not I cannot say. I think the servant, Alice Fulcher, can speak to that. There were folding doors communicating between the drawing-room and the bedroom, and it was not necessary to go on to the landing to get from the bedroom to the front room. There was some furniture put near the folding doors when the sofa was put there in December. But it was possible to pass through the door. I did not see anything unusual in the relationship between Mr. and Mrs. Bartlett. I think they were on affectionate terms as husband and wife.

Futher cross-examined by Mr. CLARKE—Whose was that small bedstead?—Mrs. Bartlett ordered me to get another bed to put in the room.

Do you mean that you bought it for the purpose?—Yes.

Then it was yours?—Yes.

At the time of their coming, or very soon after was it, she said that to you?—When they came they asked for two beds in the bedroom.

What? The first time they took the room?—Yes.

You had not in the house a bed small enough to put in, I believe?—No, and it was nearly a week before I could get out to run to the stores, and it was some days before they sent it.

But when they first took the rooms, I understand, it was stipulated that they should have two beds?—Two beds.

By Mr. JUSTICE WILLS—Were you ever present in the room when Mr. Dyson was there with them?—With Mrs. Bartlett, not with Mr. Bartlett.

Did you ever hear what he called her or what she called him? —No.

ALICE FULCHER, recalled and further examined by the ATTORNEY-GENERAL—I was servant to Mrs. Doggett. I remember Mr. and Mrs. Bartlett coming to her house in October, and I remember Mr. Bartlett's illness in December. They occupied the same bed the first week they came, and then a small bed was put into the bedroom. They then always occupied separate beds. The small bed was moved into the front room when the illness came on. After that Mrs. Bartlett used to have the sofa made up in front of the fire, and she slept there.

By Mr. JUSTICE WILLS—I waited upon the Bartletts when Mr. Dyson was dining there. I have heard Mrs. Bartlett address him as Mr. Dyson and also as George while Mr. Bartlett was

Adelaide Bartlett.

present. I do not remember Mr. Dyson calling her anything. When Mr. Dyson came to the house I have seen books about, but I cannot say whether they were open. I did not know anything at the time about lessons being given. I do not know whether Mr. Dyson brought books with him.

EDMOND BLAKE, examined by Mr. POLAND—I am an inspector of the Metropolitan Police. I understand making plans and models, and I have often made them for Courts of justice. The plans which have been produced here are correct and to scale.

Mr. POLAND—That is the case, my lord.

Mr. CLARKE—I do not call any evidence.

Speech for the Defence.

Mr. EDWARD CLARKE—May it please you, my lord, gentlemen of the jury—In this case you have now heard, in its fullest detail, the evidence which the Crown has to lay before you in support of this charge, and, having heard that evidence, and believing that I have been able, to some extent, to trace the effect of it upon your minds, I now, in Adelaide Bartlett's name, claim from you a verdict of not guilty. It might be thought that one was speaking too confidently in using that sentence. Some of my friends might think that I had had sufficient experience of the sad uncertainties of the administration of the criminal law to induce me to pause before I used an expression which only the strongest confidence would justify. But, gentlemen, I think I shall justify that claim in the most absolute and complete form. I believe that when I have taken you, as it will be my duty to take you, through the record of the evidence of suspicion which has pointed to her guilt, and through that evidence more recently given, and which has, I think I shall show you, gone nearly to demonstrating her innocence, I think you will recognise that my claim is not too confident, and that it is a claim which you will admit and indorse.

I fear I shall have to detain you some time in discussing this case, for one reason, which only applies to cases where the Attorney or Solicitor-General appears for the prosecution. There is a strange anomaly in the procedure in such cases. In the ordinary cases, which are subjects of accusation and defence in these Courts, where the prosecution has produced all its evidence, and where, as is the case in nine cases out of ten, the prisoner not being allowed to give evidence, no evidence is offered, or could be offered, on the part of the defence—in all those cases, at the end of the evidence for the prosecution, the counsel who asks the jury, in the name of the Crown, to accept the charge that has been made, has then and there, at the close of the evidence, to point out to the

66 Gresham St,
April 24th

Dear Sir

Forgive me for not
earlier expressing
my heartfelt gratitude
to you. I feel that
I owe my life to
your earnest efforts
&, though I cannot
put into words, the
feelings that fill my
heart, you will
understand all
that my pen fails
to express to you.

Your kind looks
towards me, cheered
me very much, for
I felt that you
believed me innocent.
I have heard many
eloquent Jesuits preach
but I never listened
to anything finer
than your speach.
My story was a very
painful one, but
Sadly true, my consent
to my marriage was
not asked, I only

saw my husband once
before my wedding day.

I am
much gratified that
D.. Stevenson has written
to say that he concurs
in the verdict; he
wrote so kindly of

Miss Wood, who has
been a true friend,
I received great kind-
ness at Clarkesville,
from the Governor to the
lowest, they did their
best to comfort me.
Assuring you that
I shall ever remember
you with feelings
of deepest gratitude
I am
Sincerely yours
Michael P. Parker

Speech for the Defence.

Mr Clarke

jury the facts upon which he relies, to indicate upon what ground of suspicion or of evidence it is that he feels entitled to ask them for a verdict of guilty; and when he has so pointed out the grounds upon which, in his judgment and contention, that verdict could be justified, it is then the right of the counsel for the prisoner to make answer to the suggestions so put. But, strangely enough, in those cases in which the privilege and right is most important to the prisoner, the practice of our procedure takes it away; and although I call no witnesses, though I have to content myself with comments upon the evidence put before you, when I have finished, the leader of the English bar will have to answer me, will have an opportunity—I do not say that he will use it—of pointing to topics of suspicion or of proof, which I may not have appreciated, upon which, if he were to make his statement now as counsel for the prosecution, if this were some trivial case, such as those cases which are often tried in the other Courts, if he had to make that statement now, I should hear the comments, and might be able to answer them, but they will come to you when my lips are closed.

It is an anomalous privilege, and I do not hesitate to say, as I have said in this Court before, that I hope an Attorney-General may be found some day, unless the law is altered, as it should be, to abandon the exercise of a right which does not seem to me to be defensible. It has always been felt by the Attorney-General that the exercise of that right has to be under strict conditions; and nearly one hundred years ago a great Attorney-General, afterwards an illustrous judge, speaking as Sir John Scott, said that the principles upon which the Attorney-General spoke in a case of this kind were principles which forbade the exhibition of zeal on his part. I know that my learned friend will endeavour to be as fair in his reply as he was in his opening; but I know it well, by my own experience of the conduct of cases where one meets in forensic combat—I know that there is an instinct of antagonism aroused which the strongest determination to be absolutely impartial and fair could not by any of us be trusted to clear him from prejudice or from passion. And my learned friend, coming from a country distinguished far more for its advocates than for its judges, may import that combative instinct into the conduct of this case.

Gentlemen, that consideration obliges me to deal with all the topics that are before you, because, if I were to leave any out, it might suggest itself to your minds, or it might be suggested, that I have avoided a difficulty; and unless I met, as far as I could, all the suggestions which appear to me to arise upon the facts which have been put before you, I should run the most grievous risk—a risk not for myself, for it is a matter of no moment to me what comment might be made on my speech or my advocacy, but risk to one whose interests are present to me at this moment in a very

293

Adelaide Bartlett.

Mr Clarke

far higher degree than any consideration that could attach to myself.

Whatever the history of our medical jurisprudence may be, this case will long be remembered. There have been incidents in it, there have been topics dwelt upon, which will not easily be forgotten by any of those who interest themselves in the administration of the criminal law, or in subjects of medical science and of medical jurisprudence. We have had certainly strange incidents. I do not speak now of those remarkable relations which appear to have existed between Mr. Bartlett and his wife—relations which would be almost inconceivable if they had not been, as here they are, proved to be true. Nor do I speak at this moment of that other most remarkable incident in this case, which gave to the proceedings of the second day an intensely dramatic interest, when the man who had passed, with the consent and sanction of the Crown, from his place in the dock, who had been, by their consent and upon their invitation, declared by your verdict to be free from any imputation of crime in this matter, stood in that witness-box and heard the question which was put by my learned friend, Mr. Poland, with a rhetorical point which I do not think was present to his mind when he asked the question. "You gave your evidence before the coroner and then she was arrested"; and, having passed from the dock to the witness-box, it is in great measure upon the evidence that he has given that you are asked to rely in support of the charge against Mrs. Bartlett.

But, gentlemen, there is another consideration which I think has been presented to your minds. It is a marvellous thing that you are asked by the prosecution to accept—you are asked—and when I use that phrase I do not mean that you will be urged, but what I do mean is, that this is what you must accept if you accept the idea of guilt or the contention of guilt—you are asked to believe that a woman who, for years, had lived in friendship and affection with her husband; who, during the whole time of his illness, had striven to tend him, to nurse him, and to help him; who had tended him by day, who had sacrificed her own rest to watch over him at night, had spent night after night without going to her restful bed, simply giving to herself sleep at the bottom of his couch that she might be ready by him to comfort him by her presence; who had called doctors, who had taken all the pains that the most tender and affectionate nurse possibly could, that by no possibility any chance should be lost of the doctors ascertaining what his trouble was, and having the quickest means to cure it—that woman who had watched over him, had tried to cheer him, had talked of going away, had talked lightly when they were together before the doctor in order to give spirits to that husband—you are asked to imagine that that woman on

Speech for the Defence.

Mr Clarke

New Year's Eve was suddenly transformed into a murderess, committing crime, not only without excuse, but absolutely without any object—you are asked to believe that by a sort of inspiration she succeeds in committing that crime by the execution of a delicate and difficult operation, an operation which would have been delicate and difficult to the highest trained doctor that this country has in it.

There is another aspect in which this case will be of abiding interest, and the observation which I have just made leads me to it. This is the first case that the world has ever heard of in which it has been suggested that a person has been murdered by the administration of liquid chloroform. Just let me ask you to consider what a tremendous effect that proposition and that fact ought to have upon your judgment. Forty years ago it was discovered that by the administration of chloroform a state of insensibility might be produced during which the most terrible operations could be performed on the human frame without pain being suffered from the operation; and it was recognised, by all the members of that great profession which devotes itself to the study and to the treatment of human suffering, that here a great boon, a great blessing, had been found for man, and that many lives might be saved which would have passed away under the intense agony of the surgeon's knife, or even at the very thought of what that agony might be; and for the last forty years this chloroform, its qualities and effects, the mode of administration, the symptoms of the patient, the results either for life or death, have been a constant subject of inquiry by the medical profession.

You have had the good fortune to see in the witness-box two of the greatest living authorities upon these subjects. Than Dr. Stevenson and Dr. Tidy no witnesses could be brought here of greater authority as to the history and as to the character of this matter; and I know those two gentlemen well enough to know that when they go into the witness-box they, at all events, are absolutely clear from feeling, bias, or prejudice with respect to the case in which they are concerned, and that they, speaking from the witness-box, speak with a due and strong sense of responsibility for the evidence they are giving. Gentlemen, you have had the best information which you could possibly get on this subject, and what does it come to?—that never, during those forty years, has there been a case of murder by chloroform. There have been cases of death by chloroform—there have been cases of death from the swallowing of liquid chloroform. In the great majority of those cases death may have been death by suicide; in all the others, they have been death by the accidental taking or administration of that drug. There is no case recorded in the books, but during those forty years there have been criminals in this country and in other countries who would have used that poison if it had been

Adelaide Bartlett.

possible or likely to succeed. There have been men who have committed murders, who have been supplied with all the medical knowledge and experience that would be required for the purpose of the successful administration of this poison. There is no case of the kind, and you are called upon now—it is suggested to you that you should say that Adelaide Bartlett has committed an offence absolutely unknown in the history of medical jurisprudence, and the possibility of which has never been suggested in any book on this subject so far as we know—never.

Now, gentlemen, let us just consider for a moment what this means. These forty years having passed, I think you understand now how it is, for it has been your lot to listen yesterday and to-day to an exposition of all that is known on this subject from Dr. Stevenson and Dr. Tidy—I think you understand the reasons why chloroform never has been used, and probably never will be used, for the purpose of murder, because the administration of liquid chloroform is singularly variable in its effects. Instances are given where large doses of liquid chloroform have been taken, and the patient has lived afterwards. We hear of cases of persons swallowing 2 ounces, 4 ounces—I think I saw a case in that list of 6 ounces—of liquid chloroform, and yet of life being retained. There seems no rule at all : one case will give you the instance of a man who swallows liquid chloroform and walks for a considerable distance after he has done so ; another, a case which has attracted special notice in the list Dr. Stevenson supplied us with, a case where a man, twenty-six years of age, takes a very much smaller dose of chloroform, and in three minutes he was in a heavy sleep ; so that, as to its fatal effects, there are all sorts of variety. And there is also the same variety as to the symptoms. It may produce immediate or almost immediate coma ; it may produce convulsions ; it may produce with an ordinary dose vomiting ; it may, so far as I can see, produce no immediate effects at all ; in fact, the summing-up of the whole matter, the whole testimony of medical science with regard to chloroform, is that its administration requires to be watched with so great care in order to adjust it to the characteristics of the patient—that its effects, whether inhaled or swallowed, are so various in character—that it is not altogether a trustworthy agent for producing anæsthesia. It has already been succeeded by another, the administration of which is believed to be free from some of the difficulties and dangers which attend the administration of chloroform, and medical science can only say that its effects are so uncertain that its administration cannot be undertaken without great care and study.

But now, gentlemen, let me go a step further. If you were dealing with a case of the fatal inhalation of chloroform, there would not be the same difficulty. Science tells us that the stories of immediate insensibility produced by chloroform are mere fables,

Speech for the Defence.

Mr Clarke

because, if chloroform be administered in an overdose so strong, with so slight an admixture of air that it at once produces insensibility, that insensibility means immediate death. It is not here a question of death by the inhalation of chloroform; I shall have occasion presently to point out to you that if a person were trying to commit a murder by chloroform, and administered any chloroform to the victim so as to produce even partial anæsthesia, that they would almost certainly, either with medical knowledge or without medical knowledge, go on with the administration of the inhaled chloroform and produce fatal effects; and it is impossible to suppose that a person, with medical knowledge or without medical knowledge, either knowing all these difficult details or not, would interrupt the process of anæsthesia, which, if continued, must result in death, in order to attempt another and a difficult process, the immediate result of which might be to destroy the anæsthetic influence which had already been produced, and to revive the patient to the capacity of sensation or resistance. But it is not here death from inhalation of chloroform; what is alleged or suggested here is, death by chloroform poured down the throat; and I think you will quite understand that, although, of course, there can be no admission in cases of this kind, looking at the evidence and looking at the great authority of Dr. Stevenson and Dr. Tidy, it seems to me perfectly clear—if I am entitled to say so—that there was in the stomach of Mr. Bartlett a sufficient quantity of chloroform to indicate that he had taken what might have been a fatal dose. There are all sorts of limitations to that. No one can define what a fatal dose is. A fatal dose has sometimes been very small, and a large quantity has sometimes not produced death; but, seeing how small a quantity has sometimes on some occasions produced that fatal effect, it is impossible, I think, to suggest that the quantity which Dr. Stevenson found in the stomach did not indicate that death might have been caused by chloroform administered by the mouth. There are questions with regard to the condition of the mouth, and of the upper part of the throat, and of the throat, and of the air passages upon which, of course, I shall have a word to say at another time; but, for the moment, it seems to me that Dr. Stevenson's evidence is conclusive that there was sufficient chloroform in the stomach to indicate that a dose which might have been fatal had been taken, and there are no appearances which point to death from any other cause.

When we have taken that step, just observe how very serious is the next step which has to be taken by the prosecution. My learned friend the Attorney-General recognised it, and himself expressed the difficulty, at the close of his opening in this case, because he said chloroform could not be administered by inhalation to a resisting person if you wished to cause death; and he said murder could not be done by chloroform being poured down the

297

Adelaide Bartlett.

throat of any person unless he had previously been reduced to a condition, substantially, of insensibility, unless there had been a previous inhalation of chloroform, he being unwilling, and I do not think my learned friend is going to suggest acquiescence on the part of Mr. Bartlett.

The ATTORNEY-GENERAL—Certainly not.

Mr. CLARKE—Because he said it could not be poured down, he being unwilling, so that the person must have been reduced to a state by inhalation where swallowing was possible, and where also the power of resistance had disappeared.　Now let us see what step this is you are asked to take.　You cannot come, according to this suggestion or theory, to the conclusion that Mrs. Bartlett committed this crime unless you come to the conclusion that she first, by the administration of chloroform by inhalation, produced insensibility, and that she then poured down the insensible and unresisting throat the substance that caused the death.　Well, but the moment that that suggestion is made, we have before us almost an impossibility.　I have put myself in a position in this case to be able, without hesitation and fear, to challenge Dr. Stevenson and Dr. Tidy with respect to any matter contained in the recognised books of authority in England, and I have put the question to them as to an anæsthesia produced during sleep.　The suggestion is (and you must accept every step of it if you are to say that this accusation is proved) that, Mr. Bartlett being asleep, chloroform is administered to him by inhalation, which reduces him to a state of sufficient insensibility to prevent his resisting the administration of liquid chloroform, and that, being in that state, it is done. Why, gentlemen, that process is surrounded by difficulties, and by difficulties of a most serious kind.　Look at the very first step, the administration of chloroform by inhalation to a sleeping person.　I asked Dr. Stevenson : Is there any record in the English books upon this matter ?　There is not, except by reference.　One of those references is in Taylor's book on poisons, and it is the reference to a French authority—which book lies before me—and the sentence in which this French authority disposes of this question of the administration of chloroform by inhalation to a sleeping person points out the substantial impossibility of such administration—it points out, at all events, this : that such administration would involve the great overwhelming probability that the person would awake and resist.　This French authority speaks of experiments, and you will observe that the record of all these experiments is a record of experiments made by skilled chloroformists, familiar with the operation of chloroform and the administration of anæsthetics according to their best experience and under the most favourable conditions, and administering it, one cannot doubt, only to persons whom they had noticed as being patients upon whom it would be likely to produce a satisfactory effect, because it will

298

Speech for the Defence.

Mr Clarke

be perfectly clear to you that no physician would venture to try and administer chloroform to a sleeping person unless he believed that that person was of a character and idiosyncrasy to be satisfactorily operated upon; otherwise there would be, what you have been told in one of these cases, the sudden awakening to resistance, and the objection, "You are trying to give me something," and so undoubtedly eluding the operation. Now, those cases are attempts by skilled persons, under the best conditions, and most carefully done; and, of the cases which this French authority has been able to record, in 75 per cent. the persons awakened when the attempt was made, and the summing-up of the French authority on this matter is that it is possible to administer scientifically —let me read the passage again : " It is difficult, but often possible, to render persons who are in natural sleep insensible by chloroform with certain precautions : the employment of a pure spirit "—then come the words which I translated yesterday— " Grand habitude," " great skill "—but am not sure they are not better translated " long, or great, practice—are among the conditions which may favour the attempt to chloroform in that way." Then he goes on to say : " It is possible that certain subjects are absolutely refractory—that is to say, it will be impossible to anæsthetise them in spite of all the precautions that may be taken. Other persons, on the contrary, and little children by preference, will submit to anæsthetics without being aroused from their slumber by the irritation that the anæsthetic agent produces in the air passages."

Substantially that is the summing-up of that authority. Now, I asked Dr. Stevenson : Can you give me any other authority? There is no English one, and I confess I have not followed the American authorities on the subject with which we are now dealing. But there is no American authority in the shape of a treatise. " Wharton and Stillé," the book I produced yesterday, is a book referred to in one of our English treatises, and that gives the experiences of a doctor who, giving evidence at a trial, spoke of the attempts that he made. He had made the attempt on several persons—on six persons; experiments with chloroform on six sleeping persons, and out of that number all resisted more or less. Two were awakened up immediately, and one remarked, " You are trying to give me something."

So far with regard to the authorities upon that subject. Dr. Stevenson referred me to one other authority, and I followed it; and this morning he has brought the book. I find now that this exactly bears out the letter from Mr. Dobson, and exactly bears out the opinion given in the French book—that is to say, it indicates there is difficulty in the administration, and it speaks of the administration of chloroform in this way having been represented to be very rare, and it describes the operation of removing a tumour

Adelaide Bartlett.

Mr Clarke

from the side of the knee and the thigh, and here again you have young persons. I think there is one more reference, and that is in Dr. Tidy's own book. It is a reference to the *Lancet*, and by the kindness of the editor of the *Lancet* a set of *Lancets* for 1872 was put at my disposal yesterday. I turn to that to see what it gives, and I find it refers entirely to the administration of chloroform during sleep to children, and I find this (which is of great importance with respect to this matter), that the doctor who had so administered it to children goes on to say, " The only precaution I ever found necessary to prevent them from awaking with the first inspiration of the chloroform was that the inhaler should first be held at a moderate distance from the child's face, and gradually approached nearer until the requisite degree of anæsthesia was produced, which would be judged of by the usual signs."

There is only one more observation to be made on this, and it exhausts the whole subject. This morning we have had Dr. Tidy himself here, and we have had from him the record given with that absolute impartiality with which science speaks when it goes, in the presence of its distinguished representatives, into the witness-box to inform and advise the judge and jury. He says he had made three experiments (and you cannot doubt that those experiments were most carefully made—he is himself a most experienced chloroformist, and would know all the conditions under which these experiments might be properly and favourably made), the cases in which he tried it with children succeeding, but the cases in which he tried it with adults failed, and the persons awoke.

Now, gentlemen, what do you say as to the first step—the step of administering chloroform by inhalation to the sleeping person so as to produce insensibility, which would enable the subsequent administration of chloroform by the throat? Does not all the information that the best medical authorities can give us on the subject show to you it is in the highest degree improbable that an unskilled person would ever be able to transform sleep in anæsthesia by the influence of chloroform without waking the person who was subject to that process?

Just let me take one other step with regard to this. If death had followed on inhalation, there would probably be some appearances discoverable in the post-mortem examination. Those appearances would have become less definite as the time passed by after the administration of chloroform and death from it, and it was not Mrs. Bartlett's fault that her husband's body was not examined within a very few hours of his death. She was urging it —anxious for it—saying no expense should be spared in order for it to be done; and it was only by an accident—the doctor being that afternoon engaged—that her wish was thwarted, and that the post-mortem was postponed until the next day. But if it is not presumptuous in me to say so, the indications of chloro-

Speech for the Defence.

Mr Clarke

form poisoning by inhalation, in a post-mortem examination, are not very precise, and have a tendency to disappear during the time that elapses after death. But still, if there had been inhalation, one would expect to find some indications if there had been death very shortly after, and although that inhalation had not gone far enough to produce paralysis which might cause the death—paralysis of the heart and paralysis of the respiratory organs—still, one would expect to find, though in a smaller degree, indications that inhalation had taken place. And here, although one would not expect to find indications in so marked a degree as if death had happened from inhalation alone, still, as, according to the theory of the prosecution, the inhalation of chloroform must have taken place shortly before death to such an extent as to produce a very considerable amount of anæsthesia and insensibility, one would expect to find some indications. I do not desire to lay too much stress upon this argument, but it is an undoubted fact that none of the indications of inhalation of chloroform was ever found in this body. We have got from Dr. Stevenson, and have got also from Dr. Leach, who told you, and who told my learned friend, that he had (and it is quite natural) lately directed his attention to the study of this matter and the works on it. We have got from them a statement of what the results—the ordinary signs—of chloroform inhalation are. Dr. Stevenson agrees with Guy and Ferrier that the odour will be observable in the cerebral ventricles. He demurred to one statement in " Guy and Ferrier," but he said Guy and Ferrier were high authorities on the subject, and I put to him that quotation. He agrees with Snow that inhalation may be detected after death in the urine. He agrees that in many cases, again, as recorded by Snow and quoted by Taylor, engorgement of the right side of the heart is to be discovered.

Let us take these three as the signs. There is one other which I will refer to in a moment that Dr. Stevenson did not accept. What were the post-mortem conditions in this case? The brain was carefully examined. Nothing whatever was detected in it; no odour of chloroform whatever was detected by the skilled pathologist who, with adequate assistance, was making that post-mortem examination. Dr. Green has not been able to come and give his evidence as to that at this trial, but we know he is a person of great pathological skill, and I have a right to assume that he would be familiar with the symptoms of the mischief which it was his business to detect. Now, gentlemen, the heart is described : nothing abnormal ; the brain was carefully examined : nothing abnormal. The one other part in which signs of inhalation of chloroform can be found—the urine—was never examined by anybody. So that, so far as the post-mortem examination goes, I am entitled to say this—I do not wish to push it too far, because there may be an explanation, and the observation is not a very

Adelaide Bartlett.

Mr Clarke

strong one—but of all the indications of the inhalation of chloroform before death which are in the books of the authorities, and which are recognised by the witnesses before you, not one was found on the post-mortem examination of Mr. Bartlett's body. There was one other that I mention separately, because it was not accepted by Dr. Stevenson, although I put it to him from " Guy and Ferrier," and that was intense inflammation of the air passages. But I read the passage from " Guy and Ferrier " with respect to the results of poisoning by that class of poisons to which chloroform belongs, the poisons alcohol, ether, and chloroform; and I read the passage to him : " They act as irritants to the parts with which they come in contact, producing intense inflammation in the lining membrane of the stomach when swallowed, and in that of the air passages when inhaled." Though he did not entirely agree, as far as his experience goes, with that passage, he admits the book is one of considerable authority, and I am entitled to say that in the air passages of that body no trace of inhalation of chloroform was found.

I am going, gentlemen, by steps. I have shown to you the enormous (do you not think I may add the word adopted by Dr. Stevenson?), insuperable—I have shown to you the enormous, may I not say the almost insuperable difficulty of administering chloroform to a sleeping person without waking him, and I have shown you by medical science that, whether carried to the point of fatal insensibility or preceding death from another cause, it might leave—I put it no higher—indications which would be discoverable on post-mortem examination; and, if those indications were discoverable at all, they would be now catalogued to you, and not one of them is discovered in the body of Mr. Bartlett on post-mortem examination.

Now, let us suppose this almost miracle has been worked, and that an unskilled person, alone, without any assistance, has succeeded in administering chloroform to a sleeping man—a man, observe, who would be called a refractory subject, a man upon whom these anæsthetics did not easily produce effect, who had been with difficulty affected by nitrous oxide gas a short time before. Supposing all these enormous difficulties overcome, and this thing to have been effected, and the man to have passed under the influence of chloroform; well, there are many dangers, many things that might have promptly happened. The first stage of chloroform is described as intoxication, a sort of intoxication, and there is no doubt that very often in that early stage there would be noise, and violence, and movement, which one person could not restrain, at the very time that she was administering the chloroform herself. But there is another danger : the administering of chloroform produces generally, at some stage or other—sometimes a very early stage, and sometimes a late one—produces vomiting,

302

Speech for the Defence.

Mr Clarke

and it is not at all unimportant to notice that in this case there is no evidence of vomiting of any sort or kind.

But suppose these dangers passed by—and you will observe that I am now discussing what is the scientific possibility, what one can imagine to be done by trained chloroformists, and the experienced skill of a man like Dr. Stevenson or Dr. Tidy—suppose all these difficulties are surpassed and this wonderful result to have been effected, and the man to have passed quietly into a sort of anæsthesia, then what is probable with regard to the case? I put to Dr. Stevenson the stages through which a person ordinarily passes. I quite agree that those stages are not to be found in every case. There may, for instance, in some cases be no excitement, no delirious outcry, just as in some cases there may be no vomiting; the conditions are not constant, the symptoms are not always the same; but one is bound to take the ordinary history of a case of a person under the influence of chloroform. And what does Dr. Stevenson tell us with regard to that? There are four stages. The first stage is a stage of excitement; the second stage is one where that excitement is calming down towards insensibility—I am very reluctant to use words of my own in which, in matters of this enormous importance, the alteration of a single phrase might be of consequence, so I read the passage which I put to Dr. Stevenson, and which he adopted : " There are considered to be four stages in the administration of vapour. In the first, the patient becomes excited; in the second, he talks incoherently, and sensibility is diminished; in the third, he is unconscious, but the muscles are rigid; in the fourth, the muscles are completely relaxed, and the patient is perfectly insensible. Danger commences with the third stage." That closes that passage. Yesterday afternoon we heard from Dr. Stevenson what the condition of things would be in each of those stages with respect to the possibility of administering a liquid poison of this kind. In the first stage, assuming it to have existed—assuming that the sleep did not pass to a sort of state of coma at once, in which case the person administering the chloroform would have very little indication to guide him or her of the state in which the patient was—but assume the stages to be followed : in the first stage there would be this excitement, but there would be sensation; and a sensation of the entrance into the mouth and air passages, and over the tender surface of the mouth and throat, of this irritant poison would arouse the patient to resistance, as in the case of which the doctor in America spoke. Then, in the second stage, there would still be sensibility, and there would be the resistance to anything passing down the throat. Well, but then there would be the third stage. The third stage involves a rigidity of the muscles, and the jaw itself becomes rigid, and during that period of rigidity it would need force to open the mouth down which the person is intending to

Adelaide Bartlett.

Mr Clarke

pour the poison. I agree again, and again I admit it may be presumptuous of me to use the word, but I agree that the duration of this rigidity differs enormously in different cases : on the one hand, the transition from the state of insensibility to complete anæsthesia may take place within the compass of two minutes, while, on the other, the experienced doctor administers more chloroform if he thinks it necessary, and as far as he thinks it necessary, and he cannot produce that state of anæsthesia in less than eight minutes. Just as the period of the whole four stages varies, so the period of rigidity would vary, and you might have a case in which the rigidity would last for a very few seconds, and you may have a case—that is Dr. Tidy's experience—in which for four minutes the jaw might be rigid, and during that time it is impossible there can be, without violence and force which no single person could use, the administration of chloroform. But when that rigidity has passed away, you come to the next stage. But then, according to this distribution of the stages of the effects of chloroform, the next stage is one in which the muscles are completely relaxed, and the patient is perfectly insensible. But when the muscles are relaxed, and the patient is insensible, you cannot get any liquid down the throat at all because of the act of swallowing. It is proved in evidence before you. Dr. Murray talks of the administration of this liquid by a tube, and in answer to the question, not from me only, but from the learned judge, the witnesses have described how the act of swallowing is a voluntary process, and in ordinary conditions it requires the voluntary function of different muscles in order that the substance that passes to the mouth shall pass to the gullet and down to the stomach, and shall pass over the opening of the air passages through which we speak without any portion of it getting into the air passages and causing violent irritation and rejection of it. There is a reflex action of the muscles which lasts for some time after the voluntary action has ceased, and there is a time when the reflex action will be excited by the contact of substances with the muscles of the throat, and the act of swallowing will be performed; but if the act of swallowing is not completely performed, if the action is not regular, full, and complete in its effect, the great probability will be that some of the substance will get into the air passages, it would cause choking on its reception into the air passages, and, if it did so in a case where death afterwards occurred, undoubtedly there would be found, which was not found in this case—there would be found evidence in the condition of the air passages of the transit of this irritant poison.

But now, gentlemen, what does this evidence come to? Dr. Stevenson says in this delicate and varying operation of administering chloroform by inhalation there is a time, or there may be a time, the duration of which no one can measure, the

Speech for the Defence.

Mr Clarke

existence and the conditions of which it is scarcely possible for the most careful doctor to predict, and there may be an instant of time or a few instants during which the patient would be so far insensible as not to detect or resent the administration of the poison—so far insensible as not to do that, and yet with sufficient remains of sensibility about him for the muscles to exert their reflex action, and the act of swallowing to take place. Supposing that possible, supposing that time whose duration no man can measure, the indication of whose presence no one but the most experienced man can detect, suppose that time to exist, you are asked to believe that that woman that night, alone with her husband, performed on him this marvellous operation. I put to Dr. Stevenson yesterday, towards the end of my cross-examination, a question in which I ventured to sum up and repeat to him the whole result of the cross-examination which I had directed to this point. Consider who it was with whom we are dealing. I was dealing with that scientific authority whose name is quoted by Taylor in his book as having made two hundred administrations of chloroform at Guy's Hospital, one who knows, if any man living does know, exactly the conditions under which chloroform may be administered, the precautions which are to accompany that administration, and the indications that will be given of the condition of the patient, and I ventured to put to him this question : " With all your knowledge, experience, and skill, if you had before you the problem—the object of administering chloroform in this liquid form in order to produce the death of a person sleeping before you—would it not be a delicate and difficult operation?" and Dr. Stevenson's experience gave me back the answer that it would be. Even to him, with all his knowledge, with all his experience, it would be a difficult operation and a delicate operation.

Why, gentlemen, I confess, when I had that answer, I thought that, if this had been an ordinary case, the counsel for the Crown would have felt bound to reconsider the position that they had assumed with respect to it, and that the learned judge, listening to that answer and appreciating, as I am sure he does appreciate, the great weight and importance of it, coming from Dr. Stevenson, must have himself considered how far the result of that cross-examination had modified the right of the Crown to continue the prosecution, and had left it possible for a jury to be allowed with safety to consider it as still evidence upon which they might base a conviction.

Before I leave it, there is just one more observation I want to make. I put to Dr. Murray (and I attach great importance to the answers which Dr. Murray gave at the end of his examination, and when I was permitted by my lord to put some more questions, and when, I think, one or two members of your body put

Adelaide Bartlett.

Mr Clarke

questions to him)—I have put to the medical witnesses the question
of how they can tell when insensibility has been sufficiently produced for the feeling of pain to disappear, and for it to be possible
for the operation to be proceeded with. They say, fairly enough,
that in many of the cases in which chloroform is used it is not
necessary to produce entire insensibility, and the chloroform is
used not altogether for that purpose, but only to dull the sense of
pain; but I asked Dr. Murray, " In administering chloroform for
the purpose of performing an operation, must you not try and
determine the exact time when insensibility begins, that you may
with safety commence the operation?" How does he do it? He
touches the eye, and then he notes whether the reflex action of the
muscles produces the winking movement of the eyelids. While
that reflex action of the muscles exists, he does not perform the
operation, because there will be pain and may be resistance; when
the reflex action of the muscles has ceased, then the operation may
be safely performed. But when the reflex action of the muscles
has ceased no doctor can say which portion of the body, which set
of muscles, has lost the capacity for reflex action, and in which
reflex action may still remain. It is not believed that reflex action
of all the muscles disappears at the same time. But the answer of
Dr. Murray fixed it to this knowledge by his experience, that,
when the reflex action of the eyelids has disappeared, the sense of
pain has practically gone; but, for all they know, the reflex action
of the muscles has then disappeared, and when that reflex action of
the muscles is gone, although it is possible to pour chloroform into
the mouth of a person in a recumbent position and let it stay
there, and although, to use Dr. Murray's words, " I think some
of it would trickle down the throat," the poison would be kept in
contact with the softer substance of the mouth, and that so long
that, as he stated in answer to a question from one of yourselves,
one would have looked for, and must have found, appearances
about the mouth and upper part of the throat which were entirely
absent in the case with which you have to deal.

Now, gentlemen, I hope you do not think I have kept you
too long and dwelt with too much detail on this, the scientific,
aspect of the case. I have striven to get rid, as far as I can, of
the scientific terms and phrases which might convey meanings to
the experienced physicians, but which would be unfamiliar to the
experience of yourselves and, I may say, myself. But I hope I
have shown you, by tracing this process from end to end, that
the difficulty is established not merely by the evidence of Dr.
Stevenson, but that this difficulty is established by different testimony with regard to every step of the process which we get from
the best authorities who have spoken and written on this subject,
whether in England, France, or America.

I hope I have justified to you what I said a little while ago,

Speech for the Defence.

Mr Clarke

that this case will be long memorable in the annals of medical jurisprudence. It is not only an accusation which is strange as viewed by the light of the previous relations existing between husband and wife, but it is an accusation against one who was, so far as we know, absolutely unstudied in the ways of medicine; who, from what she said herself (and, indeed, it is clear), knew little indeed of chloroform, the mode of its administration, and the objects that it would serve; and it is an accusation against her that she, alone in the room with her sleeping husband, has succeeded (was I not right in saying almost by inspiration?) in performing one of the most difficult and delicate operations possible to be performed, and has so succeeded that no trace, no spilling of chloroform by the nervous hand, no effects through the chloroform having been allowed to remain long in contact with the soft passages, no traces in the post-mortem condition of the body, reveal the fact that she had succeeded in doing that most difficult and delicate operation.

And so, gentlemen, I pass over the scientific aspect of the case—one, I am sure, which will not be allowed to escape your very careful attention, and one as to which I venture most respectfully to say that the result of the considerations which I have put before you (considerations in which I have striven to deal, with the most absolute fairness, with the evidence that has been given in this Court)—I submit to you that the result of those considerations makes it impossible for you to return a verdict of guilty in this case.

But now, gentlemen, I pass to the other matters with which I have to deal, and I want to make an observation or two at this point with reference to what I said a little while ago as to the possibility of the learned Attorney-General, in his reply, pointing out to you and dwelling upon topics of suspicion and of prejudice. I have carefully read the note of the speech in which the learned Attorney-General opened this case, and he dealt then quite fairly— for nothing could have been more fair and temperate and careful than the opening in which he introduced to your mind the consideration of this matter, and he alluded to several smaller matters in terms which showed that they were matters which might possibly, it was thought, affect your minds, and would point in the one direction of suggesting the guilt of Mrs. Bartlett. There were several of them. I hope I am not too confident in saying that they have absolutely disappeared under the test of cross-examination, and that there is not one of those suspicious circumstances which survives the examination which we have made. Let us take them in order.

It was pointed out to you that on the evening before her husband's death Mrs. Bartlett spoke about chloroform, and we know now from the evidence what that conversation was. On the

Adelaide Bartlett.

Mr Clarke

evening of that day, after Mr. Bartlett had come back from the dentist's, Mrs. Doggett went into the room. Mr. Bartlett talked to her. Mrs. Bartlett was reading at the table, but in the conversation which ensued Mrs. Bartlett did interpose. Mr. Bartlett was talking about what had happened during that day. He had had a tooth drawn, and it is said Mrs. Bartlett asked, " Did you ever take chloroform? " of Mrs. Doggett, and Mrs. Doggett said she had taken it some years before, upon which she was asked whether it was nice, or pleasant. She was not quite sure which was the word used, but there was the impression of the question, and she answered she did not remember, it was so long ago. I dare say, gentlemen, you will have observed that that conversation was at least as likely to suggest to Mr. Bartlett the idea of himself taking chloroform as it was to be connected with any thought of murder in the mind of Mrs. Bartlett. But just let us consider when that conversation with Mrs. Doggett was. We were not given in detail or with exactness the whole course of the conversation. It was not expected that we should. We often expect far too much from witnesses when we expect from them in the witnessbox the exact detail and language, the record of every conversation which, at the time it was uttered, could not suggest to them the importance which subsequent events have given to it. But we know now that on that afternoon Mr. Bartlett had been to the dentist's. We know that on the previous occasion he had had his gums treated by a local application producing cold and destroying the sense of pain when teeth were taken out, and I think—I am not quite certain, but I think he mentioned to Mrs. Doggett the fact of having his gums frozen. Whether that was so, that was the fact that he had had his gums frozen in order to prevent the sense of pain. On this occasion—that very afternoon—he had had a tooth extracted, and he had it extracted in a different way, and he had taken nitrous oxide gas, and there had been a difficulty in his taking it. Now, to the common inexperienced person nitrous oxide gas and chloroform are not very distinct. In either case there is the application of vapour—the inhalation of vapour for purposes of producing insensibility to pain. Do you think the fact that Mr. Bartlett on that evening talking to Mrs. Doggett about having his tooth out that afternoon, and having it present to his mind that he had been saved from pain by means of an anæsthetic never used with him before—do you not think it is in the highest degree probable that when Mrs. Doggett was talking to Mr. Bartlett he might have mentioned the way it was effected, and, if that was so, the most natural way of joining in the conversation would be, Did you ever have anything of the kind? Did you ever have chloroform? and the whole thing is explained. And I do beseech you, looking at the weight you are to give to the evidence as to conversations, which, as I point out, at the

Speech for the Defence.

Mr Clarke

time they occurred the persons never imagined would have any importance at all—I beseech you to consider for yourselves what, in your judgment, would have been the reasonable and probable course of the conversation between Mrs. Bartlett and Mrs. Doggett on that evening.

Just let me take another thing. I shall have to point out to you by-and-by, with regard to the evidence of one of the witnesses in this case, the way in which the moment the death had occurred all sorts of accusations and suspicions were suggested. But we have from Mrs. Doggett a statement on which some emphasis has been laid in this case. Gentlemen, I beg your pardon, I have omitted one matter which comes before it in order of time, and I will go back to it for a moment. There were two matters mentioned, also as matters of suspicion, of which the servant spoke, and which happened on the evening before the death. One was that, instead of taking, as she was told to take, the basin into the room, she was told not to come into the room again, but to leave the basin on the table outside. The other is almost too trivial to mention, but, as I have said, I must guard myself with reference to every matter of this kind—the fact that Mrs. Bartlett had not the same dress on when she awoke the servant as when the servant saw her in the evening. Let me say one word on each of those matters. The incident about the basin has absolutely disappeared, I venture to say, under the test of cross-examination, for what happened about it was this. Alice Fulcher told us that Mrs. Bartlett told her after supper to bring up a scuttle of coals and the basin, and it was at the same time she gave her the instructions about the two things. Alice Fulcher brought up the scuttle of coals, but did not bring up the basin. She took the scuttle of coals into the room at the time Mr. Bartlett was in bed. He was not in bed when the order was given, but he was in bed when she took the scuttle of coals in the room, and then Mrs. Bartlett spoke about the basin, and told her "not to bring the basin in, but to leave it outside." There is the whole thing from beginning to end, and it is perfectly obvious that the order was given to the servant to bring up the two things; she brought up one, and took it into the room, and Mr. Bartlett was in bed, and, as we have heard, was probably trying to get some sleep, and so she told her not to bring it in, but to leave it outside, and she left it outside. There was a table outside, and on that Alice Fulcher put the basin. It was there in the morning; it was not used. It would have been used in the course of the night for the beef tea, probably, because Mrs. Bartlett kept Liebig's extract in the room, and was in the habit of keeping a fire throughout the night and making beef tea for her husband, but unfortunately on that night there was no occasion or opportunity for her to administer beef tea to him.

Adelaide Bartlett.

Mr Clarke

About the dress, is that to be a matter for suspicion? It is surely the most obvious thing in the world. Mrs. Bartlett had been out that day with her husband. After the illness began, when Mr. Bartlett's bedstead was removed into the front room, Mrs. Bartlett never occupied the bed which she had previously occupied alone in the back room, but she slept upon the sofa, moved it in front of the fire, and she slept, as Dr. Leach tells us, sitting in that small chair at the bottom of her husband's bed, or lying on the sofa. But in the evening she used to go into that back room to wash, and Alice Fulcher tells us the washing-basin was generally used late in the evening in that back room. She cannot say whether it was used on that particular evening, but at all events that was the ordinary course of things. Is it not obvious that what usually took place would take place, that Mrs. Bartlett, when her husband had gone to bed, and was settling himself for the night, would go into that room to wash before returning to her post and her place for the night? She would take off the dress in which she had been out; she would put on some dress in which she would be comfortable and easy throughout the hours of the night, and we are told by one of the witnesses that the dress she then had on was a grey, and a sort of a loose jacket with it, and Alice Fulcher said it was a lighter and looser dress than the one she had worn during the day.

There are other matters on which greater stress was laid, and I ask you to consider what the real evidence with regard to them is. How about the condition of the fire? What is the evidence with regard to that? Mr. Doggett said he noticed the fire when he was called in. He noticed the fire looked as if it had been recently attended to. Mrs. Doggett comes and says the same thing. It is very remarkable about that Mr. Doggett that when he was examined first before the coroner he did not say a syllable about the fire. It cannot have impressed itself very strongly on his mind, or he would probably have mentioned it when first examined. Until his wife had been examined, and had mentioned about the fire, Mr. Doggett (whether it occurred to him or not) had not mentioned it before the coroner. So I asked the wife in cross-examination with regard to this condition of the fire. Dr. Leach, as you remember, did not remember anything about the fire at all. I asked the wife about the condition of the fire. Did not her answers put an end to the suggestion—the idea of anything remarkable about the fire? I asked her whether she had at anytime had the sad experience of watching through the night by a sick bed? She said she knew something of it. She admitted —as any woman would admit—that at night, especially with a patient at all suffering from sleeplessness and restlessness, it would be the most manifest duty of the person watching to pack the fire, to build it up and make it last for hours, that it might

310

Speech for the Defence.

Mr Clarke

go for a sufficient number of hours without being closely attended to. Then I asked: Did not this look like a fire that had been packed and remained packed, and was then broken with a touch of the poker—just a fire well packed, and after some hours, when it was crusted over, broken up with the poker, and the hot coal prepared for immediate combustion flames up and breaks into a good fire at once? She said yes, that was the appearance it presented; it must have been an appearance following on that. Is not that the most obvious thing in the world? Mrs. Bartlett, preparing for sleep that night, and having her husband composed and quiet for the evening, as she hopes, to get the sleep which strenuous efforts had been made to obtain for him, would pack the fire in that way, and when she came down from the servant's room, after sending her for the doctor, and calling down people to come to her in the room where her husband lay—is it not one of the most natural things to do to take up the poker and break up the fire into the condition in which it was seen?

Well now, gentlemen, there is one more matter of suspicion against Mrs. Bartlett with which it is my duty to deal, although not entirely at this point, but I mention it because it leads me to some other observations which I desire to offer very respectfully to your consideration on this subject. It is the matter alleged against Mrs. Bartlett of her having made untrue statements to Mr. Dyson with respect to Dr. Nichols and Annie Walker, and the relation which had existed between herself and them. I shall be obliged to discuss by-and-by some matters connected with Dr. Nichols and Annie Walker, although I should not pursue them to any very great length, but this brings me to the observation as to the position of Mr. Dyson. This matter mainly depends upon the evidence, and upon the recollection, of Mr. Dyson, because it is from him that you have got the evidence that Mrs. Bartlett told him that her husband had been to Dr. Nichols; that her husband was suffering from an internal complaint; that she had administered chloroform for the purpose of soothing him in these paroxysms, and that Annie Walker was the person who had obtained the chloroform for her, and could no longer obtain it because she had gone to America. Now, in outline, as completely as I can recall it, that is the statement alleged by Mr. Dyson to have been made by her, and to have been, so the prosecution suggests, untruly made. But, gentlemen, I cannot comment upon this point of the case without remarking what I think must have at once rushed on your minds, that, if the making of an untrue statement is any evidence of guilt, it is somewhat strange that Mr. Dyson was in the witness-box. Now observe, so far from challenging in the least the course which has been taken with regard to Mr. Dyson, I accept the conclusion at which the Crown arrived, that there really was no case to be submitted to you which you

Adelaide Bartlett.

could be fairly asked to consider against him. If my learned friend had thought that there had been any such case, of course he would not have taken the course which he did take. I am not suggesting that there is. I accept—may I add that I believe?— in the correctness of the verdict which you were invited by the Crown to give, and that Mr. Dyson is free from complicity in any crime, if crime were perpetrated. But when you are being asked to deal with the case against Mrs. Bartlett, and to use against her, or to allow to be used against her, with grave effect, the untruthful statements which she has made, and which come to you upon Mr. Dyson's evidence, and as he remembers, or says he remembers, has it not occurred to you in the course of this case that if matters of this kind are to have great weight, how fortunate Mr. Dyson is that he is not standing there himself? I beg you to note that I do not impeach his innocence in the least. I wish that no word I may say may appear to suggest—it would not be true if it did suggest—any doubt in my mind with regard to the matter. But supposing his case were before you, what would you have? That Sunday morning he walked along the side of Tooting Common on his way to preach at a chapel, and as he went he threw from him, with the gesture which you saw him use in that box, the three or four bottles that had been in his possession. Suppose some one who knew him had seen him walking along that morning, and had seen him fling away the bottles, and had thought, "It is a little odd that the Rev. Mr. Dyson should be tossing bottles away on Tooting Common on Sunday morning," and had had the curiosity to pick up a bottle, and had found it labelled "Chloroform. Poison." Suppose it had come to light, at the first meeting of the inquest, that Mr. Dyson was an habitual visitor at the house where this death had taken place; suppose it had come to light that he had been in the habit of walking out with Mrs. Bartlett, and that she had visited him at his own lodgings; suppose it came to light that the terms on which he was dealing with Mr. and Mrs. Bartlett were terms of an exceptional character, having regard to the circumstances and relations between him and the wife; and suppose it had come out by inquiry at the chemist's—whose name is on the label—that, when Mr. Dyson asked for the chloroform he had told him a falsehood, that he wanted it for stains on his coat—to take out stains which had come on his coat during his holiday at Poole—what would have been Mr. Dyson's position? That strange and hard man, Richard Baxter, used to say that he never saw a criminal going to execution without observing to himself, "There, but for the grace of God, goes Richard Baxter." I think Mr. Dyson will never in his life read the account of a trial for murder without thinking how heavily his own rash, unjustified conduct would have told against him if he had been put upon his trial.

Speech for the Defence.

Mr Clarke

I do not use this for the purpose of suggesting—I said I was anxious not to suggest, for I do not entertain the slightest doubt as to the innocence of Mr. Dyson; but I do use it to show you that where against him, an innocent man, a falsehood told for the express purpose of getting this poison might have been proved in the witness-box, and might have been considered by the jury with so fatal an effect, it would be hard indeed that the statement from the lips of that very man that Mrs. Bartlett told to him a story which was not wholly true, to explain her desiring to possess this chloroform through him—it would be strange indeed if that were allowed to weigh upon your minds as a serious element of suspicion against her.

Now, gentlemen, I said that I must make this observation before I dwelt upon the relations of Dr. Nichols and Annie Walker to this case. What is it that Dyson says? He says that he was told Mr. Bartlett had an internal complaint, and that he had consulted Dr. Nichols, and that that internal complaint produced paroxysms for which chloroform had been used, and that the chloroform was provided by Annie Walker, and that she had gone to America. I suggest that it is impossible to rely upon Mr. Dyson's recollection with regard to that matter. You may have your own opinion whether upon some points in this case Mr. Dyson's evidence is readily and fully to be accepted so far as it concerns himself. I think you will have reason to see, from an observation I shall presently make, that at all events there is very strong ground for the suspicion that he has been anxious to protect himself without much regard to the actual truth in his relation to Mr. and Mrs. Bartlett. And I suggest to you that you cannot rely upon the entire accuracy of these statements. But, gentlemen, the curious thing is this: that, when one comes to look into the facts of the case, these statements are very near the truth in many respects. I do not say true as they are given by Dyson, but at all events Dr. Nichols of Fopstone Road is mentioned, and there is a Dr. Nichols of the Fopstone Road. Whether Mr. Bartlett ever saw Dr. Nichols or not, we do not know. Dr. Nichols does not know, he does not remember any such name; but he keeps no record of the names; and it was hardly necessary for me to suggest, in my questions with regard to some matters upon which Dr. Nichols might be consulted, that a person who went to an unregistered medical practitioner, to consult him with regard to his own position, would in very many cases be very unlikely to give his own name. But Mrs. Bartlett had known Mrs. Nichols, who practised at the very same place, and it was through Mrs. Nichols that Annie Walker was recommended to Mrs. Bartlett. For what reason Mrs. Nichols was consulted by Mrs. Bartlett you cannot know, for Mrs. Nichols is dead; and Dr. Nichols knows nothing whatever about the matter. Mrs. Bartlett's account you

Adelaide Bartlett.

cannot hear, but the fact that Mrs. Nichols had been consulted is clear, and this also is clear—that Mr. Bartlett had in his possession this book of Dr. Nichols, to which reference has been made, and that when Annie Walker, the midwife who was recommended by Mrs. Nichols, was staying at the house in order to discharge her duties, this book was there. Before Mr. and Mrs. Bartlett it was made no secret of; it was shown to the nurse; it was talked about between them, and considered, and I shall submit to you, rightly considered, as a book the having of which, and the reading of which, involved no reproach upon anybody. Mr. Dyson says he does not remember hearing Dr. Nichols' or Mrs. Nichols' name mentioned with regard to the matter of the confinement; but he does admit something with regard to Annie Walker which, I think, is of considerable importance. Annie Walker's name was not mentioned first to him at Claverton Street when there came to be a question of obtaining chloroform. Annie Walker's name was mentioned one day when he was by the cemetery at Merton, and you cannot doubt how that mention came about. I am not sure that he admitted or recollected that at that time there was conversation about there once having been one child, or anything of that kind; but is it not perfectly obvious to you that the connection in which Annie Walker's name would be mentioned to him would be that, he and Mrs. Bartlett passing the cemetery, it might suggest to her the loss—which was a heavy loss to her at the time—the loss of all the hopes she had formed that their married life might give her a child to love and to grow up into her companionship? Here, at all events, was mentioned Annie Walker, and the mention of Annie Walker was long before there was any mention of chloroform. But supposing Mrs. Bartlett did tell Mr. Dyson about Annie Walker's getting the chloroform, cannot one understand why there was some concealment and some explanation of this kind, if Mrs. Bartlett's story is to be accepted by you? And I will show you reasons by-and-by for believing that it was absolutely true. If Mrs. Bartlett's account is to be accepted, the state of things was this: that the husband who so long had been, not unkind to her, but cold, was desiring again to assert his marital rights; that he, acting quite freely, had in effect given her to Dyson, had recognised the marriage which after his death might come to pass between these two, and had provided, as far as he could, for that contingency by making Dyson the executor of his will, by which the money was all left to Mrs. Bartlett—her statement is that, he again desiring to assert these rights, she felt, under those circumstances, that it would be a wrong to her womanhood to allow the revival of these long-ceased relations. Could she be expected to tell Mr. Dyson that? Could any woman with any delicacy at all have explained it so to Mr. Dyson? She gave him some

314

Speech for the Defence.

reason for desiring to obtain chloroform, and, when you come to look at it as explained by him in answer to my cross-examination here, it is not far from the explanation which she gave afterwards to Dr. Leach. Mr. Dyson's idea, he says, was that she would sprinkle drops upon the handkerchief, and that she would use that handkerchief for the purpose of soothing Mr. Bartlett, and if that were so, and those were the words in which it was communicated, is it not perfectly intelligible that Mrs. Bartlett should desire to veil by that sort of account and explanation the real truth which she could not be expected to communicate to Mr. Dyson.

I know how extraordinary are the relations which are alleged to have existed between these persons. I said before that these relations would be almost inconceivable if they were not proved. I am going to show you that they are proved, or substantially proved; and I shall show you that under Mr. Bartlett's own hand, by that letter which has been put in evidence, and which I shall ask you carefully to consider. But for a moment I am suggesting to you that this explanation by Mrs. Bartlett of the reason for which she wanted the chloroform— this veiled and hinted suggestion to Mr. Dyson, from whom she would have every reason in her delicacy for concealing the right purpose and object of her getting it—that that is by no means an untruth which should bear with it such fatal suspicion of its being an indication of a criminal purpose as would have attached to the falsehoods told by Mr. Dyson when he tried to get the chloroform, if Dyson himself were the person against whom this evidence was to be taken, and with regard to whose evidence it would be applicable.

The Court adjourned for a short time. After the adjournment,

Mr. CLARKE proceeded—Gentlemen, at the time the Court adjourned, I had been dealing with the question of the statements made by Mrs. Bartlett as to Dr. Nichols and Annie Walker. There is only just one word which I think I ought to say further with regard to that. I have pointed out to you that we do not know, and cannot know, what communication there may have been at some time between Mr. Bartlett and Dr. Nichols. I dare say that you will have observed that there were peculiarities about the earlier and about the later symptoms of the illness which commenced on 9th December which suggested to the doctor first called a cause for some of those symptoms which were not further investigated. But that Mr. Bartlett had something wrong with him no one can doubt, at all events if one accepts the evidence of Mr. Dyson. I am in this difficulty with regard to

315

Adelaide Bartlett.

the evidence that Mr. Dyson has given. That evidence may be trusted by you entirely, or may be trusted by you in part and with certain limitations; but, with regard to the facts which do not affect his interests after the death had taken place, I suggest to you that Mr. Dyson has given us the evidence of truth, and the only reason that I can see for doubting whether the whole of that evidence is true, in the sense that it is the whole truth, is that undoubtedly, when the death occurred, considerations came crowding upon the mind of Mr. Dyson suggesting to him injuries, in consequence of the result of that inquiry, upon his after-career which possibly affected to some extent the candour of the statements which he made with regard to anything that took place after the death. But if you believe Mr. Dyson as to facts, there was something wrong with Mr. Bartlett. A man does not stop in the midst of his dinner, and clutch at his side, and complain of pain, unless there is some reason for it. I do not suggest to you that there was much reason for it; but what I do suggest to your consideration is this, that in the statement, possibly—probably—of its relation to the question of chloroform, which was made to Mr. Dyson by way of explanation, at all events there is a foundation of truth in a part of it.

I shall not now, and I will not at any time in this case, pursue that question as to the nature of the indications of disease that were found in Mr. Bartlett's mouth, established at the time of Dr. Leach's first examination. It is not from any scruple as to speaking of it that I hesitate to do so. Of all those maxims that have passed through the centuries, and exercised an influence on men's minds, in my judgment the most mischievous of all is that which tells men only to speak good of the dead. It has enfeebled the moral judgment of the world, and I for one will never recognise it as an authority. But those considerations have no place here, and I do not think that it is necessary I should follow into and examine the possible causes, curious though they may have been, of the condition of the mouth when Dr. Leach saw it, and of the ultimate necrosis which set in, according to Dr. Leach's account, on 29th, 30th, and 31st December. But the marital relations which existed between Mr. and Mrs. Bartlett are certainly matters of very serious consideration. In the first place, just let me point this out to you. Mrs. Bartlett was apparently an estimable woman. The women, few in number though they were—only two, so far as we know—who came into personal communication with her, saw nothing in her to dislike. Mrs. Matthews was her friend; and Mr. and Mrs. Matthews were the persons, the only persons, who visited Mr. and Mrs. Bartlett in their home. But she had made one other friend. By the introduction of Mrs. Nichols, she made the personal acquaintance of Annie Walker; and Annie Walker, who spent with her four weeks before her confinement,

Speech for the Defence.

Mr Clarke

and spent with her those other three weeks when the disappointed mother—the mother without a child—was gradually recovering strength from the painful illness which had tried and torn her—Mrs. Walker had undoubtedly conceived for her an affectionate friendship, and the poor woman, so to speak, in the solitude of her life had taken to her friendship this hired companion of her hours of suffering; and from time to time Annie Walker went to see her, and gave her portrait to her, and seems to have been attracted by her character and her disposition. At all events, there was nothing in her or about her that alienated a woman's affection from her, and prevented that affection becoming habitual and constant.

Now, the question of the marital relations of Mr. and Mrs. Bartlett is remarkable, and is a very curious question, and it is one which connects itself, in my judgment, very much with this woman. And I venture to say that, looking at all the circumstances of the case, I am glad that statement was brought out by Mr. Dyson with regard to Dr. Nichols and Annie Walker. For if it had not been for that statement, although I feel that it may prejudice her case before you, and that it will be used to show—and it is the only instance in the case in which her statements diverge from the truth—although it will be used to show there was that divergence, I am glad that it was brought out, for that connection with Dr. Nichols and his wife directly bears upon the extraordinary moral relations of Mr. and Mrs. Bartlett. Gentlemen, those moral relations were so strange that it is only upon the most conclusive evidence that one would accept it. I am not prepared to admit that they are relations unparalleled in the experience of one's life. There are many cases where, for different reasons, either in the husband or in the wife, the sacred relationship of marriage becomes simply a companionship of love, of confidence, and of mutual help; and there have been many cases—and, so long as our nature is subject to the ailments which afflict it, there will be many cases—where a wife or a husband has been called upon to bear a burden for years of the companionship of married life with the denial of its entire happiness and enjoyment; and hundreds and thousands of men and women have gone forward on that life, and have borne it as Christians may bear it, and with a resignation which after a time would become even use. But in this case I quite agree it is so exceptional a relation that you need very strong evidence of its existence; and I look to see what evidence there is in this case with regard to that matter. That Mr. Bartlett himself was a man of strange ideas does not depend, in this case, upon one witness. I call your attention to a most singular fact. In the first sentence of that statement that was made by Mrs. Bartlett on 26th January to Dr. Leach she said that her husband was a man of strange ideas—who had an idea,

Adelaide Bartlett.

when he married her, that a man might have two wives, one for service and the other for companionship; and it is a strange thing that, curiously enough, there are two witnesses who corroborated that specific statement. I do not rest upon the evidence of Mr. Dyson. If that stood alone, I agree it would not be so material. But the other witness is a witness from whom a single word of evidence in favour of Mrs. Bartlett is a treasure beyond price to the counsel who defends her. It is that witness whose sordid and vengeful malice nourished the idea of murder, suggested it at the first moment, dwelt upon it, worked to establish it; that is the witness who did not shrink from coming into that witness-box, and repeating, against the widow of his dead son, the foul slander from which that son protected her while he was here. He it is from whom I get the acknowledgment; and he says, " I remember once he told me that a man might have two wives," and he spoke of it. How came he to remember it? He tried to weaken its force, to destroy its effect, by putting in the observation, " I heard a man say yesterday that he would like forty," and a laugh was caused, as possibly he expected. But the observation of which he spoke about his son, the observation as to a man having two wives, is an observation which had fixed itself upon his recollection, and he admitted that when I put it to him; and the very same observation as to the two wives was made by Mr. Dyson. When Mr. Dyson gave his evidence in the box, and spoke of that observation, and I was cross-examining about it, do you remember the question that my lord put upon his evidence? " Was it said jocosely or seriously? " Mr. Dyson used a strange expression; and his answer to that question was, that at first it was put tentatively, and afterwards repeated more seriously; and Mr. Bartlett, if you can accept Mr. Dyson's evidence, and according to that evidence, did ask, as a serious question, of this minister of the Gospel, who was visiting at his house, whether it was consistent with the teaching of God's Word that a man should have two wives? Gentlemen, that was exactly what was said by Mrs. Bartlett in her statement to Dr. Leach. There may be this question about it, and I pressed Mr. Dyson on the point—" Did you understand that he meant two wives, each of whom was to enjoy the full companionship and personal affection of the husband? " Mr. Dyson put that aside: " Oh, he never mentioned it with regard to himself; it was a general observation." But do you believe that Mr. Bartlett, speaking to a man whom then he knew only as a minister of a place of Christian worship, to which he himself went, that he seriously suggested to him that a man should be allowed to have two wives in the full sense of the term?

There may be an explanation, and I confess that I think it is found in this book. I have had occasion, of course, to examine this

Speech for the Defence.

Mr Clarke

book in the course of the trial; it is not for me to say what opinion or judgment I have formed about it. I shall only be entitled to read the book itself to you; but we are not unacquainted in our criminal procedure with the publication of works which have had for their vicious object the spreading about to the public of explanations of the way in which physical passion may be gratified without the risk of responsibility being incurred. This book, whatever it may be, is no book of that kind. So far from that being so, I asked Annie Walker (and I am very anxious not to transgress my right in the matter), whether she had read the book, and whether there was anything immoral or improper in it, and she said there was nothing of the kind. I asked Dr. Nichols, when he was called, whether the statement in the preface, that he tried to make this as well as his other books good and useful, the books true in science and pure in morals, and contributing to the highest state of humanity, was true, and he said it was, and there was no suggestion to him at all of any observation conflicting with it. So far from this book being an immoral book, it contains counsels of perfection too high for the ordinary life of men and women. It lays down the rule that it is only for the continuation of the species that the indulgence of sexual passion is permissible; that the moment that indulgence is supposed to have resulted in a natural and legitimate consequence, from that moment the wife is sacred from the husband until the time of the nursing of the child has expired. I do not discuss these doctrines; I have nothing to do with them; their truth, their application, is indifferent to me; but the book, such as it is, is a book which, so far from lending itself to the lower influences and the lower passions of men, is a book which endeavours to restrict, to guide, and to limit the indulgence of those passions according to rules which, in their strictness, would be almost impossible to ordinary human nature, but which undoubtedly are compatible, as the sentence in this book which I before read pointed out, are compatible with the lives of a very large number of men amongst us. I will read no passage from this book which I have not read before; but you will remember that I read a passage as to the one way which the danger and responsibility of childbirth could be naturally and effectually prevented, and that was abstinence; (and here is the importance of it, it belonged to, and was habitually considered and talked about in Mrs. Walker's presence by Mr. Bartlett, as well as by his wife) that is, " to refrain from the sexual act." It is easily done by most women and by many men. In every civilised community thousands live in celibacy, many from necessity, many from choice. In Catholic countries the whole priesthood and great numbers of religious of both sexes take vows of perpetual chastity. This practice has existed for at least sixteen centuries.

Adelaide Bartlett.

Mr Clarke

You can easily imagine that I do not desire in this place, and in these surroundings, to enter into these questions in this book. I have anxiously thought how far I was entitled to limit my observations with regard to it, and I hope my lord, who no doubt has seriously considered the aspect of this case, will not think that I have transgressed the limits which I have imposed upon myself in discussing it; but the importance of it is not in the teaching of the book; the importance of it is that this book is found in the possession of people with regard to whom there is so much other evidence as to the relation in which they lived. The great improbability of the account which has been given as to their lives has, of course, struck you all. I have more than once referred to it, but just let us see what the facts are about which there can be no dispute. And I was going to say providentially, and I do not see why I should shrink from the word " providentially," for Mrs. Bartlett's protection there has been preserved one letter, the importance of which in this case, I think, it is impossible to overrate. It is the letter about whose authorship there is no doubt, as to the occasion for the reading of which we have clear evidence, and which remains to-day in the handwriting of her dead husband. Then Mr. Dyson is called. I do not know if you thought, or that my lord thought, he dealt quite fairly with some of my questions. It occurred to me, but I think it is a matter for your judgment entirely, that, when he came to the question of the relations between himself and Mrs. Bartlett, he was anxious as far as possible to escape from the admission of the relation that he had been in, and the position he held, and the same lack of courage, to put it mildly, which led him to try and get from her possession the poetry which he had written and given to her, and which her husband had seen, led him to try and tone down as much as he could the relations existing between them. But you remember the mode in which he gave his answer to the first important question carrying him back irresistibly to the earlier period of the strange relationship between himself and Mrs. Bartlett. He described that in October, at Claverton Street, when paying there one of his frequent visits, Mr. Bartlett had found some fault with his wife and scolded her, and Mr. Dyson said, in substance, these words, for I do not pretend to recite them with verbal accuracy, " When she comes under my care," or, " I have charge of her, I will do so and so." Of course, it strikes every one at once that could not be the first observation—a man does not go to a friend's house to see a friend and his wife, and say, " When your wife is under my care, I will do " this, that, or the other. It irresistibly carried him back to the earlier time, and he was forced back step by step; he was brought back to the month of September, and to the conversation that took place with Mr. Bartlett when he came back from Dover and came and called

320

Speech for the Defence.

Mr Clarke

on Dyson. Now, that conversation was a remarkable one, strange and unexplained, but it is in evidence before you on oath as part of the evidence upon which you are to decide this case, and the conversation was this—Mr. Dyson told Mr. Bartlett that he was feeling uneasy, that he had conceived an affection for Mrs. Bartlett which interfered with his work, and that he thought it would be better that he should discontinue the visits. He had at that time spoken to Mrs. Bartlett of that affection, and so he told the husband; and instead of the husband resenting it, as you would expect, the husband not only did not resent it, but he indorsed it; he gave it his sanction, his consent and approval; and from that day to the day of his death he, the husband, cherished and nurtured, as far as he could, the opportunities of communication and of growing affection between his wife and the young Wesleyan minister. It is a strange story. If it rested alone upon the evidence given after the husband is dead you might doubt it; but it does not. We have got three documents, which are of considerable importance, with regard to it. On 3rd September Mr. Bartlett made his will at Herne Hill. Now, observe, there was no question of anybody influencing him in making that will; he was not with his wife, he was not with Mr. Dyson; he signed it at his place of business at Herne Hill; it was witnessed by the two assistants in the shop, who came up and saw him write his name to it. There can be no suggestion of any influence that anybody exercised on him with regard to that. How did that alter the disposition of his property? Until that time, so far as the evidence goes, it was believed his will had left Mrs. Bartlett his property upon the condition that she should not marry again—that it had been one of those wicked wills which men are making every day, and with which they are outraging the feelings of the wife they leave behind. But on 3rd September he altered it, and, instead of leaving it to her only in case she did not get married, he left it to her absolutely, and he appointed as one executor of that will the Rev. George Dyson.

But now, gentlemen, early in September the interview took place between these two men, and the young Wesleyan minister told the husband of the love which he had conceived for the wife, and of which he had assured her. There are two documents more. There is the document—the letter written by Mr. Bartlett to Mr. Dyson on 21st September, and there is the answer of Mr. Dyson to Mr. Bartlett on the 23rd. Now, gentlemen, nothing can exceed in this case, having regard to this part of the question with which you have to deal, the importance of that letter from Mr. Bartlett. Let me read it to you, and let me ask you to listen to it, having present in your minds the statement that has been made by Mr. Dyson with regard to the communication that he made to Mr. Bartlett. " Dear George,—Permit me to say that I feel great

Y

Adelaide Bartlett.

Mr Clarke

pleasure in thus addressing you for the first time." That letter shows that shortly before that letter the relationship of the parties had changed, and that Mr. Dyson had been admitted to a confidence and intimacy which had not been given to him before. " To me it is a privilege to think that I am allowed to feel towards you as a brother, and I hope our friendship may ripen as time goes on, without anything to mar its future brightness." Now listen to this, gentlemen : " Would that I could find words to express my thankfulness to you for the very loving letter you sent Adelaide to-day." Now, when you consider that letter, and consider that it is written by a husband to another man, and that in that sentence he mentions his wife by her Christian name, you have gone a very long way indeed to confirm the statement which is made as to their relations. A " loving letter " written to Adelaide ! Why did he speak of her as Adelaide to another man ? Why did he write to express thankfulness to another man for having written that letter to his wife ? A loving letter to his wife ! There is, so far as I can see, no conceivable explanation of it but this—that the relations between his wife and himself were not the relations of marriage in its deepest and in its closest ties, but that they were such relations that he could quietly, calmly, without any pang of jealousy, look upon the rising and growth of an affectionate attachment between that wife and another man. Hear how he goes on : " The very loving letter you sent Adelaide to-day. It would have done anybody good to see her overflowing with joy as she read it whilst walking along the street, and afterwards as she read it to me."

There must be something exceptional, something extraordinary, something very difficult to believe about the story that was given to you of the marital relations of these persons ; there is nothing more remarkable than the fact which is shown in that sentence of that letter that the husband should write in thankfulness to another man for that letter that comes—the loving letter—so loving that Adelaide overflows with joy as she reads it when she walks along the street, and afterwards when she reads it to her husband. If that sentence stood alone, if there were no corroboration of it either by Mr. Dyson, no statement made to Dr. Leach by Mrs. Bartlett—I say that sentence alone is capable of no explanation whatever save this, that the marital relations between Mr. and Mrs. Bartlett were relations of a strange and unusual character, relations which allowed the husband to speak of another man with regard to his wife, and of his wife's affection for another man, and I say that can only be explained by the suggestion that husband and wife were to each other loving and faithful companions, but companions and nothing more. " I felt my heart going out to you. I long to tell you how proud I felt at the thought I should soon be able to clasp the hand of the man who from his heart

Speech for the Defence.

Mr Clarke

could pen such noble thoughts. Who can help loving you. I felt that I must say to you two words, ' Thank you '; and my desire to do so is my excuse for troubling you with this. Looking towards the future with joyfulness, I am yours affectionately, Edwin." Of all the strange things that this Court has heard, and the multitude of cases which have here been tried, involving the closest and deepest relationship of lives, nothing stranger has ever been read than that letter, where " yours affectionately, Edwin," is with humble and apologetic humility thanking the man who had written a loving letter to the wife which made her overflow with joy as she read it to her husband. That letter is the key of the whole case. Without it, it might not be possible to believe the statement that Mrs. Bartlett made as to their marital relations; with it, I venture to say it is impossible to disbelieve that statement and to suggest an intelligible explanation of the words and phrases that that letter contains.

Now, there are two other matters before I pass to their marital relations. One is a little matter that has arisen to-day. Of all the learned counsel who have appeared in this case on the part of the prosecution there is not one whose diligence has so exacting an effect as my learned friend Mr. Poland, and nothing whatever will be lost or forgotten when that scrutinising and all-remembering intellect is brought to bear upon it. This morning Alice Fulcher was recalled, and Mrs. Doggett was recalled, for the purpose of giving you some information as to the habits of life at Claverton Street. I have already commented, and the observation my lord was good enough to make upon it entirely answered the part of the comment, upon the way in which the witnesses were asked were they living as man and wife—a phrase which may imply a good deal, and the value of the answer to which depends absolutely on the means of observation, and the reason for observation, of the witnesses. But I am very grateful to my learned friend for the scrupulous care with which every item of evidence is brought before you, for the evidence brought before you this morning has established a very remarkable thing with regard to the lives of these people. When they went to take these rooms at Claverton Street, Mr. Bartlett was in good health, but it was stipulated when they went there that they should have two beds, and it was only because Mrs. Doggett could not go to the stores for two or three days to order it, and then that the stores took two or three days to send it home—it was only owing to that that a week elapsed during which there was only one bed in that room. And as soon as could be that second bed was supplied to the back room, and from that time both those beds were used. It is not so very remarkable even in our own, but it is much less common in this country than in countries not far off, where the use of two beds is frequent. But there it is, and as far as it

Adelaide Bartlett.

Mr Clarke

goes it gives support to the statement you have heard as to their marital relations. The statement, you observe, relates to matters so absolutely private that it is impossible to suspect you would ever get very much evidence to support it.

But there is another point to which I attach a great deal of importance, and that is given in the evidence of Dr. Leach. Dr. Leach, in the witness-box, was a self-conscious witness, and undoubtedly Dr. Leach was very anxious as to his own appearance before the world, and to protect himself from misunderstanding and from complaint in the matter. Gentlemen, I own I feel a great deal of sympathy for Dr. Leach; to a man like him, carrying on an ordinary practice in a place where he may not be too much known, and going through the daily round of the ordinary general medical practitioner's life, it is an appalling thing to have suddenly thrust into his life all the responsibility, and public responsibility, of a case like this. He is confronted with medical problems which perplex men who have spent years in that special study. He is called upon, in the fierce light of public observation, to recount, to explain, to give statements as to fact, and to vindicate medical opinion in a way which would test the capacity and the nerve of the ablest and best men in his profession. And I must say for Dr. Leach that, apart from that question of self-consciousness, I think he has been most anxious to give full information to the jury and to the coroner when he was called as to all that he had observed with regard to this matter. And in the witness-box, it is for you to judge whether he did not seem to you, under that crust and appearance of self-consciousness, at all events most anxious to bring to his evidence and to the answers which he gave to questions in examination and cross-examination the honest desire to tell you, without favour on one side or the other, what it was he had observed in this case. Well, now, Dr. Leach, before he was first examined before the coroner, asked Mrs. Bartlett to tell him what had happened on that evening, and she gave to him an account over which at this moment I need not travel, but which was absolutely identical with the account which she gave to other people. Of all the events of that night, so far as they referred to the finding of her husband, and the condition in which he was, the matter which awoke her, and so on, she has given four accounts. She gave an account to Mr. Doggett; she gave an account to Dr. Leach; she gave another to Mrs. Matthews; she gave another to Mr. Dyson. Those four witnesses have, here in Court, repeated the accounts she gave, and there is absolutely no difference of any material character—no difference, I mean, except in just the merest form of words, between the accounts she gave on those four different occasions. That was before Dr. Leach was first examined, but at a later time another statement was made to him by Mrs. Bartlett. It was on 26th January. He had seen

Speech for the Defence.

Mr Clarke

her twice in the interval, on the 14th and on the 18th, and on those occasions she had consulted him, not with reference to the inquest, or these matters at all, but with regard to her own private condition of health. On 26th January he had a conversation with her, and there was a matter about this conversation which I brought out in cross-examination, and the full bearing of which I do not suppose was obvious at the moment that I was making the cross-examination. That statement was never intended for a public statement. In this country a doctor has no privilege. There is one country at least in civilised Europe where the privilege of the doctor is recognised, and where he is not called upon—just as we do not call upon a solicitor—he is not called on to reveal what has taken place in consultation. In this case Dr. Leach seems to have thought that he would not be called upon, and could not be called upon, to state what was then said. The first time he had asked for a statement to enable him to give his evidence before the coroner; the second time he receives the deepest and most delicate confidence of Mrs. Bartlett, and it was so impressed on his mind that that confidence was given to him in his character of a physician that when before the coroner he struggled to escape from the necessity of giving in evidence the statement which had so been made. I think you will follow me when I say that that fact is a very material one for my case. That statement was never made for the public ear. She never knew that those words then spoken would go upon the coroner's deposition, and be published to all the world. They contain her statement made to the physician to whose skill she herself had applied for her own personal necessities, and I claim for that statement this: it was not a statement offered to an accusing world as an explanation of circumstances which had cast suspicion upon her, it was a private communication of the most private matter to the physician in whose skill she was trusting for her own treatment, and it was a statement which comes to you in such circumstances as to bear with it almost the irresistible presumption that that statement is true.

Now, what is that statement? I need not read it to you in detail—I am speaking in your correction, and in the correction of those that heard it, and, if I do not read all that document in detail, I will carefully give as far as I can its exact effect. It began by a statement made to Dr. Leach with regard to the marital relations between her and her husband. How was that statement brought about? At that moment nothing had been said by her as to her having possession of chloroform, but curiously enough, in a way which is absolutely inconsistent with any consciousness of guilt, she had been discussing and refuting, to use Dr. Leach's own remarkable word, refuting the suggestion that had been made as to the other causes of death. On the 26th, Dr. Leach says to her: " I have good news for you, Mrs. Bartlett; they say that

Adelaide Bartlett.

chloroform is supposed to be the cause of your husband's death."
And he says—you will observe he had heard before about the relatives, and the suspicions that they entertained—" It is fortunate
enough for you that it was not prussic acid, or some matter
of that kind, because then it is possible, although he might have
taken it himself, strong suspicion would have attached to you,"
upon which she gives this answer; she says, " I wish it had been
anything but chloroform." Why? Then comes the answer :
"What I have to tell you now requires a preface," and then, to
her thinking, in the absolute secrecy of a confidence between herself
and her medical man, she goes on to give him this account of their
marital relations. A strange account. She says : " I was very
young, and when I married my husband he had the idea that a
man should have two wives, one for companionship and the other
for use, and it was for companionship that he chose me." She
says : " I was so young I did not understand the contract I was
making." And that is true, for nearly three years after she was
married the greater part of her time was spent at a boarding-
school or one of the convent schools of Belgium. She said : " I
did not understand the contract when I made it, but I was loyal to
it. For six years that contract was kept between us, and then
there came to my heart the wish that I, too, might be a mother, and
have a child at my knee to love me, and on my entreaty my husband
broke through the contract that had been made, once, and once
only." And there is a strong light upon this from that book of
Dr. Nichols', a book in which he speaks of the proper and moral
condition of men and women after conception has once taken place
—" Once, and once only," she says, " I was admitted to my husband's love, and when the months had gone by, instead of the child
there came the weeks of agony, and of life nearly lost in the
labour-struggle, and from that time my hope and wish for a child
went, and we resumed our old relations."
 Now, gentlemen, the circumstances under which that communication was made were circumstances which, in my contention before you, give it the sanction of truth. But there is another remarkable thing which is stated by Dr. Leach. He went to work
—I do not complain of him; I think, looking at it, he was right
in this, that, when he found how important these matters were
getting, he should sit down quietly at home, undisturbed by the
clash and wrangle of examination and cross-examination at the
inquest and the trial, that he should set down on paper, so far as
he, quietly thinking, could remember, the statements that had been
made. But, gentlemen, what was the impression on his mind? He
wrote that down, and he says after the passage which I have paraphrased, although correctly paraphrased, I believe, " I personally
was to some extent cognisant of the facts up to this point before
the 26th; they had been partly told me, partly implied, and partly

Speech for the Defence.

Mr Clarke

gathered from observation. The rest was nearly all new.'' I tried with great care—I think you will bear me out—to sift that statement, and to see how far it was observation, how far it was information, that had given him knowledge of these facts, and we do get this from him, that when she made that statement to him it did not strike him as being an extraordinary and unbelievable thing, but the relations which he had seen existing between her and her husband, the way in which they spoke to each other, the habitual tone of their companionship, came back to his mind as to some extent supporting that statement. I can go no further than that. There is no more evidence to support it. It is amazing that there should be so much, for in this case, where marriage itself has become a platonic relation, I do not imagine that others visiting at the house, simply meeting the husband and wife, would guess, or have any means of knowing, what the real state of things was. But what I point out is this : so far as there is any evidence at all in the case, it goes to support that statement. The statement itself is one made in circumstances—circumstances of confidence with Dr. Leach—which removed Mrs. Bartlett from attempting an untruth—gave her no object for inventing a story ; and that statement, so far as the other evidence in the case is concerned, is supported by that evidence, and not contradicted by it. I do not pause to speak of the trivial nature of that conversation in the cab as they were going to the dentist ; there, again, is a suggested contradiction, and, in the course of a case like this, little matters toss up to the surface and disappear, and that, I think, disappeared when Dr. Leach said that Mrs. Bartlett was always trying to be cheerful and keep up her husband's spirits, and in conversation and other ways would make suggestions that would lighten the burden on him—the burden of anxiety, and no doubt at that moment the apprehension of pain, for an operation was going to be performed.

But now, gentlemen, there is a word I ought to say here. I have called your attention to the circumstances in which that statement was made, and I should not make another comment on it but for the extraordinary way in which my learned friend Mr. Poland insisted on examining Marshall, the police constable, as to the fact that Mrs. Bartlett was not called to give evidence as a witness before the coroner. I may say at once it was not Mrs. Bartlett's act, and could not be on Mrs. Bartlett's election. I have been greatly assisted in this case by my friends Mr. Mead and Mr. Beal, and my friend Mr. Mead will be the first to agree with me in the observation I am about to make, that I think Mrs. Bartlett is greatly indebted, and I know that I myself am greatly indebted, to the judgment and ability with which Mr. Beal discharged the anxious and onerous duties that fell on him in representing her at the inquiry before the coroner and before the magistrate. If there

Adelaide Bartlett.

Mr Clarke

had been a question as to whether Mrs. Bartlett should be called as a witness or not, I know him well enough to know that he accepted, as I in a similar situation would accept, the full responsibility of the course that was taken; and my learned friend the Attorney-General, I thought, had relieved me from any question of that kind at all when he told you in his opening that no prejudice or inference was to be drawn against Mrs. Bartlett from the fact that she was not called as a witness at the inquest. But I go further. Dr. Leach had given at the inquest a kind of statement that she had made to him, and my point to you is this: If that statement had been made at the inquest—had been made for the purpose of diverting suspicion from herself, and of justifying her acts in circumstances which otherwise would have looked and told heavily against her—it might have been the subject of suspicion. But Mrs. Bartlett had confided to her doctor that most strange and delicate explanation of the relations with regard to herself and her husband. He had given it in evidence, and there was nothing for her to add. She made that statement to Dr. Leach on 26th January; she stands by that statement now; there was nothing for her to add; no reason for her to have gone into the witness-box and exposed herself to cross-examination (I was going to use an epithet about it, but I refrain) of the solicitor whom Mr. Bartlett, senior, had employed at that inquest. It would have been to expose herself to a trial as severe and terrible as a woman could ever have undergone, and would have added nothing to the statement she had already made, and which, through Dr. Leach's lips, had been put on the public record, of her share in the transaction.

I pause for a very short time to call your attention to the history of the illness, because my learned friend the Attorney-General, in opening this case, suggested that there were only three alternative explanations of his death: either that the man took the chloroform by accident, or, said my learned friend, he took it with a suicidal intent, or he took it by being administered to him by another person with the intent to murder. I have called your attention fully, I hope not too fully, to the medical questions which have arisen in this case, and which affect the third of these theories, namely, murder; but, with regard to the others, I have a word or two to say; but the matter is reduced to the idea of suicide, accidental taking, or murder. You have heard from Dr. Tidy that of the cases of death from the administration of liquid chloroform that are recorded, by far the larger proportion and the overwhelming majority are cases of suicide. So that suicide is by far the most common of the causes of death from liquid chloroform. Gentlemen, let me make this observation to you before I enter upon the consideration of the history of that illness; it is not for you to decide whether Mr. Bartlett committed suicide, or whether he was murdered. That is not the question that is put to you; there

Speech for the Defence.

Mr Clarke

being two alternatives, you are not to call upon the defendant here to establish before you that Mr. Bartlett committed suicide. No such burden falls upon those who represent the defendant. The prosecution have got to establish before you beyond reasonable doubt that he was murdered, and murdered by the hands of the defendant here; and that is the matter to which I have to address myself. But, when we have to consider this question of the probabilities of the case, we start thus: Dr. Tidy, who knows the history of all these cases, says that, apart from the evidence, the enormous preponderance of probability would be on the side of suicide. Well, let us examine what the condition of things was during the illness. I am not going day by day through the record of those days, but as one's mind goes back over the evidence that has been given, and traces the salient points in the history of the illness, there are matters to which it is not undesirable to call to your attention. The first point I should like to put before you is this—that you have as complete and exact a record of all that took place during that illness as probably a jury ever had in a case of this kind; and it is by no means unimportant. From 9th December to 31st December this illness was running its course, and during the whole of that time Mrs. Bartlett was under the immediate inspecting eye, and under to some extent the hostile inspection, of those who have been called as witnesses before you. Under whose eye was this illness running its course? She wrote every day to Mr. Baxter, or nearly every day. Her husband's heart was in his business work; he was a man of whom we hear that, when they were staying at Dover, he would get up at three in the morning to catch the boat-train and come up to London, go to Herne Hill, attend to his business, and go back to Dover so late at night that he did not get back to his wife sometimes till ten o'clock, so that he would sometimes only spend five or six hours practically out of the twenty-four in her company. And when his illness began, the first thing he told the doctor was that he had been overworked both physically and mentally; and the first advice which the doctor gave him was this— that he should abstain altogether from all talk and all thought of business, and keep his mind to different subjects for a time.

Well, gentlemen, every day the prisoner wrote to Mr. Baxter, just to say how her husband was getting on, and from time to time Mr. Baxter came to visit at the house, and he visited at the house so late as the last three days before the death, when he brought the mango-chutney, or something that has been mentioned in the course of the case. Immediately after the illness began she called in another witness, Dr. Leach. He knew nothing of them; he was a perfect stranger. The great advantage was, with regard to him, that he lived close by, and that he could come in constantly to attend upon her husband; and Dr. Leach has told you that he never could have wished for a more attentive, a more faithful, or a more affec-

Adelaide Bartlett.

tionate nurse than she proved herself to be during all the period of that illness. She had one failing, and only one—her memory was not very good; but she kept a record from hour to hour of the little incidents of the day and of the invalid's condition, and she kept that record for the doctor to see. She tried to cheer her husband from time to time; she talked of going away; she did all she could to raise his drooping spirits; she provided for the doctor every sort of information that he could possibly want, in order that, by testing the contents of the stomach when those had been rejected, he might be able to understand exactly the course of the trouble and the course of the treatment. Dr. Leach was there, not daily only, but two or three times a day, on many of the days during that period; and Dr. Leach had arranged, on the night of the 31st, that he was to come again on the morning of the 1st in order to visit Mr. Bartlett; so that, from the beginning to the end, she was under his independent judgment.

But there was another thing she knew, and her husband knew, that there was one member of his family who looked upon her with jealousy, suspicion, and dislike—there was one member of the family who used to visit at that house—it was the father, who had been promised a home for life, and who, for reasons which you can well imagine, had not been allowed to continue an inmate of that home. He was the one member of the family who visited at the house, and on 18th December, in consequence of what the father had said, Dr. Leach was asked to find another physician. The father had said, according to himself, that he would like to send down a physician. Well, that was very kind of him, for his money was obtained from the son, and he would have sent down a physician at the son's expense; but his statement that he would like to send down a physician was repeated to the husband, and the husband, with an anxious desire to save his wife from any chance of that terrible suspicion which now, in spite of all his care, has fallen upon her, and which has condemned her to the agony of this trial—the husband speaks to the medical man, and tells him that the family have not liked her, and had not understood her; that, if the illness goes on and he does not get better, the family may say that she was poisoning him; and so he asked Dr. Leach to find some stranger, upon whom no suspicion could fall, with whom there could be no fear at all of his absolute *bona fides*, and to call him in and let him see the case. The husband says, " I will not be treated by him. You alone," he says to Dr. Leach, " shall treat me, but, for my wife's protection, call in a doctor to see me once, and let him express his opinion, and be able to express an opinion if need be." And so, on 19th December, Dr. Dudley was called in, and that absolute independent judgment we have; and that independent judgment was intended for the good purpose of shielding the wife against that malice

Speech for the Defence.

Mr Clarke

which he knew existed, and which would suggest in any case that there had been foul play. But she was under the inspection of the father-in-law himself. He has been called into the witness-box, and he has told you what he had to say. He complained, or suggested, rather, that there should be another doctor; he complained with regard to the nursing, and suggested that there should be another nurse. Another nurse! Why? The man who was ill, and who was tended thus by his wife, as Dr. Leach told you—I think it was Dr. Leach—would not have listened to the suggestion of another nurse. Dr. Leach did suggest another nurse afterwards —but for what reason? Not because there was a failure of care in the loving wife who was tending her sick husband, but because that love had carried her to a devotion which was telling upon her health—because night after night, for thirteen or fourteen nights, she had spent the restless and broken hours of the night, sitting by and watching over her husband, and because the doctor feared, not that the patient would be neglected, but that the nurse would break down under the strain. But Mr. Bartlett cherished his suspicions; he complained that he was kept away. He was one of the first persons to be communicated with. When the death took place it was not to Mr. Dyson that she telegraphed. She wrote to Mr. Dyson, just as she wrote to Mr. Wood, the other executor; but the three telegrams that were sent off that morning were sent to Mrs. Matthews, to Mr. Baxter, and to Mr. Bartlett. Mr. Bartlett did not get that telegram until a little later. He had heard from Mr. Baxter, before he got his own telegram, that the death had taken place, and he rushed off to the place where his son was lying dead; he went up to the bed where his son was lying, and smelt at his lips for prussic acid. Why? Because that preconceived idea—that idea against which the husband had tried to shield her—was in his mind; and he was smelling there at his dead son's mouth with the idea that he should find something to implicate and to blame in that death the daughter-in-law whom he had always disliked, and against whom the husband knew that he bore a revengeful feeling. That is not all. He smells for the prussic acid; he turns to the doctor, and says, " We cannot let this pass—there must be an examination—we cannot let this pass. I will not have a doctor from the neighbourhood, or one connected with the case. I insist that some independent doctor shall come down to test the cause of death." And it does not stop there. He goes and finds a solicitor, and he takes a solicitor down to Somerset House to inspect the will, which he hopes to upset. He comes here—and I describe not, because you saw it, his conduct when the will was put before him, and he was asked about the signature; and he does not scruple now—now that the wife has no husband to protect her—he does not scruple now to tell you—now from the witness-box—that the foul accusation that

331

Adelaide Bartlett.

he made against her seven years ago—for which he had then in writing expressed the greatest penitence—as to which he then confessed that it was an absolutely unfounded slander on his part —he does not scruple now to repeat that slander, and to stand by its truth, and to persist in the odious accusation which he desires to revive after these years against the reputation of one of his own sons and the honour of the widow of the son who kept him. Gentlemen, this was the sort of watching under which this illness passed—this was the sort of test that has been applied to her conduct. There was no resource of suspicion, dislike, and malignity which has not been given to the conduct of this case—for that witness instructed the solicitor to cross-examine the witnesses at the inquest.

Now then, gentlemen, that was the illness passing under that scrutiny, and subject to that construction, and what was the history of that illness? I will take this as rapidly as I can. On the 10th Dr. Leach was called in, and there was something very remarkable about Mr. Bartlett's condition. It was not so much that physical mischief was betrayed in the frame and condition of the man, but he was hypochondriacal, he complained of suffering from great sleeplessness, he was depressed in spirit, and when his mouth was looked at there was a very curious result impressed upon the doctor's mind. The condition of the gums, and the characteristic blue line, told Dr. Leach that there had been mercury taken. We know not what had produced this result, which might be produced either by large quantities of mercury, or might be produced by a small quantity of mercury administered in the case of a patient who had a peculiar idiosyncrasy for that drug. But there it was, and, whatever the cause of it, it so impressed itself on Dr. Leach's mind that he waited until Mrs. Bartlett was out of the room, and then he asked Mr. Bartlett, "Have you been taking any medicines?" The answer was "No," and Dr. Leach has recorded the impression which was then on his mind, namely, that Mr. Bartlett had been to some quack, who, for real or supposed syphilis, had administered mercury, which had produced this result. It was absolutely denied by Mr. Bartlett. He explained it afterwards as being caused—and certainly it was a very odd explanation—he explained it as being caused by a pill that he picked out of a box of sample pills. It is a curious thing for a man to take a pill in that way, and one is not surprised that Dr. Leach did not readily accept this explanation; and hence the suspicion in his mind that there was some other explanation of the matter. But the symptoms of gastritis or dyspepsia that existed on 10th December disappeared to some extent under Dr. Leach's treatment; and undoubtedly when Dr. Dudley was called in on 19th December the physical condition of Mr. Bartlett had greatly improved.

Speech for the Defence.

Mr Clarke

Well, gentlemen, but there was a very curious relapse, in this sense. Dr. Leach has said that things got better—a good deal better—from the 19th, I think, until the 24th or 25th. But he used this expression : " On the 26th the appearance of the lumbricoid worm upset everything again," and we know from the evidence that the appearance of that worm had very seriously affected the spirits and the mind of Mr. Bartlett. We have got the evidence of Mr. Dyson, who returned on 26th December, and who, on the 26th and 27th, visited at the house, and he describes Mr. Bartlett as being at that time in a very depressed condition. The improvement which had taken place during the earlier days of the illness had been an improvement of physical symptoms, but there had been no great improvement in mental condition, because, if you will remember, when Dr. Dudley tried to describe the condition Mr. Bartlett was in on the 19th, he described him, I think, as restless, disinclined to move, disinclined even to open his eyes, looking at him through half-closed eyelids, and altogether in a condition which, if it were not physically one of a serious character, was at all events one which, as far as one can see, mentally and morally was a condition of great depression. But the condition was enormously increased in its gravity when you come to 26th December.

Let us just see what happened on that day. The lumbricoid worm made its appearance, and Dr. Leach says the man was greatly alarmed and troubled about that worm. Some vermifuge was given, santonine was given, to treat this. What is Dr. Leach's statement on that treatment? That if vermifuge was given, and was not speedily removed by purgatives from the system, the effect on the mind and spirits would be very serious indeed—so serious that Dr. Leach says, " I have experienced them myself, and I wish nobody to experience for themselves those serious consequences." What was the effect? The santonine was administered, and Dr. Leach made every effort to relieve the bowels and exclude the vermifuge. What was the effect? None whatever. The drug remained in the system, and its effect must have been very great. He had had two purgative draughts and two globules of croton oil, and exactly the same sort of thing was observed with regard to those purgatives as Dr. Leach had observed as to the sedatives. Something was given him to procure sleep. It had no effect at all; he was as restless as ever. Croton oil was administered—a remedy so strong that one would have supposed it would have produced immediate evacuation with considerable looseness; and this amazing patient said to Dr. Leach that it was very comforting, that he felt very comfortable, and he was very glad to have it. But it had no effect. He had taken these things into the stomach, and no effect was produced; he had hot tea and coffee, that were used to try and give them efficiency, in vain. At last Dr. Leach galvanises the abdomen, still all in vain; and Dr. Leach says, " I gave it up

Adelaide Bartlett.

in despair ''; and on that day, the 26th, having exhausted all the means he had adopted to remove this vermifuge, which was absolutely necessary, Dr. Leach went away. He comes again, I think, in a day or two. But just let me remind you of another thing. Dr. Leach said he should not come and see him again, and he tells you there was no real reason, in his judgment, for coming to see this man constantly, but whenever he suggested that he would not come, Mr. Bartlett was distressed; and he says on that day Mr. Bartlett seemed distressed at his threat not to come. On the 27th he had a somewhat better day, I suppose. Dr. Leach says, '' On the 27th he obtained some relief,'' and undoubtedly if, after all the accumulation of remedies, he did get relief, the probability is it was a relief of that kind which left him in a very low and depressed condition. Then two days pass. He got relief on the 27th, and on the 29th a fresh trouble comes. He had been twice to the dentist's already. He had had removed from his jaw a number of roots of teeth, and he had also had removed a number of stumps which were left, and had been sawn off, and now on the 29th, Dr. Leach says, '' The jaw symptoms became alarming.'' Gentlemen, that word has been used by Dr. Leach over and over again. When they came afterwards to examine the jaw, it turned out that the necrosis was of a superficial and not of a very important character; but on the 29th, the 30th, and the 31st Dr. Leach says those symptoms were alarming. Now, gentlemen, what does that mean, or what would it mean to him? We know that Mr. Bartlett knew it, and I will tell you why; necrosis had been discussed between Dr. Leach and Mrs. Bartlett before the visit to the dentist on the 31st; and so nervous was Mr. Bartlett with regard to a matter of this kind that Dr. Leach endeavoured to spare him the horror and dread of going to the dentist by not telling him anything about it till arrangements had been made and they were ready to go. Then he did go. Before that time there had been a conversation about necrosis.

The next piece of evidence is of enormous importance—it is the evidence of Mr. Roberts, the dentist—because he says, when the operation had been performed, as we know it to have been with some difficulty under nitrous oxide gas, double the usual time being taken in the operation—he said it was mentioned before him that necrosis was setting in. What would that mean to him, '' Necrosis was setting in ''? '' Necrosis '' is a word of itself suggestive of most unpleasant imaginations; it means death; and in its adopted form of city of the dead, necropolis, has probably become familiar to people who would not attach any meaning to the word otherwise —it means death of the structure, whatever it is. Necrosis of the jaw means the death of the bone, coming usually, as the witness told you, either from syphilis, or from an administration of mercury, whether syphilis be present or not. Sometimes it may be checked,

Speech for the Defence.

Mr Clarke

sometimes only involving a purely superficial injury; the bone may be removed; but sometimes, as the doctor told you, involving grave effects to the bone, until the bone structure itself of the jaw has to be interfered with and removed, and occasionally involving, if it progresses, consequences which are actually fatal to life.

It is true, when his body was examined after death, necrosis was found to be limited, and of a superficial character. On the 31st, it is true, Mr. Roberts did not attribute the most serious aspect to the presence of necrosis; but on that day, in Mr. Bartlett's presence, it was said necrosis was setting in; and such an intimation coming to a man who had gone through the illness which has been detailed to you in evidence, and which I have but sketched in the merest outline, would necessarily and severely affect his spirits.

Now one has come to the evening on which this happened. We have got the account of that evening. The supper went up, the oysters and the mango-chutney and so on, and it was partaken of by Mr. Bartlett. The conversation with Mrs. Doggett; then the servant takes in the coals and says " Good-night," and goes downstairs at, I think, about half-past eleven. Twenty-five minutes past eleven she goes downstairs—I am not quite sure about the exact time—it may be twenty-five minutes past eleven, or at twenty-five minutes to twelve, she takes in the coals, is told, as Mr. Bartlett is in bed, that she is to put the basin outside, and there the evidence of eye-witnesses stops. The next time that other persons, Mr. and Mrs. Doggett and the doctor, go into that room, Mr. Bartlett is dead. Now, gentlemen, just let me ask you to consider the statement that Mrs. Bartlett has made with regard to that matter. Let us consider what would, in the ordinary course of things, happen after that. Observe, the day is over. Mrs. Bartlett has no friends with her with whom she is going to say farewell to the old year and exchange congratulations on the birth of the new one. She is alone with her husband in that front room. In the ordinary course of things, now that he has gone to bed, she would make up the fire for the night, she would go into the back room and wash according to her usual wont, and she would change the dress she had worn during the day for that lighter and looser dress she was going to wear through the hours of the night. Then, in the ordinary course of things, she would come back to her place at the foot of his bed, and there settle to sleep. If the statement of Mrs. Bartlett be, as I suggest to you it is, the true statement of all that she can speak to as having taken place on that night, what was it that happened? I have called your attention to the circumstances in which that statement was made to Dr. Leach; I have called your attention to the first part of it, and his comment upon it. Now let me call your attention to the statement which she made as to that night.

Adelaide Bartlett.

Mr Clarke

She told him that she had felt it a duty to her womanhood to resist the resumption by her husband of the marital rights so long abandoned; she told him she had prepared herself to resist, and to assist herself in her resistance to that attempt by supplying herself with chloroform. Nobody who ever knew anything about the use of chloroform would have dreamed of doing such a thing as that. Mr. Dyson and Mrs. Bartlett were probably equally ignorant of the effects of chloroform, and of the way in which chloroform could have been used. But then she said this. She told Dr. Leach that she possessed herself of a bottle of chloroform, and secretly resolved that, in the event of her husband approaching her, " she would put some of the chloroform on to a handkerchief and wave it in his face, believing thereby to make him lie down again to sleep, as often as the occasion required. I congratulated her on not having to try the experiment, saying that its accomplishment would have been impossible, and in the scramble the bottle would probably have capsized." " She said, never having kept anything from her husband, the presence of that bottle in her drawer troubled her mind, and she felt she would do a very wrong thing if she really used it, so determined to tell her husband and make a clean breast of it; so, on the last night of the year, she sat down and broached the subject to him while he was lying in bed. She told him to what extremes she was driven, and gave the bottle into his hands. They talked affectionately about their relations one with the other for a short time, and he seemed much grieved. She told me no details of their conversation, but I gather it was not a long one, for he soon turned round and pretended to sleep or to sulk. Then, soon after midnight, she fell asleep, and once waking, heard her husband breathing in a peculiar manner, but her suspicions were in no way aroused. She next awoke, probably an hour or two later, with a cramped feeling of her left arm, the one round his foot; she saw he was lying on his face; she got up to turn him into a more comfortable position, and was greatly alarmed at his condition; she rubbed his chest with brandy." Now, that statement, made in the circumstances I have suggested to you, gives it a great probability of its being the absolutely true account. Is it a possible account? Why, the facts that we know fit in with that statement in a way which, I venture to submit to you, makes the account which I gather from that statement, and from the facts given in evidence, not merely the most probable, but almost the certain, history of the transactions of that night. Observe those curious relations that had been set up between them. The husband who was to succeed him had been in fact, with his assent, selected. Mr. Bartlett had so behaved as in fact to have given or dedicated his wife for the future to Mr. Dyson. Then he desires to re-assume his rights, but is resisted; and on this night, when he has suffered during the day, when he has undergone this operation, and must

336

Speech for the Defence.

Mr Clarke

undoubtedly have suffered from his condition, he is told by her, substantially, that the consent which he has given with regard to Dyson's relations is treated by her as an irrevocable decision, that to her he has ceased to enjoy the rights that a husband may exercise, that she has taken him at his word, that written word, in fact, which I have read you in that letter, and that, from this time afterwards, copartnership must remain copartnership, and shall never be allowed again to pass into the associations of marriage. He was grieved, he appeared very grieved, and he turned over.

Suppose you now sketch in imagination what took place. Suppose she left the room as usual to wash, and he had placed on the mantelpiece this bottle of chloroform. There was a wineglass there, that wineglass was found afterwards, and while she was away it was perfectly easy for him without leaving his bed, lifting himself only upon his elbow, to pour into this wineglass the less than half a wineglass of chloroform which may have constituted that fatal dose, having poured that into the wineglass, having replaced the bottle, then to have taken it off. If he swallowed it in that way, and swallowed it up quickly, there would not be, as there were not, appearances of long exposure of the softer substances of the mouth and throat to the chloroform. Having drunk it, he reassumes his recumbent position, the chloroform passes down his throat and reaches the stomach. There is no difficulty, nothing unreasonable, nothing extraordinary, as tested by the cases which have been quoted here; within two or three minutes after that he might be passing into a state of coma, that might have been when she came back, or when she awoke, because how can she tell if this was done when she was absent from the room, or while she was dozing at the foot of his bed? There might have been when she awoke or when she came back this stertorous breathing, which is one of the signs of having taken chloroform, and which, if she had been a murderess, she never would have mentioned as she did mention it to the man to whom she was giving the account; there may have been this breathing which did attract her attention, and was mentioned by her when telling it. Then she herself goes to sleep, and her husband's coma deepens into insensibility, and insensibility passes into death. There has been before the death just the turn upon the pillow, the turn into the uncomfortable attitude described with the head turned over on the pillow, but except that there has not been, nor would science predict or expect to find, any other disturbance or convulsion. And then the hours go by. She has heard them, happier than she, in the other part of the house speaking to each other of the brighter hopes of the New Year that is beginning, but the first thing she awakens to in that New Year is the sad consciousness that the husband who might not have fully deserved the love that he received, but who, at all events, had treated her with affection, with confidence, with the desire to

z

Adelaide Bartlett.

Mr Clarke

protect her—she awakens to find that husband apparently cold and dead. She springs to his side; there is close to the end of the mantelpiece, for we know it, this wineglass from which he has taken that fatal draught; the woman's instinct is at once to administer brandy in hopes to restore him to himself. She pours into the glass some brandy and tries to pour it down his throat, I am not sure she does much; with shaking hand she spills some brandy on his chest which the doctor smells afterwards; she tries to rub his chest with a little brandy. It is no use; she puts back on the mantelpiece, where it was found when they came into the room, this wineglass with the brandy in it, a wineglass which only contained brandy; there was no admixture of chloroform with it, but a wineglass which her husband had used for chloroform it well may be. Mr. Doggett, on first going in and smelling the glass, may have detected the odour of chloroform about it, though it was only brandy it contained. All we know is the glass was there, we know that that part of the mantelpiece was within his reach. If you believe—and how dare you reject the statement which she in those circumstances made as to what took place on that night?—accept that statement, the whole history is clear. There was no scientific miracle worked by the grocer's wife under circumstances where it could not have been worked by the most experienced doctor who ever gave himself to the study of this matter. There was unhappily the putting within the reach of a man who was broken by illness, and upon whom there had come this disappointment, and absolute and final severance of the effectual marriage tie between himself and his wife—there was the putting within his reach of the poison which he might have used, and which he probably did use, but there was nothing more, and from that moment there was not a word of hers, there was not an action, not a look, which was not the look, or the word, or the action of the loving wife who had nursed him through his illness to this point, and who now found him suddenly gone for ever. She rushes upstairs, she calls the servant, she bids her go and fetch the doctor as soon as she can; not content with that, she arouses the people in the house in the hope that they may give some help, and then she breaks the fire, and she waits till help comes, and the first who comes in to whom she can ask the question, and on whose judgment she relies, the doctor, she says, " Doctor, is he really dead? " And the doctor goes to the bedside and looks, and feels, makes his examination, and tells her he is really dead; and then the widow bursts into a passion of tears, and, when that passion of tears has subsided, she is the first person to ask the doctor, " What can he have died of? " She was anxious to have the mystery solved. The doctor says, " I do not know; I think a small blood vessel may have broken, but I cannot tell; there must be a post-mortem examination." A post-mortem examination she does not shrink from. She said, " Must

Speech for the Defence.

Mr Clarke

there be an inquest?" as almost every one has said when death in sudden form has come and stricken down the dear one. Must this be open to public investigation—must all this be gone through? The inquest she shrinks from, but the post-mortem she of all people is the one most anxious to have. She desires not only to have the post-mortem examination, but to have it as promptly as possible, and to have it conducted by the highest skill. "Spare no expense. Cannot he come to-day?"

Why, gentlemen, "Squire's Companion" has been produced, from which it is said she would know about chloroform. It tells you nothing but that chloroform is volatile. If there had been the smallest knowledge or idea in her mind of chloroform having produced the effect, and of her being blamed, the delay in the post-mortem examination would have been delightful to her, a relief. But she must have it. She chafed and was restless in the idea that for one hour this mystery should be left unsolved. "Spare no expense; fetch any one," she suggested. "What could it be?" The doctor says, "Can it be prussic acid?"—"No." "Could it be any other poison?"—"There was no other poison he could get without my knowing it." "Could it be anything else—opium?" —"I am so glad I did not give him the pills"; and she goes to the cupboard and takes out the two pills from the box and shows them to Dr. Leach, and she has not given them to him. And from beginning to end her every action and word and thought appears to be the act and word and thought of a woman who is chafing under the cruel uncertainty: what can it be that has suddenly robbed her of her husband?

There is another suggestion made about the death. I am not sure if at that moment, or, if not then, afterwards, the doctor suggested chlorodyne—it was afterwards, after the post-mortem examination; but on that morning she was combating the idea of poisoning.

Mr. JUSTICE WILLS—It was then, Mr. Clarke.

Mr. CLARKE—I am obliged to your lordship. It emphasises what I said; I am glad. There was a bottle of chlorodyne on the mantelpiece. To show how little you can rely on the evidence of witnesses as to what they found at that particular time, you know Doggett swore he made a careful examination of the room, and there was no bottle on the mantelpiece, and Dr. Leach as distinctly swore there was a small bottle containing chlorodyne. Dr. Leach suggested, "Could he have died of chlorodyne?"

Gentlemen, if there had been any thought in her mind of guilt of this death, she would have sprung at the idea. How could she tell the difference between chloroform and chlorodyne—the difference there might be in post-mortem appearances? But when the doctor suggested chlorodyne, she would not have it—the last thing in the world. "Chlorodyne! No, he never swallowed it."

339

Adelaide Bartlett.

Mr Clarke

" If he took it into his mouth he might have swallowed it?" " No, it is impossible," she said; " he only used a little chlorodyne to rub his gums with; he could not have swallowed enough for that purpose"; and there ends the interview. She has demanded that immediate examination which, if she had been guilty, she might have known would be the surest way of finding out her own guilt. She has repudiated and refuted the suggestion of the doctor with regard to other modes of death which would have freed her from any imputation.

But, gentlemen, what happens afterwards? She sends immediately for Mrs. Matthews, for Mr. Bartlett, and for Mr. Baxter. Mrs. Matthews is an old friend. Mrs. Matthews comes and spends the day with her. There is no attempt to get into solitude in order that she may run no risk of letting out to others that terrible secret of a crime. She is with the people she has been in the habit of meeting. She spends the day with Mrs. Matthews. On the following day, the Saturday, the post-mortem examination takes place. Now observe, was there in her mind on that day of the post-mortem examination any doubt, any anxiety, as to her being incriminated? What did she do? The post-mortem examination took place. The doctor communicated to her that there had been a smell of chloroform, and he told her at the same time, on the Saturday, that he believed that the doctors were wrong, and that it was not chloroform, but chlorodyne. But what was her act? That bottle of chloroform was at that moment in the drawer in that room—in one of those rooms; but what was her behaviour after the post-mortem examination? She did not go and touch the drawer. She did not suggest that she should be allowed to take anything away. She took her keys from her pocket. She gave them to Dr. Leach to go and fetch the drawer, and he brought the drawer. She took from it the hat she was to go away in. He took the drawer, and put it in its place; and, except the hat she wore to go away, the only other thing she took away was the cloak, the cloak which she was actually willing to go without, about which that witness Bartlett said, " I will be responsible for the cloak," and he felt whether there were pockets in it, and whether anything was being taken away in those pockets, before he gave her the cloak. In the hat and cloak she went away from the house. It was suggested that the keys should be given to her solicitor. That was resisted; they were not given; they were given into the impartial hands of Dr. Leach; and away she went from that house. And it was not until days after, when Dr. Leach said that the coroner's officer—Mr. Dyson gave it in evidence—had got all he wanted from the rooms—it was not until after that she went back to the rooms and took away this bottle of chloroform. Then she threw it away.

Gentlemen, it is true she threw the bottle of chloroform away,

Speech for the Defence.

Mr Clarke

just as Dyson threw away the bottles from which he had taken the chloroform; but she did not throw away that bottle of chloroform until three days after Dyson had thrown away those bottles; and before she threw away that bottle of chloroform there had occurred that remarkable conversation between her and Dyson with regard to which Mrs. Matthews spoke.   Gentlemen, on Monday, 4th January, there was that conversation, there was the conversation between them, and when Mrs. Matthews went into the room she heard Dyson say, "You told me that Edwin would die soon"; she heard her deny it, and then she saw him bow down on the piano and then go out, saying, "I am a ruined man."   He had been at that interview bothering her about a piece of paper—what piece of paper?   Why should he bother her about that piece of paper? It was a piece of paper on which he had written some verses to her which I suppose he thought were in tone and character inconsistent with his position, and verses which he did not wish to have come before the public eye, and therefore at that visit, when she was under the grief of that awful calamity which had come upon her three days before, he was bothering her to return his wretched verses to him.   For what purpose?   In order that he could get rid of them, and that they should not rise up in public witness against him.   You will decide whether or not his answer to the question as to whether he had not required to have all his letters back again was true.   It is a trifle—she was angry on the 4th about his bothering about a piece of paper with verses on it at such a time as that; but she behaved to him far better than he behaved to her—she did keep his verses for him, she gave him those verses on Saturday, 9th January, and when she was in confidence telling Dr. Leach the story of that night, and Dr. Leach asked her, "Who got the chloroform for you?" she did not tell him; she did not bring Dyson or his name into this controversy, but she gave him back his verses; and since then she has never had a conversation with him; since then the only time during which she has heard the voice which had become familiar to her during those months has been the time when she heard it from the witness-box against her when she stands upon trial for her life.   But upon that 9th of February one thing happened; it was from her lips that the first challenge came to him, or to any one, to accuse her of this crime.   He got his miserable paper on 9th January, and then he was satisfied.   He got rid of the bottles, and his verses had disappeared, and he, I suppose, felt himself a little safer; but then he says something about the chloroform, and she turned on him angrily and said, "Do not mince matters; say, if you want to say it, that I gave him the chloroform."   Gentlemen, apart from all the scientific aspects of the case, apart from all the matters I have discussed, I am sorry, at such length, and I desire not to occupy your time unnecessarily

Adelaide Bartlett.

Mr Clarke

on this—apart from all the scientific difficulties there stands that fact, that from the moment of that death every word and act and look of hers has been the word and act and look of a woman conscious of her innocence, though shrinking, and naturally shrinking, from the suspicion which at last she saw would gather with awful force and strength around her. Every word and look and action has been the word and look and action of innocence. The first challenge to the world to bring this charge came from her lips.

I have now, I think—I hope I have—to the best of my ability dealt with the topics in this case, and to you the responsibility will shortly pass. I do not desire to touch you or to influence your judgment by anything more than by a reasonable and fair appeal to you as to the conclusions formed on the evidence before you, but it has not been possible for me to discharge during these days the duty which I have been honoured to bear without a deepening feeling of the intensest interest in the result of this case.

This woman has not had the happiest of lives. She has been described to you as one who had no friends. She found a friend in Mrs. Matthews, she found another friend in continuing the acquaintance of the nurse who was called before you, but beyond that we know of no friends, and the habits of her husband's life left her much alone. There is no hint of misconduct or wrong upon her part at any time of this association of husband and wife except the trivial and malignant invention of that witness who came first. She had no friends in the sense that has been mentioned, but she had one friend—her husband. He did stand by her, strange as his ideas may have been, disordered, as it would seem from some things that have been said, as his intellect in some respects must have been. Witness the statements that were made by him, for instance, to Dr. Leach. Yet still in his strange way he stood by her and he protected her. He was affectionate in manner, and, when her reputation was assailed, he defended it as only the husband could defend it. And to her at this moment it may seem most strange that he to whom she had given this persistent affection, even during the years of such a life, should be the one of whose foul murder she now stands accused. And if he himself could know what passed among us here—how strange, how sorrowful, it might seem to him—how strange that such an accusation should have been formulated and tried in Court in spite of the efforts which he endeavoured to make to prevent it; the precautions which perhaps, by his own rash and despairing act, he too completely defeated.

Gentlemen, that husband too has gone, but she is not left without a friend; she will find that friend here to-day in the spirit which guides your judgment and clears your eyes upon this case. It is a great responsibility for men to be called suddenly

Speech for the Defence.

Mr Clarke

from their business and their pleasures, and to be shut off as you have been from the ordinary habits of your life, to decide upon issues of life and death. There are trivial incidents sometimes about the conduct of every case, but we, the ministers of the law, are ministers of justice, and I believe that, as a case like this goes on from day to day, there comes into your hearts a deep desire which is in itself a prayer that the spirit of justice may be among us, and may guide and strengthen each one to fulfil his part. That invocation is never in vain. The spirit of justice is in this Court to-day to comfort and protect her in the hour of her utmost need. It has strengthened, I hope, my voice; it will, I trust, clear your eyes and guide your judgment. It will speak in calm and measured tones when my lord deals with the evidence which aroused suspicion, and also with the evidence which I hope and believe has demolished and destroyed that suspicion, and that spirit will speak in firm and unfaltering voice when your verdict tells to the whole world that in your judgment Adelaide Bartlett is not guilty.

The Court adjourned.

Sixth Day—Saturday, 17th April, 1886.

Mr. CLARKE—My lord, before my learned friend the Attorney-General begins his reply, I wish to mention one matter, which I regret did escape my attention in addressing the jury, but I hope it is a matter that has not escaped your lordship's recollection or that of the jury—as to the relation of the conversation said to have taken place with Mrs. Doggett, and with relation to the question of motive; and I would desire to say that there is an entire absence of motive. I should say that Mrs. Bartlett's money had been in the business; that she was entirely dependent upon her husband's income; that they were aware that Dyson's means were scanty; and also that she had been given to understand by Mr. Dyson, according to his belief at the time, that no marriage could take place for two years.

Closing Speech for the Prosecution.

The ATTORNEY-GENERAL—May it please your lordship, gentlemen of the jury—With reference to the statement which my learned friend has just made, I would call your attention to the fact, as it has been mentioned, that there is no evidence that Mrs. Bartlett ever had a penny of money, or brought anything to her husband; and that the facts, so far as they make any disclosure on the subject, seem to point rather in the opposite direction. So far as regards this lady's previous history, we have not heard anything. He sends her to school for some time; and, except as my learned friend made the suggestion from his instructions, there is no evidence to suggest, much less to show, that this lady brought one penny of money——

Mr. CLARKE—It is her statement; her statement is in evidence.

The ATTORNEY-GENERAL—Oh, yes. I say, except her statement to which you refer, there is no evidence, in fact, of anything of the kind.

Gentlemen, in endeavouring to do my duty respecting this case, I shall endeavour to observe two rules. I shall not appeal to passion or to prejudice, but I shall feel it to be my duty to put together the facts of the case, as far as I am able to do, in the most forcible, but I hope in a perfectly fair, manner, because, in my view of the duty of those who represent the Crown on these occasions—the Crown being the public, the interests at stake being the interests of society and of justice—in my view, while it is not right to struggle for a verdict, as in a civil court, it is the duty

344

Closing Speech for the Prosecution.

The Attorney-General

of those representing the Crown to see that there is put before the jury, who have to decide upon the question of guilt or of innocence, the full strength and bearing of the case with which they have to deal.

My learned friend, I will not say made a complaint, but suggested that the Attorney-General should not claim his right, which comes down to him from olden times, of having the last word in a case of this kind. I will merely observe in reference to that matter that, although that claimed right may undoubtedly seem anomalous, it could not have been allowed to continue to this day if, at all events in recent times, there was any suggestion that it had been abused. But I beg leave to add to that, that if ever there was a case in which it was proper that that right should be exercised, it is a case like the present, and for this reason : upon the occurrence of the death of her husband, Mrs. Bartlett gave no explanation before the coroner's jury. I am not mentioning that in order that you may draw an inference to her prejudice. Probably she was acting under the advice of counsel, and did not even stop to inquire whether that advice was well judged or not. The first, if it could be so called, the first attempt at explanation is at the interview on 26th January, to her friend Dr. Leach, who takes down from her the statement, the greater part of which has been read to you in the course of this case, but which statement contains no suggestion of explanation upon her part of how this tragedy—her husband's death—was brought about. And it is not, in truth, given until my learned friend, speaking no doubt upon his instructions, in a few sentences addressed to the serious part of the case, presented to you what he conceives to be a plausible theory as to the way in which this man compassed his own death. Nay, more, I might observe that of late it has been the habit of judges to allow prisoners, in addition to availing themselves of the benefit of defence by counsel—to allow prisoners to make their own supplementary statements ; and I have no doubt that, if my friend had thought fit to make such application before the point at which we have now arrived, my lord would have done that which judges do in these circumstances. And therefore it is, gentlemen, I think you will see—and I apologise for dwelling even for this moment on the topic—therefore it is that I think this a case where, if, at the last moment, there is anything like an explanation, counsel for the Crown should have an opportunity of discussing that in the presence of my lord, who will have to direct the jury as to the facts of this case.

There are one or two introductory matters which I must refer to. My learned friend says this is the first case of suggested death by the use of the irritant poison, chloroform.

Mr. CLARKE—Liquid.

Adelaide Bartlett.

The ATTORNEY-GENERAL—In a liquid form. The counsel who defended Palmer might have said the same of strychnine; the counsel who defended Lamson might have said the same of aconitine; it is no answer, it has no weight, to suggest this is a medium for destroying human life of which there is no prior recorded usage. The question in this case is, has the evidence been reasonable—has the evidence with reasonable certainty brought home to your minds that here there was criminal use of chloroform, and that that criminal use was by the prisoner at the bar? One other introductory point to which my learned friend adverted, and I come to the substance of this case. My learned friend was good enough to express his approval, and, knowing the value of my friend's opinion and his capacity as a lawyer, I am not surprised he did so, of the course that, after very careful and anxious consideration, my learned friend and myself thought right to take with reference to Mr. Dyson. And my learned friend was good enough to state that he agrees that there was no case proper to be presented to you against Mr. Dyson. But he pressed that circumstance with a good deal of rhetorical ingenuity in favour of the prisoner at the bar, and said, " If no criminal intent is to be drawn against Mr. Dyson because of the misstatements he made when he got the chloroform, and no criminal inference is to be drawn against him because he threw away the bottles of chloroform in secret, then no criminal inference is to be drawn against her." Let me ask you to consider for a moment, does my friend fairly complete the parallel? If, in addition to Mr. Dyson having done those things, which are suspicious, but suspicious only, it could be shown that Mr. Dyson had the possession, and that he alone had the possession, of the poison which caused the death, that he alone, if it was intentionally and criminally used, could have been the person to use it, then he alone was the person who could have given explanation, if explanation were to be given consistently with innocence, as to how it came to be administered, then indeed the antecedent circumstances of possession and concealment would have accumulative force. At least it would be for the jury to say whether it had not accumulative force pointing to the conclusion of guilt.

One other word. My learned friend thought it was right for him to make an attack upon the father of the dead man. Gentlemen, I think some allowance must be made for that father. He came to the conclusion, a conclusion which the facts have made but too apparent, that this was not, as Dr. Leach at first suggested, a death from natural causes; he came to the conclusion that this was a death from unnatural causes, and he was right; his suspicions further pointed to death from unnatural causes brought into operation by criminal means. That question, of course, is un-

Closing Speech for the Prosecution.

The Attorney-General

determinable, and must remain undeterminable, until your verdict has been pronounced. But when my learned friend goes on to attack the father of the deceased, and to point to his evidence in the witness-box as evidence of the malign feelings that he entertains towards the prisoner, it is but fair to remind you that it was upon cross-examination, and not by any voluntary statement of the witness, that Mr. Bartlett, the father, referred to the antecedent charge that he had made against the prisoner in the dock, and for which he apologised in writing. But my learned friend, I think, for the moment forgot that letter written on the Sunday night on the illness of his son by Adelaide Bartlett, in which she says : " Dear Mr. Bartlett,—I hear that you are a little disturbed because Edwin has been too ill to see you. I wish, if possible, to be friends with you, but you must place yourself on the same footing as other people—that is to say, you are welcome here when I invite you, and at no other time." That is to say, he might not come to see his son, who is ill, except at the time it pleased her to permit him. " You seem to forget that I have not been to bed for thirteen days, and am consequently too tired to talk to visitors." As we know, the illness began on the 10th, and this letter was written on the 23rd. " I am sorry to speak so plainly. I wish you distinctly to understand that I have neither forgotten nor forgiven the past. Edwin will be pleased to see you on Monday evening any time after six o'clock."

Now, gentlemen, when he was examined, he was asked to what that referred, and at first you will recollect he declined to make any reference to it. It was only when the matter was persisted in, it was, so to say, brought in in cross-examination, he stated that opinion—into the justice, or otherwise, of which I do not stop to inquire, namely, his belief in the accusation which had originally been made, although he had undoubtedly unequivocally and absolutely withdrawn it.

But, gentlemen, those are, after all, small matters. I come to the real question in this case. At a quarter-past four on the morning of 1st January Dr. Leach finds the deceased, his patient, at 85 Claverton Street, and, forming the best opinion he can, thinks that death must have taken place about three hours previously ; that brings us back to half-past one o'clock in the morning. We have it proved, in the statement which the prisoner made, that before the prisoner composed herself to sleep on that night she had heard downstairs the kindly New Year's greeting between friends, and in her statement to Dr. Leach she makes some reference, I think, to the same incident. Therefore we have got the important part of this inquiry to which your attention must now be addressed practically confined to what took place in that period, probably not exceeding an hour and a half, if it amounted to so much. However, inquiry has established that the dead man met his death by

Adelaide Bartlett.

the effects of an irritant poison introduced into his stomach, and the question in the case—and the only question in the case—is, how came that there? It is not suggested—I followed my friend's able speech with the attention which it certainly deserved, and I noticed that my learned friend did not suggest the question of accident; nor could he. He confined his case to suggesting the difficulties in the way of the administering of this irritant poison by any one else, and marshalled his facts and arguments in support of one suggestion, and one suggestion only—suicide, deliberate suicide, on the part of the deceased.

Now, let me remind you that this is one of those cases in which you can never have—the nature of the thing forbids it—proof to demonstration of the crime committed. In a case of poisoning, those who are endeavouring to find a clue to the truth, and to follow that clue to the end until it legitimately leads to the guilt or innocence of the accused, must, so to speak, grope in the dark. Murders by poison are not committed, like crimes of sudden passion, often in the light of day. They are necessarily mysterious and hidden in their operation. Gentlemen, it seems to be necessary in order that you may follow, not only my learned friend's line of defence, but in order that you may appreciate its true weight, and in order also that you may follow the points to which I respectfully call your attention, it is necessary that I should say a word or two, and only a word or two, descriptive of the antecedent history of these persons.

The prisoner at the bar was born in 1855. She was some years younger, therefore, but with no marked disparity, however, than her husband. She was married in 1875. Therefore, she was, at the date of her marriage, between nineteen and twenty years of age. She told, indeed, in what I must ask leave to characterise as that extraordinary statement to Dr. Leach—she told him, indeed, that she was married at sixteen.

Mr. CLARKE—No; he said he was not sure.

The ATTORNEY-GENERAL—Yes; I have it before me.

Mr. CLARKE—He said, in cross-examination, he was not sure.

The ATTORNEY-GENERAL—Very well; he took it down at the time——

Mr. CLARKE—No.

The ATTORNEY-GENERAL—I was going to say he took it down at the time when he alleges the matter was fresh in his memory.

Mr. JUSTICE WILLS—He put it down.

The ATTORNEY-GENERAL—Yes.

Mr. JUSTICE WILLS—I thought you meant he took it down.

The ATTORNEY-GENERAL—No.

Mr. JUSTICE WILLS—He put it down on 4th February.

The ATTORNEY-GENERAL—On 4th February he took it down; he said he took it down when it was fresh in his memory, but he says

Closing Speech for the Prosecution.

The Attorney-General

he is not quite certain if she said she was married at the age of sixteen; but he then at a later stage begins by stating, " At the age of sixteen she was selected by him in the former capacity," and then he said, " I did not know what she meant, that ' I was married at sixteen,' or thereabouts." But the suggestion is in relation to that under-statement of age, that she did not understand in its fullness the nature of the marriage contract into which she was entering, and the obligations it imposed and the rights it gave. You must deal with a suggestion of that kind, and I ask you whether it is reasonable to give effect to such a suggestion as that?

The deceased man seems to have wished to improve her education, which was apparently somewhat defective, and, as has been shown, in the interval of the vacations, at which she was not at school, he and his wife cohabited; and their ordinary relations, so far as observers and friends could judge, were those of man and wife. And, finally, we take up the story of their life with her coming, I think for the first time, in 1877, to live with her husband at the shop in Station Road, Herne Hill. Then in the next year (1878) was that distressing incident in which the father-in-law of the prisoner played the part of accuser, and for which he afterwards in an unqualified and absolute manner apologised. Then next in order of date is the event of the birth of a child, about Christmas of 1881. Then my learned friend made some observations, in referring to that incident, the justice of which, the probability of which, you must judge. It is alleged that at that time, and previous to that time, she had conceived a desire to be a mother, and that she had submitted to one, only one, act of sexual intercourse as between her and her husband.

This part of the case, in my judgment, is important to be considered. If you believe, as men of common sense, the story which without any corroboration, as I think I can show you, she told to Dr. Leach of those unutterably unnatural relations between herself and her husband, it may go some way to account for what is otherwise unaccountable; but, if you cannot accept that statement, regarded fairly and justly, but always by the light of common sense, your rejection does not stop in its effect merely by cutting out of the story so much of the statement which is so repugnant, and which is so much rejected. One act of coition in order to gratify her desire to have a child! How did she know—how could she know—that one act of coition would place her in the position to count with certainty or probability on the fruition of her hopes? Does it suggest itself as possible to be accepted as the truth? Yet that is the statement—married in 1875; that in ten years of married life there was one act of sexual intercourse between man and wife, and one act of sexual intercourse only. The birth of that stillborn child—that dead child—seems to have been a source of great physical anguish and trial to her, and she seems to have

Adelaide Bartlett.

then expressed the resolution that she would not have any more children. Her desire to be a mother, to have a child of the marriage (as my learned friend touchingly expressed it) at her knee, to grow up and be a comfort to her, and to be a thing which she could cherish, and round which the best feelings of her nature might cling and cluster, seems to have soon disappeared from her mind; but the language she used to Annie Walker was consistent only with the desire to avoid childbearing. It does not necessarily point to a cessation of marital intercourse; and there is one fact proved in this case—I mean the fact of what was found in the clothes of the dead man at No. 85 Claverton Street—which at least suggests the probability that, while there may have been sexual intercourse, means were resorted to to prevent any conception from the act of coition.

But take the whole of the story—the whole of the evidence given on that part of the case, and up to the date that, in October, 1885, they came to live on the first floor of 85 Claverton Street. Is there one scintilla of evidence to support the suggestion that Mr. and Mrs. Bartlett were living upon any other than the ordinary terms of husband and wife? So far as I know—and, if I am wrong, I, of course, will only be too glad to be corrected and put right—up to that time there is not even the suggestion that they had separate beds. There is no suggestion at any time that they had separate rooms; and so far as I know—and again I say that, if I am wrong, I shall be glad to be put right—there is not up to the month of October, when they went to No. 85 Claverton Street, the slightest suggestion that they did not habitually sleep in the same bed. At 85 Claverton Street, unquestionably, for the first week they continued to sleep in the same bed, but that was because, apparently, the landlady, Mrs. Doggett, with whom a stipulation had been made that a second bed should be bought, delayed somewhat in buying it, and apparently after that date up to 10th December they used the same room, sleeping, however, in separate beds.

Why, gentlemen, if during their whole married life they had been using the same room and occupying separate beds, that certainly would have gone but a little way to suggest that there was not the habitual and ordinary intercourse between man and wife. You know that is the habit of many persons in different classes of life, although no doubt in what are called the lower classes it is rare and uncommon. After 10th December, when that illness begins, the deceased's bed was moved into the drawing-room, and she, Mrs. Bartlett, occupied principally the sofa, which was wheeled before the fire, and at times slept in the armchair which has been referred to.

But now I get to that part of the story, and I do not wish to come back to the story of their relations. Early in 1885 Mr.

Closing Speech for the Prosecution.

and Mrs. Bartlett make the acquaintance of Mr. George Dyson.
What is the character of the acquaintance between those three persons? What were the relations they in truth stood towards one
another? What were the relations between the prisoner at the
bar and George Dyson? We probably cannot be certain that we
have got before us fully and completely reliable data upon which
to form a completely reliable opinion. Some things, however, are
quite clear. It is quite clear that George Dyson was received upon
terms of close intimacy, and I will say dangerous intimacy, by
Mrs. Bartlett and by Mrs. Bartlett's husband. There is no doubt
that she was interested in him, and that she probably thought he
was equally interested in her; but it is fair to the prisoner to say,
it is fair to Dyson to say, that whatever may have been their terms,
and their expectations of what was possible in the future, there
does not seem to be any just ground for asserting that she was
unfaithful to her dead husband, and that Dyson had, in that
particular at least, abused the friendship and confidence which
the dead man had shown him. I am sorry to say that, as I gather
the tenor of my learned friend's argument, it pointed in a very
different direction. My learned friend's argument, as I understood it, was in effect this : that the dead man saw a growing
affection and admiration between George Dyson and his wife;
that he recognised the fact that it was a growing friendship and
admiration which in the future, and in the possible event of his
death, was to culminate in a closer and nearer relation—that is
to say, in the relation of man and wife; and that he had so far
contemplated the possibility of his own prior death—he, a man
but a few years the senior of either—as to have, in that extraordinary language which Mrs. Bartlett used to Dr. Leach, made
over in reversion his living wife to a man whose friendship he
was then cultivating. The sequence of that argument—and I must
come back to this point later—the sequence of that argument is
that this compliant husband, who had in this way made over his
wife as the future wife of his friend George Dyson, finally, when
he was told by his wife, " You have made me over to Dyson; it is
unfair to him that you should exercise your rights as a husband "—
her husband turns on his pillow, and does an act which removes the only obstacle which stands in the way of the union which
he, the dead man, while living had contemplated.

My learned friend has spoken of what he described as the devotion of the prisoner at the bar. I shall have a word or two to say
on that; but it is certainly, I think you will feel—I think my
learned friend must have felt—the sad necessity of this case, and
the sad necessity of her defence, that she should, by the mouth of
her counsel, be obliged to cast this grievous stigma, this damning
slur, on the memory of her dead husband. Is there, outside her
statement, anything in the case to warrant that stigma with which

Adelaide Bartlett.

the memory of the dead man is to be branded? We are referred to two letters.

Mr. CLARKE—What stigma?

The ATTORNEY-GENERAL—My learned friend asks me what stigma? The stigma that the living husband, with obligations and with rights, caused those obligations and rights to be forgotten; he entered into a compact by which, in the event of his death, his wife was handed over to the embraces of another man, and that he stood by complacently agreeing. Does the correspondence warrant that stigma? I will read the two letters—the two principal ones referred to. One is in September, 1885; it is from Bartlett to Dyson—'' Dear George,—Permit me to say I feel great pleasure in thus addressing you for the first time. To me it is a privilege to think that I am allowed to feel towards you as a brother, and I hope our friendship may ripen as time goes on, without anything to mar its future brightness. Would that I could find words to express my thankfulness to you for the very loving letter you sent Adelaide to-day. It would have done anybody good to see her overflowing with joy as she read it whilst walking along the street, and afterwards, as she read it to me, I felt my heart going out to you. I long to tell you how proud I felt at the thought I should soon be able to clasp the hand of the man who from his heart could pen such noble thoughts. Who could help loving you? I felt that I must say to you two words, ' Thank you,' and my desire to do so is my excuse for troubling you with this. Looking towards the future with joyfulness, I am yours affectionately, Edwin.''

What is the answer? '' September 23, 1885. My dear Edwin,—Thank you very much for the brotherly letter you sent me yesterday. I am sure I respond from my heart to your wish that our friendship may ripen with the lapse of time, and I do so with confidence, for I feel that our friendship is founded on a firm abiding basis—trust and esteem. I have from a boy been ever longing for the confidence and trust of others. I have never been so perfectly happy as when in possession of this. It is in this respect, among many others, that you have shown yourself a true friend. You have thanked me, and now I thank you. Yet I ought to confess that I read your warm and generous letter with a kind of half-fear—a fear lest you should ever be disappointed in me and find me a far more prosy, matter-of-fact creature than you expect. Thank you, moreover, for the telegram; it was very considerate to send it. I am looking forward with much pleasure to next week. Thus far I have been able to stave off any work, and trust to be able to keep it clear. Dear old Dover, it will ever possess a pleasant memory for me in my mind and a warm place in my heart.—With very kind regards, believe me, yours affectionately, George.''

Is there anything in this letter to suggest, I mean reasonably

Closing Speech for the Prosecution.

The Attorney-General

to suggest—recollect, we have now got within three weeks, less than three weeks, in fact, of the termination of this sad story of the last days of Edwin Bartlett's life—is there anything to suggest, in the light of commonsense, any state of things except this: that Dyson, a man of education, as he has told you, probably a man of some literary ability, had become interested in Mr. and Mrs. Bartlett, particularly Mrs. Bartlett, and that they, particularly Mrs. Bartlett, had become interested in him? Is there anything in that letter to suggest that there was anything in any letter to either one or the other of those—any feeling other than a feeling of mutual respect and admiration, with one exception—and that is the statement which, I understand, my learned friend—I may be wrong—accepted from Mr. Dyson as the witness of truth—when Mr. Dyson went to Mr. Bartlett and said to him, straightforwardly, that he found he was becoming interested in Mrs. Bartlett, and suggested whether it was prudent that their intimacy should continue? Mr. Bartlett had confidence, apparently, in Dyson, and apparently had confidence also in his wife.

Now, gentlemen, nothing, I think, took place which it is important to call your attention to until September, the same month that I have mentioned, when the deceased man made his will, and by that will he shows his confidence in Dyson, for he makes Dyson one of his executors, and he shows his confidence and affection for his wife, because she is the person benefited under that will.

We now come to the story of the illness beginning on 10th December. What was that illness? Of course, my learned friend exerted his ingenuity and his ability, and most properly so, to present the story of that illness to you in a grave and serious aspect; but does it truly and properly bear that complexion? What is the worst that has been said of it? He was found to be suffering from sub-acute gastritis. Well, gentlemen, that sounds very formidable, just as ecchymosis of the visual organ sounds appalling; but just as the one means a black eye, so does the other mean an attack of indigestion. From that, and that only, was he suffering; for that, and that only, was he treated until the appearance of the worm, which, of course, Dr. Leach is too sensible a man to attach serious importance to; and the only apparent difficulty in the treatment, according to Dr. Leach's experience, was that the bowels of his patient were apparently obstinately costive. He is suffering from his teeth, and pays several visits to the dentist, and gets relief; and it stands on the evidence of Dr. Leach that on 25th or 26th December, I forget which, he was in exceptionally good spirits; and on 31st December he was also in very good spirits. " I cannot say good," said Dr. Leach, but said, " I must qualify it for this reason, that on the 25th and 26th he was in exceptionally good spirits." On 31st December he pays another visit to the dentist.

1A

Adelaide Bartlett.

The Attorney-General

I said in opening this case, and I repeat it, that there is no ground for suggesting that Mrs. Bartlett has, so far as can be judged, failed in her attention to her husband; but you must be good enough to bear in mind, in that connection, that if you should come to the conclusion, after patiently hearing the case, as you have done, that there was the criminal resolve in her mind, and that criminal resolve had taken a definite shape on 28th or 29th December, when she requested chloroform to be bought, you would expect the conduct of a person who had formed such a design to be such as not to attract observation, or to suggest any apparent want of affection and change of feeling in relation to the person as to whom she had conceived the criminal intent. I will ask you whether—I say no more than that—whether that scene to which Dr. Leach has spoken in the cab on the way to the dentist's, under circumstances not particularly romantic, or suggestive of the expression of romantic feeling, on the way to the dentist's to get out another stump, or two or three stumps, she expressed her wish they might be married over again, her married life had been so completely happy, and it is suggested, and very likely, if the scene described took place, he honestly joined in the expression of the same sentiment. Well, gentlemen, on that night of 31st December, he retires to bed, so far as one can judge, with but little to complain of. He was so well in his general health that the doctor said it was really unnecessary for him to keep attending him from day to day. He had eaten a hearty dinner of jugged hare; he had eaten a hearty supper of oysters; he had even ordered of the servant what he would eat for breakfast next morning. It was intended that in a day or two (I do not know exactly that the day was fixed) he should go to the seaside for a change; and it was suggested that the doctor should go with him, and the wife who was spoiling him should not come.

That was the condition of things up to the last moment when the servant closes the door on them in that front room and is told by the prisoner that she need not come unless she is called for. But something had taken place before that. On 27th December she asked Dyson to get her chloroform. He tries to get her —and even does get for her a considerable quantity of chloroform. I won't stop to inquire whether it is possible to suppose that Dyson, even if he desired to invent, could have invented that statement which the prisoner is supposed to have made to him about Dr. Nichols, of Fopstone Road, or about Annie Walker, now in America, who had previously got the prisoner the chloroform she needed, or about the story of its being wanted for external application, because Edwin was suffering from an internal affliction. I do not stop to inquire into the details of this statement. And, even if you see any ground for supposing that Dyson could have invented that matter, some excuse ought to be given, some

354

Closing Speech for the Prosecution.

The Attorney-General

reason ought to be given. You cannot doubt some reason was given. She obtains the chloroform, and why does she obtain it? That she knew, or said she knew, something about medicines, and something about poisons, seems to be clear from her own statement, if it be reliable, for Dyson thought she had a medicine chest.

Mr. CLARKE—There was not a syllable about poisons.

The ATTORNEY-GENERAL—I beg your pardon—that she had "Squire's Companion," which spoke of chloroform, and which speaks of it as an irritant poison.

Mr. CLARKE—Where is the book?

The ATTORNEY-GENERAL—Whether the book does or does not—and you can, if I am wrong, look at it—whether it speaks of it as poison, or whether it does not speak of it as poison, the chloroform is labelled "Poison," as you have heard. The chemist sells it properly so labelled, because it is in fact an irritant poison. I am asking you to ask yourselves this question, because it seems to me, with great deference, to be important : Why did she want it then? For what did she want it then? The statement is—and the only statement, I pray you to bear in mind—that she had had no act of intercourse with her husband during the whole of her married life but one, which resulted in the birth of a stillborn child ; that when he was beginning to get better, about 16th December, he began to show signs of returning passion and desire to have intercourse with her again. Is that likely? Is it likely that passion, which, according to her statement, had lain dormant for all those years—ten of married life, with that one single act excepted—should in this conjunction of circumstances, and at this time, be again aroused within him? He then lying upon his sick bed—he then being, on that 27th of December, treated as an invalid, although not suffering from a serious illness—why was it, how came it, that at this time this passion manifested itself, and how came it that that was the first time that it manifested itself? And how came it, further, that the necessity for attempting to meet and to repel the assertion upon his part of a legitimate right —to which it would be her duty, if it were asserted, to submit—how came it that it occurred to her, as a potent means of resisting the exercise of that right on his part, that she should sprinkle chloroform upon a handkerchief, and, when he was seeking to approach her, wave it over his head? Gentlemen, if you can accept that statement or that explanation, by all means accept it. Nay, I will go further. If you do not feel compelled, by the exercise of your common sense and your judgment—if you do not feel compelled by the exercise of that common sense which in the ordinary affairs of life would govern and control all your views to reject it, by all means give fair effect to it.

I come now to the matter in hand still more closely. I re-

Adelaide Bartlett.

minded you that the doctor has sworn that, at half-past four he
judged, forming the best opinion that he could, that Edwin Bartlett had been dead three hours, which brings the period of his
death to about half-past one. I reminded you that, upon the
statement of the prisoner herself, she had not gone to rest until
after midnight on that night, for she heard the people of the house
exchanging kindly New Year's greetings; and therefore the period
of time is reduced to a period at the most of an hour and a half;
and probably it is reduced to a period even less than that in which
the administration in some way or other, or the acceptance in some
way or other of this poison took place, and in which it worked its
fatal result, because, as you have heard from the medical evidence (which is in agreement on this point, whatever differences
may exist in it upon others) that it is not infrequent that a considerable time elapses, even after a considerable and a fatally strong
dose, before death ensues.

Now, gentlemen, what are the theories and what are the suggestions that have to be dealt with now? I have pointed out that
there is no suggestion, and there could be no suggestion, of accident in the matter. I remind you that death must have been
caused, and could only have been caused, either by the intentional
administration, or by the intentional suicide, by the taking of
this poisonous irritant. There are two ways in which it may have
been administered. The one which was suggested by the medical
evidence before the magistrate at the Police Court was that the
administration down the throat might have been preceded by a
state of insensibility produced by inhalation—a state of insensibility total or partial. With that my learned friend has dealt,
and dealt at great length. It is not for the prosecution to suggest theories, or to ask the jury to accept theories. It is for the
prosecution to see that the full facts of the case are before the
jury, to point to the result which seems to them to be fairly the
result deducible from those facts, and to leave the jury to apply
their own judgments as to what is the theory upon which this
result of guilt, if it were guilt, should be based.

I took the liberty of suggesting to my learned friend yesterday, at the adjournment, that there was, of course, another possible
view of the administration of this poisonous irritant. But my
learned friend, in his discretion, did not think it necessary to
deal with it, and I shall merely utter a sentence about it, and leave
you to deal with it. For I do not desire to conceal from myself
—on the contrary, I wish to make it apparent to you—that, whatever theory is suggested in this case as to the mode in which the
poison got into the stomach of the dead man, about every theory
there is a difficulty. But there are, in the case of the suggested
theory of suicide, difficulties which, it is my submission to you,
are insuperable. The suggestion which I ventured to make was

356

Closing Speech for the Prosecution.

this : that, in addition to the possibility of the prisoner having administered chloroform while the man was lying on his back, and with his mouth open, in a state of partial or total insensibility, there was another way—that, if the draught had been handed to him in a glass, and given to him as if for an ordinary purpose, with drops of chloroform in it, and water or some other thing, to drink, then it was conceivable that the dying man would have gulped it down, believing in its innocence, and not suspecting that the prisoner had administered something which was wrong and injurious.

Mr. CLARKE—My lord, it is with great reluctance, but I feel bound to interpose at this point. I protest against any such suggestion being put forward, for the first time, at this stage of the case, when it was not even hinted by the learned counsel for the prosecution in his opening, or in the examination of any of the witnesses. My lord, it is the fact that yesterday the learned Attorney-General, at the adjournment, told me that he thought that the case was open to that suggestion. That was when I was in the middle of my speech, when I had dealt with, and had finally left, the medical evidence in regard to this case. I founded my comments and my cross-examination on the passage in my learned friend's opening, in which he said : " There remains only one other mode (apart from the one pointed out) by which it could have been taken. You will say that, if it was administered by a third person, the physical effect would be the same; and you will be quite right, provided the administration into the stomach was not preceded by an external application by which the person was lulled into a state of stupor." But I really do not recognise any private communication in the course of this case as a matter with which I have to deal; and I do respectfully protest that this suggestion ought not to be made in substitution of the original suggestion that has been made.

The ATTORNEY-GENERAL—I am not making any suggestion, or any substitution of any suggestion; but when my learned friend is erecting one theory—namely, the theory of suicide—I am entitled—nay, I will not put it so low as that—I am bound, as I think, to submit any theory which would point in a more probable direction, and which would go to negative the suggestion which my learned friend would make. I was adding to my comment at the moment when my learned friend interposed, that I do not suggest that that theory is one which is free from difficulties either. It is not; because it will immediately have occurred to you that the theory that it was administered by the hand of the prisoner, and that it was taken by the deceased man in confidence and gulped down, might possibly have removed some difficulties, but it would not have removed all, because he would be conscious of the presence in his stomach of an irritant poison, or at all events

357

Adelaide Bartlett.

of the presence of something in his stomach which was causing him pain and anguish, the result of which would probably have been violent exclamations and violent physical effort on his part. I am not, therefore, at all putting it forward to you as a theory which is free from difficulties, but I do put it forward as a theory to which the medical evidence mainly was addressed; and I do put it forward also as a theory which presents difficulties which are nothing, or which sink into insignificance, as compared with those difficulties which meet one upon the theory that under these circumstances this man deliberately did an act to take away his own life. My learned friend, indeed, in his speech seemed to me rather to have had present to his mind the other theory which I have suggested, although he did not think it right to deal with it, even when I spoke to him on the matter, because my learned friend said in his opening that chloroform could not be poured down a person's throat unless he or she, being unwilling, had been rendered practically insensible before.

Mr. CLARKE—I think that was by way of reference, and in fact it was almost a quotation from my learned friend's own speech.

The ATTORNEY-GENERAL—So much the better.

Mr. CLARKE—It begins, '' My learned friend said in his opening.'' Those were my words.

The ATTORNEY-GENERAL—Quite right. I say it shows that my learned friend appreciated that when I was speaking of the administration, first by the preliminary step of inhalation causing insensibility, and then followed by the conveyance into the stomach, of the chloroform—that my learned friend had in his mind, as I had apparently in my mind, the case of the patient being unwilling, and therefore that I was contemplating the case where the patient—the dead man—had the glass handed to him, and gulped it down willingly and in confidence, believing that it did not contain anything poisonous or noxious.

Gentlemen, in reference to the theory as to which the medical men have spoken, let us examine it for a moment or two. They say, in relation to that question, that causing insensibility to a person asleep is possible, although attended with some difficulty. But does it follow in this case, if that course was followed at all, that the attempt to render insensible the deceased man even began when he was asleep? Why may it not have preceded that stage? If that was the difficulty, the difficulty as to causing insensibility by inhalation by a man who is asleep disappears. Then comes the second point. My learned friend's argument is this: that the evidence shows that, in a position such as I have described, a state of insensibility is reached which is accompanied by contraction of the muscles, and probably a contraction of the jaws. My learned friend will remember that the evidence did not point

358

Closing Speech for the Prosecution.

The Attorney-General

to that as an invariable accompaniment at all; and in the next place that they spoke of that as not being a constant accompaniment of the administration of chloroform by inhalation. It is true they went on to say, and it is quite right that that should be considered fairly and fully by you, that in that condition which I have suggested, and assuming that no difficulty of contraction was to be got over, that the administration into the gullet was a matter of some difficulty—" delicacy," I think, is the word used. It might be said, I should have supposed, that a medical man desiring to perform this operation would do so so as to run no risk to the person to whom he administered the chloroform. But, gentlemen, considerations of delicacy have no place in the consideration of counsel in judging of the probability of the thing being done, if you should, in view of the whole of the facts, after carefully weighing them, come to the conclusion that the object of the person administering was not that it should be performed with surgical delicacy, but that it should be effective for the only purpose which, according to the criminal intent, it supposes it could be effective. Gentlemen, we start from this fact: death caused by the introduction into the stomach of an irritant poison. How did it get there? is the sole question in that case. It is not suggested, and could not be suggested in any view of the case, and my learned friend saw the difficulty of arguing it upon that suggestion, that it could have got there accidentally. Then it is reduced to the two points of whether the man did it himself with a suicidal intent, or whether some one else did it with criminal intent. If some one else did it with a criminal intent, that some one else can be no one but the prisoner at the bar. Now, did he do it with suicidal intent? Everything seems against such a theory. He was prosperous in business. He had apparently known no illness until 10th December. By 25th December he had practically regained his health, and was in exceptionally good spirits, and on 31st December he was also in good spirits, and, if that statement in the cab is to be relied upon, he was on good terms with himself, and on good terms with his wife, while his arrangements of that night, and his arrangements for the next morning, and his contemplated arrangements in reference to his leaving town for a change of air, all point—you must say whether they do not conclusively point—to a man who then felt the enjoyment of life, and you must say whether these facts do not conclusively negative the probability—I would almost say the possibility—of a sudden idea of interfering with his own life. One can understand, indeed, if some appalling misfortune had come upon him, if some extraordinary revelation of horror had been made to him, that, in sudden disgust of life, he might resort to the weak and criminal resource of ending it by his own hand. But is there anything of that kind here? Again we have only the statement which the

359

Adelaide Bartlett.

prisoner made on 26th January to Dr. Leach. What is that statement? That having, through the instrumentality of Mr. Dyson,
procured this large quantity of chloroform upon 28th December,
she does nothing with it. She mentions its possession to no one.
She says nothing about it to Dr. Leach. She says nothing about it
to her husband, but on 31st December she says she could not
have a secret from Edwin; she tells Edwin why she had got it. She
tells him the purpose for which she intended to use it, namely, to
resist the embraces of her husband; and she says to him, " It is
an offence to my womanhood; nay, it is an injury to Mr. Dyson,
to whom you have made me over."

Mr. CLARKE—She does not say that exactly.

The ATTORNEY-GENERAL—I do not pretend to use the exact
words, but it is the substance which I am seeking to convey. I do
not care for the exact expression—" You have given me over to
Mr. Dyson; it is not fair that you, my living husband "—as to
whom, looking at the ordinary duration of human life, it is fair
to say that he might have looked forward to twenty or thirty years
of life—" it is not fair that you should approach me; should you
live to be seventy years of age, during the whole of that interven-
ing period you are to be debarred all exercise in my regard, the
exercise of which it is my wifely duty to submit to." Does your
common sense—can your common sense—accept that suggestion?
But what follows upon that? Is there expostulation? Is there
angry remonstrance? No suggestion of the kind; but the husband
turns upon his pillow, is sullen, and sulks, or appears to sulk;
and it is suggested that she leaves the room, and she comes back,
and notices him breathing; she composes herself to sleep in the
chair at the foot of his bed, with her left hand and arm upon his
clothes. The suggestion is that, in that short interval of absence
from the room, he had done the act which had for its result to
deprive him of his life. Can that be accepted as the explanation?
Let me follow this out a little more closely. What does it suppose?
What does it necessarily involve? If he takes the bottle, and out
of the bottle directly he takes a fatal dose, is it to be supposed he
had sufficient consciousness and self-control to have repressed in
that awful moment a cry of anguish and despair? Is he supposed
to have had sufficient control to have re-stoppered the bottle and
put it back upon the mantelpiece? Or is it supposed—which I
understood to be rather my friend's suggestion—that in the very
brief interval of absence of his wife, he stretches from the bed, or
gets from the bed, and takes the bottle, and takes a wineglass, fills
the wineglass with a necessary quantity, re-stoppers the bottle,
puts the bottle back upon the mantelpiece, gets back into bed,
takes the wineglassful of chloroform, and puts the wineglass, I
know not where? Is that possible? Is it probable? Well, but we
are only at the very beginning of the difficulty in testing this

360

Closing Speech for the Prosecution.

The Attorney-General

theory. Is it conceivable that if he had availed himself, as it is the suggestion, of her absence from the room for the space of what he could not count upon being more than a few minutes——

Mr. CLARKE—Why not?

The ATTORNEY-GENERAL—My learned friend asks me why not? I am dealing with the theory which is put forward—which I understood to be the theory—that she had temporarily left the room for the purpose of preparing herself for rest for the night.

Mr. CLARKE—She absolutely went into the other room to wash and change her dress for the night, as was usual.

The ATTORNEY-GENERAL—I assumed that to be my learned friend's theory, and was doing so, and supposed he could not count upon her absence from the room beyond a few minutes—I care not whether it was three, or five, or ten, or fifteen—for this purpose it matters not. She then is supposed to have come back. And recollect, this theory falls to pieces and crumbles up on examination, unless you are also prepared to believe that when she comes back—the man having taken the fatal dose; she has meanwhile heard no sign, no utterance of pain or distress—that when she comes back she finds him apparently tranquilly sleeping in his bed in such a condition that she, the anxious, the affectionate wife, is able to compose herself at the foot of the bed, and go to sleep.

It is my duty, and it is not a pleasant one, to put these facts strongly before you. Again I say, we are only at the beginning of this difficulty in testing this theory. The theory is that he has, in one or other of the ways which I have mentioned, administered to himself this poison. The theory involves the presence of that bottle of chloroform, according to the suggestion made, upon the mantelshelf. I will pursue this story in order to test it with reference to that point. What became of the bottle of chloroform? I do not stop to dwell upon—they are too insignificant, in view of the wider considerations which rush upon one's mind—the suggestions of change of dress, which may be extensive as my learned friend says, as I do not stop to dwell upon the statement of Doggett or of others. The fire had been carefully attended to, which is too insignificant also to dwell upon—but before the servant is called, before the house is roused, before the doctor comes, that bottle of chloroform has been removed. By whom? When? Why? You, gentlemen, will gravely ask yourselves these questions. For this at least is clear, that when the doctor comes and finds the patient whom he had left the day before practically in good health, when he comes and finds him dead, and when he sees nothing to account for his death upon the surface of things, he, as he swears, made an examination to see whether there was anything in the room which could in any way afford a clue to the cause of death. He made an examination, of course, much more exact, as you would expect a medical man in such circumstances would do, than Doggett

361

Adelaide Bartlett.

did. Whatever may be said of Dr. Leach's evidence, this seems to be clear : that he swore—and you will probably think him reliable—that he searched the room upon that occasion, the mantel-shelf, and the stand, and the other parts of the room, and he swears there was no bottle of chloroform there.

Gentlemen, it may be possibly suggested that, if this lady had indeed done this criminal thing, she would have left the bottle of chloroform, and probably have put it in close proximity to the deceased in order to suggest the possibility of his having used it. If it had been so left, other suggestions, I think, of a cogent kind might be made. But if you have had any experience of, or in your observation in life have watched the history of crime, you will find that it constantly occurs, as if by the operation of a mysterious Providence, that plans of a criminal character, carried out with firmness, and apparently thought out to results intended to shield from the consequences of guilt, have failed because of some short-sighted omission which the criminal has made. But, again, we are at the beginning of grave difficulties in consideration of this theory. When Dr. Leach comes, he puts to her pointedly and strongly, not then only, but on subsequent days : could he have taken poison? Was there anything he could have taken? She says, " No," and it is not, gentlemen, until 26th January that to Dr. Leach she gives the detailed and circumstantial account which you are asked to accept, and in which she explains the possession of chloroform upon her part. By themselves, if you have to take account of these single things, each one by itself, indeed, the demand for the chloroform, and the reasons, the untrue reasons, given for wanting it, each one by itself is not very cogent; but when you have circumstance after circumstance gathering accumulative force as they are massed together, and when you support them by the fact—the admitted fact, I may say—of a death from an unnatural cause, and that unnatural cause the presence of chloroform evidenced in excessive doses in the man's stomach; and when the circumstances of the case negative, as we say, *a priori*, the probability of this man contemplating suicide in the circumstances in which he was, with years of life and prosperity before him—when those circumstances negative the probability of his contemplating the suicidal act of interfering with his own life—when you have all those circumstances leading up to, and when the suggestion is made of suicide, when the suggestion is made of the mode of suicide, and the circumstances of suicide do not bear the test of critical examination in all its phases, then you must ask yourselves : are these circumstances reasonably consistent with innocence on the part of the person who alone, if it was administered by anybody else, was, or could be, the person who administered it?

Again let me remind you, as I took the liberty of doing at the outset, that in this class of case you cannot expect demonstration.

Closing Speech for the Prosecution.

The Attorney General

Crimes of this kind are not performed in the light of day. The steps leading to the consummation of guilt are not perpetrated step by step under the eyes of living witnesses. It would be deplorable indeed if, when direct evidence or proof to demonstration is not forthcoming, juries were to shrink from doing their duty in fixing guilt where guilt lies if, in their opinion, with reasonable cogency and certainty, the conclusion is forced upon their minds that guilt does lie upon the person against whom the crime is charged.

Gentlemen, a little more. It will be said: oh, but if this lady was on these terms of affection towards her husband, if she was the devoted wife which the evidence suggests she was, what possible motive can she have had? Gentlemen, this is a matter which again you are the judges of. Short of the suggestion of criminal guilt as between her and Dyson, short of the charge of actual unfaithfulness to her husband, is there no evidence pointing to the probability of what was the actual state of feeling between Mr. Dyson and her? That she had become interested in Dyson is manifest; that she was a woman of stronger will and firmer purpose than Dyson is, I think, manifest; for while he, in the face of this death, was appalled, and when it was suggested that chloroform was the cause of death, he saw the risk that he ran, and the culpable part that he had played, although unwittingly, and he wishes to, and, in fact, he does confess, to Mrs. Matthews his part in it, and afterwards before the coroner. She, you will remember, makes a statement to him showing that she at least was resolute: " If you don't incriminate me, I won't incriminate you; " or, I believe the converse is the way it was put: " I won't incriminate you if you don't incriminate yourself "; she was firm to the purpose. He was not conscious of having been a party to any possible criminal use of this chloroform, but she knew the injurious effect of the fact that he had procured it for her, and procured it from three different chemists; and on the very day of her husband's death, in addition to the cheque, she presents him with her husband's watch, and says that Edwin told her to give it to him. When did he tell her? Under what circumstances did he tell her? What shadow of evidence is there to suggest that, at any time before 31st December, this man had contemplated anything but a life of ordinary duration, such as his age and circumstances would suggest as probable? It is true, if you are to believe some of the witnesses, she had suggested something of the very kind. She had suggested an internal affliction—paroxysms of pain; and Mrs. Matthews overheard a conversation in which Dyson had charged her with having stated to him that Edwin would die sooner, or would die earlier.

Mr. CLARKE—" That he would not live long " was the expression.

The ATTORNEY-GENERAL—I am much obliged to my learned friend: that Edwin would not live long—meaning his condition.

Adelaide Bartlett.

The Attorney-General

Do not the facts point to some such relation between Dyson and her as that which I have suggested to you? One cannot but see, looking to his physical condition, the state of his gums, the state of his teeth, the offensively fœtid breath which is spoken of, that her husband may have become personally distasteful to her; that she had begun to see in Dyson a man of superior education, although apparently of no physical attractions; a man with whom her husband unfavourably compared; may she not have felt—did she not feel then this feeling growing upon her? And when she knew—I am not now suggesting motive—that the will had been made in the September previously by which she was benefited, that the will was free from the restriction which was supposed to have existed in the earlier will, namely, that she did not receive the benefit merely during her widowhood, but was absolutely the beneficiary under the second will—in this condition of things the evil comes into her mind to avail herself of this illness, and of the presence there of a medical man, who arrived on 10th December, and who was a stranger to her, and a stranger to him, and as to whom I think one may safely say he would hardly be described as a strong-headed man : this chain of circumstances occurred to her as one in which she might take advantage of the opportunity of ridding herself of a husband who had become distasteful to her, and for whom she had ceased to care, that she might clear the way to a union with the man for whom she had of late conceived admiration and apparently affection.

But, gentlemen, it is no part of the necessity of the case to establish the motive, although I admit the importance of it. The question of motive undoubtedly is important, or the absence of motive undoubtedly is important; but if the facts of the case lead you to the conclusion, step by step, that you must reject the other theories of the mode in which this chloroform was administered, and if the logic of the facts drives you to the conclusion with practically irresistible force that it must have been administered with criminal intent by some one, then the fact that you will not be able to satisfy yourselves about the strength or even about the character of the motive cannot, I am afraid, relieve you from the responsibility which rests upon you of giving effect by your verdict to the view which you take of the criminal responsibility of the person charged.

Very early after this death there was a suggestion of chloroform—I think as early as, or earlier than, the 6th; the exact date is not material. But she takes away the chloroform. She makes away with it. I want to ask you again, how is that consistent with innocent thought; how is it consistent with innocent act in the matter? Above all, and this idea I wish to emphasise, or rather wish you to emphasise—above all, if she, for she must have known, believed that the theory of suicide, which is suggested so forcibly

Closing Speech for the Prosecution.

The Attorney-General

and so ably by my learned friend, was the explanation of the cause, how came it that not even in that intimate communication to Dr. Leach, which Dr. Leach so sympathetically received, is there a suggestion on her part as to how the thing could occur? If this was present to her as the mode in which the thing did occur, how comes it that she takes such pains apparently to remove from the room that which would have needed some explanation, and to remove from the house at a later date that which, so far from being proof of her guilt, would have built up the story which would account for her innocence? All these are circumstances, gentlemen, with which you must deal. I have done my duty, with the assistance of my learned friends, in putting the case before you, and in endeavouring to urge upon your attention the points which seem to be worthy of that attention.

My learned friend Mr. Clarke was good enough to say that I opened this case fairly and moderately. Gentlemen, I said then, and I repeat now, that it is not, and never ought to be, in a criminal case, a struggle, a personal struggle, for a verdict—to that I subscribe; but I do not subscribe to this—that the prosecuting counsel discharge their duty unless they fully and strongly, but always fairly, put before the jury all the matters which in their judgment, and according to their experience, ought to inform the mind of the tribunal which will ultimately have to decide the question. Gentlemen, that done, our task and our responsibility end.

My learned friend has said that the spirit of justice in the jury-box will be the friend and the protector of the prisoner at the bar. Let me say the spirit of justice, and whose friend it is to be proved to be, depend upon the antecedent question which is not yet determined—is there guilt here, or is there innocence here? The spirit of justice, if there be guilt, cannot be invoked to conjure up doubts or to protect a criminal. Even as justice is blind, so ought justice to be deaf to appeals, to prejudice, or to passion. Justice is open to the impression of the truth. The truth is the point to which your attention is to be drawn, and upon which it is to be fixed. The law requires that you should give—and it rightly requires that you should give—the benefit of any fair and reasonable doubt which, upon the facts, remains in your minds. I ask you to give the benefit of that doubt, if that doubt does remain, but it must be a doubt which would operate upon your minds in the ordinary important affairs of life, and it is not to be a doubt which you may or must conjure up for the sake of having a doubt. It must be a doubt which presents itself to your minds as reasoning men anxious to discharge your duty between the prisoner and the public—the Crown, whom we represent—a doubt which you cannot overcome. Apply your minds, I pray you, gentlemen, in that spirit; consider and weigh the facts of the case in that spirit;

Adelaide Bartlett.

and if you come to the conclusion that still a doubt of the nature that I have mentioned remains, in God's name give this woman the benefit of that doubt. But if, after you have heard my lord, and you have retired from that box, and find yourselves face to face with the responsibility of the duty that devolves upon you, and the conviction is borne in upon your mind that you cannot receive this theory of suicide; if the conviction remains in your mind, although you may not be able to state with accuracy to your own satisfaction the exact methods or means by which it is accomplished, that guilt lies at this woman's door, then I ask you, by the duty you owe to your oaths, and to the country which you represent, not to shrink from the responsibility which in that event will be cast upon you.

Mr. CLARKE—Before your lordship begins, a communication has been made to me by Annie Walker, or from Annie Walker, who was called as a witness. We have, of course, had no communication with her. I don't know, whether your lordship, before beginning to sum up, would ask Annie Walker one question with regard to anything she knew as to the single act—your lordship will know what I mean; she was attending at the confinement—if your lordship thinks it right to ask the question as to whether, at that time, she became aware of that matter. I say no more.

Mr. WRIGHT—Whatever course your lordship thinks right and fair to be taken in the matter—I do not mind what the point is or what the question is—anything that can elucidate the truth.

Mr. JUSTICE WILLS—It is very late, but I think one should never shut out anything that may be material. Let Annie Walker step up.

Mrs. ANNIE WALKER, recalled, examined by Mr. CLARKE—At the time you nursed Mrs. Bartlett in her confinement, did you become aware from anything she said to you with regard to its having been the result of a single act?—Yes, sir.

By Mr. JUSTICE WILLS—What was it?—That it happened only once—on a Sunday afternoon.

She said so?—Both of them; that there was always some preventive used.

You say you had that from both of them?—Both of them.

Charge to the Jury.

Mr. JUSTICE WILLS—Gentlemen of the jury, before I address myself to the complicated facts of this difficult case, I should like, on public grounds, to say one word about a matter to which a good deal of reference has been made in the addresses both of the learned

Charge to the Jury.

Mr Justice Wills

counsel for the defence and of the learned Attorney-General, and that is as to the exercise by the Attorney-General of his undoubted right of reply in this case. I refer to that which has but a small bearing upon the result, because I am always anxious that no erroneous impression should go forth as to the spirit in which justice is administered in this country. A rule has existed for a very great number of years back—I cannot tell you when exactly it arose, but it has been for generations the established practice, that where the Attorney-General or the Solicitor-General, representing the Crown is personally present, conducting the business of the country on behalf of the Crown, the Attorney-General or Solicitor-General or the counsel associated with him may exercise a right which belongs to no one else, namely, of claiming a reply, although no evidence be given on behalf of the prisoner. It is, as has been said, in a certain sense an anomaly, but a great many things in our legal system are more or less tinctured with anomaly; and the fact that it exists at the present day must be taken, I think, as an evidence that it has been found to work well, and that on grounds of public advantage it is desirable to retain it, or else it would very soon be abolished. Probably, there was a danger of the right being strained too far, because at no very distant period it was the habit of counsel who were instructed by the Treasury, although the Attorney-General or Solicitor-General might not have been present, to claim, and exercise, this right. I have exercised it myself when I was at the bar under these circumstances. And it was felt that there might be a danger of that practice degenerating into an abuse when the Treasury had taken upon itself so important a part of the criminal work of the country as it has done of late years by replacing the public prosecutor. I myself was present at a council of the judges at which it was determined that for the future the right should be claimed and exercised only by the direct representatives of the Crown—that is, in cases in which the Attorney-General or Solicitor-General is or has been personally present conducting the case on the part of the Crown. Under these circumstances it was felt that there should be no attempt to tamper with the right which has existed for so long, when exercised by or under the sanction of the highest legal officers of the Crown, under sanctions and circumstances such as make it certain that it will not be abused. At times it may be exercised, and ought to be exercised, in the public interests, and the learned Attorney-General in this case has no more right, as representing the Crown, to make a present of that prerogative, which is vested in him for no personal purpose or private ends, but simply for the public advantage, than I should have to dispense with the usual marks of outward respect which are paid to judges, many of which by a man of simple habits and careless so far as he is personally con-

Adelaide Bartlett.

cerned about such matters, might very well be forgotten or over-looked. Such things are vested in the officers of justice for public purposes. Those to whom they are entrusted must keep undiminished the power and authority of the office they exercise, and hand them down unimpaired by any acts of their own. I have thought it right to say thus much, because it is eminently undesirable that it should be supposed that in matters of this kind the law is harsh or unreasonable, or that due consideration has not been given by those who are concerned in the administration of justice to the exercise, and to the limitations in the exercise, of a prerogative of this kind.

Before I refer more in detail to the facts of this case let me also make one comment upon the course which the Crown have pursued here in presenting no evidence against Mr. Dyson, and offering him here as a witness instead of treating him as a prisoner on his trial. I think, gentlemen, that the interests of the prisoner now under trial, at all events, have not suffered by that course. The advisers of the Crown, having the best means of judging, and having very often in matters of this kind the means of exercising a judgment on more or less reliable materials beyond those which come before the Court, approach such a question with the deepest sense of duty and responsibility. The matter is in the hands, in this case, of the highest representative of the learning and the knowledge and the judgment of the bar; and the advisers of the Crown, approaching it undoubtedly in a spirit of unflinching justice, and nothing else, have come to the conclusion that it was not proper to present the case of Mr. Dyson as one deserving investigation before you, and, they having done so, this case must be conducted—as far as any observations which I have to offer upon it are concerned—upon the principle that Mr. Dyson is innocent. No one who has been present throughout this investigation can doubt that, if Mr. Dyson had stood in that dock, he would have had a good deal to get rid of, and a good deal to get rid of which, had it been given in evidence—and, in my judgment, it must have been given in evidence—against this prisoner, would have told with more or less fatal effect against her as well as against him. I refer to the circumstances of uncommon suspicion under which he made the purchase of the chloroform. Now all that is gone as against the prisoner at the bar, and she is relieved from the stress of considerations which, if you had been told to neglect, you would have been incapable of neglecting, and which, in my opinion, must have been before you even if the case had proceeded against this prisoner alone without Mr. Dyson standing by her side in the dock. Gentlemen, I need not tell you that before this case came into Court I had well considered the matter, and I had come to the conclusion that the circumstances attending the purchase of the chloroform by him could not

Mr. Justice Wills.

Charge to the Jury.

Mr Justice Wills

have been excluded even in the consideration of the case against this prisoner; and if Mr. Dyson had not been relieved from suspicion by the action of the Crown, there would have been a state of circumstances given in evidence that, as it turns out, ought not to weigh against her, but which, though we had talked about them and attempted to explain them away till midnight, you would never have been able to discard, which, without the emphatic and absolute acquittal of Mr. Dyson by those best able to form a judgment upon his share in the transaction, must have affected the whole atmosphere of this case. And, inasmuch as this case must now be looked at, from beginning to end, from the point of view that he is innocent of any malpractice tending to the death of this unfortunate man—inasmuch as his entire innocence is to be accepted, not merely as an intellectual exercise, but as the fact which is to dictate the attitude of mind in which we approach the case, I cannot help thinking that, so far from the course which the Crown have pursued in this matter having been of any disadvantage to the prisoner now on her trial, it has been an immense gain to her. It has had this further advantage, that Mr. Dyson has been subjected to cross-examination, that Mr. Dyson has been seen in the witness-box, and that we—that is to say, you and I whose arduous task it is now to approach the investigation of this difficult and, in some sense, mysterious case—are not fettered by any difficulty which necessarily and inevitably stood in the way of the learned counsel for the prisoner in dealing with Mr. Dyson's evidence; and we may take so much of it as we feel it safe to rely upon, and we may reject so much as we should not choose to act upon in the serious concerns of our own lives. To what extent that limitation ought to go I shall have the opportunity of observing hereafter; but I do feel anxious to give this preliminary expression of my opinion with regard to a matter as to which, upon the first day of this trial, my opinion was more or less invited, but about which necessarily I forbore to express an opinion until the whole course of the case should have been run. I am now in a far better position than I could then be to form a judgment as to the effect of such a step upon the course of justice and the fate of the person who has such supreme interests at stake in this matter. I have the satisfaction of feeling that the step which has been taken, and which, as I pointed out then, was within the undoubted competence of the Crown, has not only conduced to the ends of justice, but has been of great advantage to the prisoner at the bar.

Now, gentlemen, the history of these people whose lives we have more or less to consider, and the death of one of whom forms the immediate subject of our inquiry, begins with the year 1875, when at the age of between nineteen and twenty this woman was married to Mr. Bartlett. She was a Frenchwoman, or a foreigner

Adelaide Bartlett.

Mr Justice Wills

at all events, and she seems to have been imperfectly educated, for after her marriage, although at the age of twenty, which is an age at which the formal instruction of women has generally ceased, she was sent to school, first in England, and then in Belgium, and for two or three years she saw her husband but occasionally, when he went over to visit her, or when her holidays gave her the leisure of joining and associating with him.

In 1878 they were living at Station Road, Herne Hill, for a considerable time, and there the father, upon the death of his wife, went to join them. He had not been long with them before they quarrelled, and a deep-seated quarrel no one can doubt took place then, which has left its traces in considerable animosity, I think I am right in saying, on both sides. Towards the close of last December the prisoner wrote to him in language which unmistakably stamps her feelings towards him. She wished him to know that she had neither forgiven nor forgotten the past. He certainly has, and had, no goodwill towards her, because, without going further than is necessary into matters of this kind which have but a remote bearing on this case, there is something that calls to one's lips unbidden the name of Judas in the kiss with which he parted from his daughter-in-law on 1st January —when he was undoubtedly entertaining suspicions that she had taken away the life of his son. But fortunately, as it seems to me, very little indeed depends upon the evidence of the senior Bartlett, and with the sole observation which Mr. Clarke made yesterday, and to the benefit of which his client is certainly entitled— that from the hour of his appearance on the scene after his son's death, she must be regarded as having lived under the observation of keen and suspicious eyes—with that remark I really think I may dismiss him from the scene, and shall have no occasion further to refer to him. I do not pause to inquire even into the merits of the dispute of 1878, save to say this, that I view with the natural instinct of a trained lawyer—and that is synonymous with saying with the instincts of a man trained to try and get at the truth—I view with the natural instincts of a lawyer the statements of a man who says, " I put my hand to a document which I now say was false," and I prefer to accept the document rather than the statement of its falsehood.

In 1878 or 1879 Mr. Bartlett would seem to have had a little discomfort with his teeth. It is possible that may have a bearing upon the matters connected with his later illness. The father said they were all running into one another, which, I suppose, means this, that there was some carious and unhealthy inflammation. This led to their being sawn off—a most exceptional treatment, I should suppose—and from that time he seems to have used false teeth. In 1880 he insured his life, and was then in excellent health, and was accepted as a first-class life by the insurance office.

Charge to the Jury.

Mr Justice Wills

In 1881 a child was born—begotten under circumstances certainly remarkable, and as to which the evidence we have heard to-day is, to my mind, of very considerable importance in trying to ascertain the truth in this case. I will not conceal from you, gentlemen, that at a very early period of my own study of this case—for, of course, I had to study it through the depositions, before I came into this Court—I was struck by a fact which is scarcely mentioned in these depositions, and of which, but for a memorandum accompanying the exhibits which were laid before the coroner, I should have known nothing—possibly you would have known nothing—that is, that, after this man's death, French letters were found in his pockets; and I thought that before this trial was over it would turn to have an important bearing upon the case. It is an unpleasant subject. The case is full of unpleasant subjects. There is another unpleasant subject which cannot be dismissed either, because, unless we understand who and what these people were, and unless we divest them and their doings of false and meretricious romance, we shall have no chance of exercising an unbiassed judgment. There was a very unpleasant book that formed one of the articles of his domestic furniture. Whatever shame may attend the possession and the reading of such books should not fall too heavily upon the wife. One can scarcely think that in any decent household, and with any decent husband, such books would be put before the wife; and, if this was part of his daily food, it is no wonder she should partake of it. Apparently there are people who can read these books and see no shame in them. Annie Walker, who saw it, seems a respectable woman, and she says there is not a word immoral or improper in the book from the beginning to the end. Gentlemen, it has been my unpleasant duty to look at this book. I entertain myself an entirely different opinion, and there is one passage, notably, which instructs the ladies and gentlemen of our land, to whom this book's outpouring of impurity is supposed to be addressed, in the last invented means of procuring abortion; and yet we are invited to look upon this book as an effusion of purity, and an honest attempt to help people in the conduct of their lives. If I thought that the strictures I am compelled to make on this book would tell materially against the woman in the dock, I should say much less about it, but I cannot, sitting here, have such garbage passed under my eyes and then allow it to go forth that an English judge concurs in the view that it is a specimen of pure and healthy literature. It is one of those books, in my judgment, which, under the garb of ostentatious purity, obtains entrance, probably, into many a household from which it would be otherwise certain to be banished. It scatters its poison and does its mischief. The women of the present day are used to strange things—things which would have

Adelaide Bartlett.

startled us in the time of my boyhood; and it is such reading as this that helps to unsex them, and to bring them to a place like this day after day to listen willingly to details which, even to men of mature life, like yourselves and myself, and to men like myself unwillingly steeped in the experience of criminal Courts and in knowledge which untainted men would gladly dispense with, are distasteful and disgusting.

If you care to verify what I say, I have put down upon a piece of paper references to passages met with in my inspection of this book, which, in my judgment, not only justify me in expressing myself with regard to it in language such as this, but compel me to do so. To my thinking, it should excite a feeling of pity for the unhappy woman, made in early life the companion of a man who could throw such literature in her way, and encourage her to read it. She must have got rid of much of a woman's natural instincts before she could lend it to her friend Mr. Matthews—to a man. It excites a pity that I can scarcely venture to indulge in, because we have sterner matters here to deal with than pity, and one must reject all influences and all thoughts which could tend to disturb the judgment or to ruffle the calm of intellectual inquiry. Oddly enough, when the copy was handed up to me, it opened of itself at the passage to which Mr. Clarke referred. It is true that the passage, which at the first moment I thought was of the usual character, recommends abstinence as the only means of preventing the natural results of married life. I thought, gentlemen, though I should not have said so but for what happened this morning—I thought it would be strange if, whatever the suggestion was, the desired result should be brought about in *that* fashion ended there. One has learnt to-day what is the natural and to be expected consequences of indulgence in literature of that kind.

Now, gentlemen, in 1885 these people, who, with all the vulgar facts now known, which make it impossible to hold up this man as more than a Joseph, and to treat him as the hero of an absurd romance, and capable of an almost superhuman self-restraint, still were living, after their fashion, happily and contented together—there is one unbroken chain of evidence that they were happy together—and between whom, except upon one occasion, with regard to the father, no quarrel seems to have come—had the great misfortune to make the acquaintance of the Rev. George Dyson. I say, the misfortune—and I am justified in saying so—because, even upon the theory which was so eloquently put before you yesterday by Mr. Clarke of the last moments of this unhappy man, it was the shadow of the Rev. George Dyson that had fallen on his path. But for that acquaintance, they would have continued probably to this hour to be living happily and comfortably together.

Charge to the Jury.

Mr Justice Wills

And whatever you may think—and I earnestly press upon you, with your whole minds and wills, to approach this case with the conviction, and to act upon that conviction throughout, that Mr. Dyson is guiltless of any complicity in murder or designs of murder —whatever you may think of his innocence in this respect, it is not a pleasant spectacle that of a Christian minister entering into this unwholesome discussion about the two wives, one for companionship and one for service—joining in it apparently with little touch of those sentiments which you would naturally expect such matters to arouse in the breast of a Christian minister—gradually becoming the intimate friend of both husband and wife; according to his own account, before there had been a shadow of a justification for it or a hint by the husband that it was welcome, addressing to the wife the words of unhallowed and unchristian admiration; steadily taking advantage of the husband's weakness, increasing the frequency of his visits, and kissing, according to himself, in the presence, and according to himself also, in the absence of the husband, the wife; under the guise of giving lessons (as to which, however, there is scarcely a trace of corroborative evidence), passing hour after hour—twice, three times, or four times a week—with the woman; letting her sit at his knee on the ground and with her head reclining on his lap, and justifying all this to himself by the miserable pretext that he was listening to the maudlin nonsense of the husband, and accepting his invitation to succeed him when he should be no more. Gentlemen, if such talk did take place in the presence of the Rev. George Dyson, the Rev. George Dyson should have put his foot down upon it and stamped it out. You cannot doubt—and I grieve to have to point it out to you, because it is one of the material circumstances in this case that can never be thrown out of it from beginning to end—you cannot doubt, because you have it on the statement of the wife as well as on the statement of the Rev. George Dyson, and they both agree to this—that they got to that state of intimacy when in some fashion or other the possible death of the husband and the possibility of Dyson succeeding him were matters of familiar discussion. When a young wife and a younger male friend get to discussing, whether in the presence of the husband or out of his presence, the probability of his decease within a measurable time, and the possibility of the friend succeeding to that husband's place, according to all ordinary experience of human life that husband's life is not one that an insurance office would like to take at any premium.

I cannot forbear to make these observations. They arise upon the case, and they ought to be made, and it is part of my duty—its painful nature no one feels more keenly than I do—but I cannot discharge the duty which I am put here to discharge, and fail to point that out to you. Whatever may become of the case by your verdict, no human being can say that the actors in such a drama

Adelaide Bartlett.

as this, when the very thing had occurred which had been the subject of discussion between them, and had occurred under very suspicious circumstances—no human being can say that either of them has any cause of complaint if grievous suspicions are entertained that he or she, or both of them, has had a hand in it. And as far as those suspicions are concerned, one must not be too hard upon the father, because sometimes there is an instinct as to things of this kind, and sometimes people who would be puzzled to give an account of their reasons are not entirely without justification in their suspicions.

Now, gentlemen, on 3rd September, 1885, the late Mr. Bartlett made his will, and by that will he left all his property to his wife absolutely. The will was a natural and a proper one, and, in my judgment, a much better one than the one which he had made before, because I agree entirely with one passage, as I do with many others, in the remarkable display of forensic eloquence and power to which we listened yesterday, and which was as distinguished for the fairness with which the subjects were dealt with, and the evidence treated, as for its power and ability—I agree with Mr. Clarke that, where a man who has a young wife and has no children, and has no particular reason for leaving his property away from her, makes her enjoyment of life or even her means of subsistence dependent upon the condition that she should remain a widow for ever, it is a cruel will. I agree with Mr. Clarke that the will which he made in 1885 was a much better one than its predecessor; and I think that no shadow of distrust ought to rest upon her, because, in the course of 1885, or whenever it was that Annie Walker was visiting, she commented, in the presence of her husband, upon the harshness of such a will, and remonstrated, or said something by way of remonstrance against it. I think the later will was a wise, a good, and a proper will in every respect, and it was a natural thing to name as executor of that will a gentleman in whose ministrations he professed to have found, and I dare say with perfect genuineness said that he had found, great comfort both to himself and his wife. I cannot go further. I cannot see that in the fact of his making Mr. Dyson his executor there is any trace of a suggestion that he thought that he himself was not likely long to survive the making of that will; I cannot understand that. I made my will when I was a young man, and I should have been surprised if, because I selected my executor, it was to be suggested that I thought he was likely necessarily to outlive myself, or that there was anything more in it than an indication of the confidence reposed by the writer of the will in the person so named.

Well, they go to Dover, and they spend a month at Dover, and during that month at Dover Mr. Bartlett must have very severely taxed his physical energy. He seems to have been a man,

Charge to the Jury.

Mr Justice Wills

if you accept the father's statement—and I do not see any particular reason for doubting it—who was engrossed in business. He had been very successful. Shop after shop had been added to the list of his acquisitions; such a man would naturally take a keen interest in business, and he emphasised it by putting a strain upon his physical powers under which it was not unnatural that they should break down. You hear how he used to start at three o'clock in the morning, take the boat-train, and come back at nine or ten at night. Flesh and blood won't stand that. In the course of that month at Dover Mr. Dyson visited them; and, according to Mr. Dyson, Bartlett visited him at Putney. With regard to everything that Mr. Dyson has said, both about the extent of his own relations with Mrs. Bartlett and about the extent of the knowledge of the husband of how far those relations had gone or were likely to go, I must put it to you, as men of the world, as men of experience, and as men exercising sound judgment, whether you can place more than a very slender faith in Mr. Dyson's statement. Mr. Dyson had to make the best for himself of his relations—which from any point of view, as described by himself, were discreditable to him, discreditable to Mr. Bartlett, discreditable to Mrs. Bartlett—and a large part of his statements, although they came to us to-day in the witness-box out of his mouth, are nothing but repetitions of statements to which he had already committed himself in his evidence before the coroner. At the time he gave that evidence, there can be no doubt that the Rev. George Dyson entertained very serious fears that his own life was in danger; and I should think there can be very little doubt on the part of anybody who has seen him here, that there is one person in this world that the Rev. George Dyson was determined should suffer as little as possible by this history—that is, the Rev. George Dyson himself. And therefore you cannot give yourselves over with unlimited confidence to statements which he has made of any kind; and wherever you find that they touch upon things which affect himself, I should think you would say you would have to exercise great reserve in accepting them.

Now, he tells a story as to which I do not know what you may say about this part of it. I confess to my mind it presents some features of almost revolting improbability. He says Mr. Bartlett came down to see him at Putney. " I told him I was growing too fond of his wife." I do not mean that " too fond " was his expression; but I am translating what he said into something like plain and intelligible language—" I told him I was getting too fond of his wife." A young unmarried man thrown in the fashion in which he was into the company of a young married woman would be likely enough to be getting too fond of her. He said to the husband, " It distracts me; I cannot attend to my duties; do you not think it had better cease? " He also told him, as he says,

375

Adelaide Bartlett.

that he had addressed to his wife words which she should not have heard from her minister. The Rev. George Dyson would have you believe that, after that explicit statement, Mr. Bartlett invited him to continue his intimacy with both of them. If there is anything in the atmosphere of this case which ought to make one part with the ordinary faculties which God has given us, and by which alone we can hope to test the truth of stories which are placed before us, by all means accept that statement. Am I putting it too strongly when I say you must part with a good many of them before you can accept it?

It is said that two letters have passed which indicate that something of this kind had taken place. Gentlemen, you have heard them read this morning. Are they of that extravagant character? They do use strong terms, and terms which are not usual—at least they are not usual among educated people brought up in the ways of speech to which I am accustomed. One difficulty I feel in dealing with this case, and a difficulty which never must be absent from your minds, is that the ways and thoughts of these people are very different from ours. I have passed a large part of my professional life in seeing quarrels and litigations—and those are the occasions upon which unvarnished human nature crops up to the surface—in a district in which a great deal of these more emotional forms of religious belief and action exists; and I am more prepared perhaps than many persons would be for the odd mixture which we have here of religion and coarseness—the things told to Annie Walker about the sexual relations between the parties, and the fervent religious exultation roused by Mr. Dyson's services. Still, it is difficult to put oneself quite in the position of these people; and one always runs a great risk if one judges from one's own standpoint other people whose ways and thoughts are quite different. You must beware of that danger. But, after all, can you find in these letters anything of the extraordinary nature which Mr. Clarke claims for them? "Dear George" (you know the intimacy had gone some distance, and it looks as if that was the first time he was addressed as "George"),—"Permit me to say I feel great pleasure in thus addressing you for the first time." It is in evidence that they called him "Georgius Rex," and looked up to him, and were proud of his friendship. They felt him, it is evident, to be a little above them in education and social standing, notwithstanding his want of means. "Permit me to say I feel great pleasure in thus addressing you for the first time. To me it is a privilege to think that I am allowed to feel towards you as a brother, and hope our friendship may ripen as time goes on, without anything to mar its future brightness." There is absolutely nothing there, except a tendency to a little over-sentimentality—some people, perhaps, might be inclined to say it was getting towards maudlin—that is

376

Charge to the Jury.

the extent of it. Now we come to a little more: "Would that I could find words to express my thankfulness to you for the very loving letter you sent Adelaide to-day. It would have done anybody good to see her overflowing with joy as she read it whilst walking along the street, and afterwards, as she read it to me, I felt my heart going out to you. I long to tell you how proud I felt at the thought I should soon be able to clasp the hand of the man who, from his heart, could pen such noble thoughts. Who can help loving you?"

Mr. Dyson gives his explanation of these expressions. It comes, indeed, from Mr. Dyson; you will receive it with all qualification and all suspicion, but, after all is said and done, does it, or does it not, in your judgment, adequately explain this language? Mr. Dyson says, "He had talked to me about his wife, and he said that she had benefited by my ministrations, and he showed me one of her highly devotional letters, and he seemed as if he would be glad if I could bring her back into the same line of thought and devotion, and so on. It was a letter of that character I wrote to her." Now, which is the more probable—that that was so, or that this was a letter which was founded upon the desire of the husband that Dyson should look on his wife in a manner that no husband except Mr. Bartlett ever could be content with? You must judge for yourselves. I do not mean to detract from the powerful and able observations which Mr. Clarke made to you; they must be considered by you along with, and side by side with, these observations of mine; those observations would present a different view. "I felt that I must say to you two words, 'Thank you,' and my desire to do so is my excuse for troubling you with this. Looking towards the future with joyfulness." I can see nothing very suggestive—nothing very exceptional. Here is a man who says, "I am allowed to address you for the first time by your Christian name, on terms of close intimacy; I hope nothing will mar our future or prevent its being delightful. I hope nothing will come between us, and I look forward to the future with joy." I dare say a good many of us, if writing the same thought, would say "with pleasure," but does that shade of difference of expression, especially when used by a person who was certainly familiar with a mode of life and a mode of expression in which strong and fervent language is frequent, imply anything so very extraordinary? I confess, whatever that letter might be taken to mean standing by itself, when I come to view Mr. Dyson's answer to it I find it difficult to see in the correspondence anything much above the common prose level. Is it possible that this really stamps the commencement of a new phase of life, in which this woman had been in some mysterious way consecrated as the object of his special personal interest in a sense and under conditions probably without a precedent in human experience?

Adelaide Bartlett.

Here it is—" Thank you very much for the brotherly letter you sent me yesterday. I am sure I respond from my heart to your wish that our friendship may ripen with the lapse of time, and I do so with confidence, for I feel that our friendship is founded on a firm, abiding basis—trust and esteem." It is not " you and I have some mysterious relationship to the same lady "; that is not the centre of interest—the centre of common interest is trust and esteem. " I have, from a boy, been ever longing for the confidence and trust of others. I have never been so perfectly happy as when in possession of this. It is in this respect, among many others, that you have shown yourself a true friend. You have thanked me, and now I thank you; yet I ought to confess that I read your warm and generous letter with a kind of half-fear—a fear lest you should ever be disappointed in me, and find me a far more prosy, matter-of-fact creature than you expect." What is there there? " You expect too much of me; you look forward to our future intercourse. I am afraid you make too much of me. I am a mere matter-of-fact person." He goes on—" Thank you, moreover, for the telegram; it was very considerate to send it. I am looking forward with much pleasure to next week. Thus far I have been able to stave off any work, and trust to be able to keep it clear. Dear old Dover. It will ever possess a pleasant memory for me in my mind, and a warm place in my heart." I don't know how it strikes you, but is there anything about a mystic union—such as nobody ever heard of before —between two persons, one unmarried and one married, with the consent, sanction, and approval of the husband?

We come now to Claverton Street, and there, according to Mr. Dyson, the probable or possible death of Bartlett formed the subject of conversation between the prisoner and himself. Again I say, receive what he says with becoming caution, not to say mistrust. But, except for mere accident of time and place, she is at one with him, because she told Mrs. Matthews at a later period that Mr. Dyson would not believe her that Edwin was likely to die soon, or not to live long—the exact phraseology is unimportant. Mr. Dyson says that this topic formed the subject of conversation soon after they went to Claverton Street, that it was referred to from time to time, and he says, " I could not say exactly when it was; all I can say is, at my first visit to Claverton Street it was referred to, and referred to more than once afterwards." If this were true, Mr. Dyson's account of what followed sounds probable enough. Mr. Dyson says, " I could not understand it, and I asked her what was her reason for supposing that Edwin would die soon, and then I was told this story about the internal complaint, about which he was so sensitive that it should not be mentioned to him, and for which he had seen Dr. Leach; this gradually led up to a series of conversations which

Charge to the Jury.

Mr Justice Wills

culminated some time or other in the mention of chloroform—chloroform to be used when he was violent or in a paroxysm." If you believe that, it is a serious circumstance in this case, because the story is all moonshine—and it seems to me very difficult to doubt, seeing what Mrs. Matthews afterwards overheard, and what Mrs. Bartlett afterwards said to Mrs. Matthews, that for some reason or other the subject of Edwin's possible decease was talked of. And I mean his decease at a not very remote period, because, of course, if it was talked of in any other sense, there is nothing in it at all. If you only talk of your death as a thing which may happen, and of which nobody can say whether it will be to-night or twenty years hence, there is nothing remarkable about it. But that does not seem to have been at all the character of the conversation. And one thing I have watched, from the beginning to the end of this case, with anxious care, I assure you, and that has been to see whether any sort of reasonable foundation had been established for the notion that Edwin's life was not likely to be lasting. You have attended to this case with as much care, I am sure, and under as much sense of responsibility, as myself. My responsibility is great from any point of view, and I feel it the more because it is, in my opinion, no part of a judge's duty to make his summing-up a wholly colourless thing. It is not my theory of judicial responsibility, and not one on which I propose to act in this case. I feel you have the right to call on me to give you the help of a trained mind, and of the experience which years, many years, spent in investigating difficult questions of fact of one kind and another cannot have failed to give.

Now, gentlemen, what foundation is there for this? One must go into this with minuteness and some care. Baxter had known him for thirteen years, and had never known a case of serious illness.

Mr. CLARKE—I hope your lordship will not think I am improperly interrupting. I will remind your lordship that no evidence was given, except by Dyson, that Mrs. Bartlett ever said he was likely to die soon. Mrs. Matthews says she overheard the statement made by——

Mr. JUSTICE WILLS—After that " How did you come to tell Dyson such a lie? " and Mrs. Bartlett said Dyson " would not believe what I had told him, that Edwin was likely to die soon."

Mr. CLARKE—Your lordship has got into one note the answer to two questions. She said he did not believe her when she told him the truth. Then the witness was asked what was the truth, and she said, " Her husband was going to die soon," and your lordship immediately put this question in these words, " Had anything passed between you and her to indicate what you were talking about? " and the witness answered, " No."

Mr. JUSTICE WILLS—I am very much obliged to you, Mr.

379

Adelaide Bartlett.

Clarke, and I hope if you think I am going wrong you will tell me; I know you will not interrupt unnecessarily. But, gentlemen, I will give it you: "On the 11th of January I had a conversation with her. I asked her why she had told Mr. Dyson all those lies. I had not told her what Dyson had said." You know pretty well what Dyson had told Mrs. Matthews. We are left to guess; we do not know exactly, but you may guess very nearly what it must have been from what followed. "She said he had bothered her so; he did not believe her when she told him the truth—that Edwin was going to die soon, and she said he did think so latterly." Now, gentlemen, if you think there is any doubt of that, of course you will not accept it on the evidence of Dyson alone, because Dyson, as I told you, had got a story to tell before the coroner, and Dyson was very determined, whatever happened, that he should run no unnecessary risk, and I should think he was perfectly careless how much he put on this woman, and how little he left on his own shoulders. Now, this conversation with Mrs. Matthews that I have read was on 11th January. I will read it again to fix it on your mind: "I asked her why she told Mr. Dyson all those lies." We know what that relates to; it relates to this, that Dyson had told her at Dr. Leach's when, on 6th January, they were waiting for her while she was in——

Mr. CLARKE—There is no such evidence, my lord.

Mr. JUSTICE WILLS—Do listen to me. Mrs. Matthews had had a conversation with Dyson, Dr. Leach had gone in with Mrs. Bartlett; Dyson and Mrs. Matthews were left outside, they were left in the waiting-room, and Mrs. Matthews said, "We were in there together, and we had a conversation," and then it must have been he told her something, I am not saying what, because we can only guess what it was, but Dyson says he mentioned chloroform on that occasion. Mrs. Matthews must have heard something, because she said, "Why did you tell him all those lies?" Now, we know both of them knew that some lies had been told. She said he had bothered her so, he did not believe her when she told him the truth, namely, that Edwin was going to die soon, and so she told him a lie. "I said I did not know that Edwin thought he was going to die soon; she said he did think so latterly; she said she had had the chloroform to soothe Edwin, but she had never used it." If you think that that does not point in the direction of confirmation of Dyson's story, of course, you will reject Dyson's story, because you will never think of accepting his uncorroborated evidence on a point on which it is of vital consequence to him to exculpate himself and as to which he cares nothing how much difficulty and danger he throws on another person. If you doubt that a conversation of this kind had taken place, of course it must be discarded as an element in the case.

Charge to the Jury.

Mr Justice Wills

That is for you to judge. You have heard the evidence; it is for you to judge whether the right complexion has been put on it or not.

Baxter said he never knew this man except as a strong man; that he had one illness before of a very trivial character, and that was all he had known of him in the way of illness during the thirteen years he had been acquainted with him. This illness does not seem to have been of a very serious character—it was a very disagreeable one, no doubt; the man overstrained himself, and overworked himself. He had taken those extravagant journeys from Dover, day after day and week after week, and done himself injury by it, and he broke down, and there were symptoms of mercurial poisoning. It is quite possible, when you find the way in which this man went about with French letters in his pocket, that that mercurial poisoning, and that necrosis of the jaw, may have a very different explanation from that of Dr. Leach. Indeed, to me it seems an extravagant notion of his that the disease of the bone of the jaw could be due to an oversized blue pill picked out of a sample box, and it is possible that he was a man suffering from syphilis. The course of that illness certainly did not point to approaching death, and, although he was sleepless, wretched, morbid, hypochondriacal, presenting the symptoms of a nervous breakdown, the illness had run its course; and as to that there is a strange concurrence of testimony. The doctor tells him on the 19th he had nothing to do except to go out. Dr. Leach told him he should discontinue attendance, and that it was a ridiculous idea about his dying soon. It is very likely that a man of that kind would say, as Dyson said he said to him, " Can a man feel so ill as this and recover?" Very likely he talked of his death, but not as a man does who is, or feels himself, in real danger. Dr. Leach said, " I always ridiculed the idea," and the last three or four days of his life it is scarcely possible he can have supposed that there was any danger of any sort or kind to his life. According to Mrs. Matthews, Mrs. Bartlett told her that Edwin did think latterly that he was going to die. But he does not seem to have thought so on the last day of his existence. Anything more unlike the conduct of a dying man it is impossible to conceive. On 31st December he ate heartily of jugged hare, so heartily Mrs. Bartlett tells Mrs. Doggett that she thought he would eat three dinners. He went and had a tooth out, and then that evening he was better than usual, and he expressed himself in a way which certainly did not look like the thought of a man to whom early death was present. He ordered a large haddock for breakfast in the morning, and told the servant—the last thing he said to her—that the very thoughts of it would make him get up an hour earlier that he might enjoy his breakfast. And on the 28th he told his father, and on another day close to the day of

Adelaide Bartlett.

his death he told Dyson, that he was going to Bournemouth shortly, and it seems that Dr. Leach had promised to take him down to Bournemouth, and place him there under the care of a doctor.

Now, gentlemen, assume, if you will, that this talk of Edwin's dying was very late in his illness, and not, as Dyson says, soon after they went to Claverton Street. Surely the passage I have read from Mrs. Matthews' evidence shows that some such conversation did take place between Dyson and her, and shows that Dyson was reluctant to believe that he was ill to the death, and shows that she was urging him to believe it, and told him some lie or other in order to account for the fact that she represented her husband as likely to die. Dyson says the particular lie was that he had an internal complaint, and that Dr. Nichols said he would not live another twelve months. But I would rather not rest on anything Dyson has said unless corroborated by other people, and if I had to form an opinion of this case I would not form it on uncorroborated statements of Dyson, and I would reject them unless there was a violent probability in their favour.

We come now to the most critical time in the whole history. I have stated to you one side of the question up to that night. Let me now put before you the other, and it is one I dwell on with much more pleasure, and one I know that has not been absent from your minds in considering this question, for it is one of the strongest circumstances in favour of the prisoner, and one to the full benefit of which she is well entitled. Every piece of evidence we have throughout the case points to the conduct of a devoted wife, and I must say everything given in evidence seems to me perfectly natural. I can detect no trace of anything that does not look like the natural, spontaneous flow of affection and of unusual devotion. During the three weeks preceding this critical time, she had scarcely had her clothes off; and a most unpleasant illness it must have been. You have heard the sort of state he was in— his wretched hypochondriacal melancholy; and if any of you have had any experience of that kind, you will know the tax there must be on any one attending upon such a man. He had all the irritability and all the moral disturbance which attend such a condition. Perhaps, gentlemen, I have had unusual opportunities of knowing myself what that means, because it was my unhappy fate at one period of my life for twelve months together never to have one tolerable night's rest; and I know, as no human being who has not gone through it can know, the misery of that state of things and the discomfort the patient must bring on all those about him. But she seems to have been entirely true to her trust and her duty. She performed the most disagreeable duties, keeping the man's stools and urine for the doctor to see, and doing everything with patience and devotion. That must never be lost sight of in this case, and that ought to stand her in the fullest

Charge to the Jury.

Mr Justice Wills

stead. I have been myself unable, as I say, to see any trace of anything like acting in the matter; and I can see no trace, no legitimate trace, of anything which should tend towards suspicion, either in the possession of books about poisoning, or conversations about poison—a class of evidence which it is very rarely that a case of this kind wants. And if I put the truth faithfully before you as to the circumstances which have told against her, and have helped to bring her to this pass, where dreadful suspicion has fallen on her, and naturally fallen on her, it is equally my duty, and far more my pleasure, to point out those circumstances which, as I say, must never be lost sight of, and as to which I hope you will not attach the less importance, because necessarily they take me less time to deal with, and therefore, in one sense, are passed off more lightly, than the opposing considerations. Certainly I have no disposition to extenuate their importance or take away from the great force that they ought to have when you consider the difficult question you have to answer. She was perfectly devoted, perfectly affectionate, perfectly natural in her conduct. Extending as the evidence on this point does over a great number of years, and coming from many different sources, it is entitled to the greatest weight. Gentlemen, I have summed up this part of the case in a few words, but I hope in words which will be thought even by those representing the prisoner adequate to the occasion.

That being the state of things, we come to the night of 31st December. There is absolutely nothing, in my judgment, either in the few words spoken about chloroform (which came in very naturally after the operation he had undergone), or in the trivial directions given for the night, which affords ground for suspicion. Ten o'clock comes. She and her husband were left alone, and all we know about what passed there in the interval between ten and four is from herself, and she has said that up to twelve o'clock she was awake, and some time after twelve she says she went to sleep. At four o'clock in the morning she awoke, and then this man had been dead two or three hours. Now, what he died of seems to me to be no mystery; and although the medical evidence occupied a long time—necessarily a long time—and was a most important part of this investigation, yet all of it that is worthy of consideration may be really summarised in half a dozen sentences, or very little more. There is cogent evidence that this man died from swallowing chloroform. How much we cannot tell; all we know is, it was a fatal dose. There is, as it seems to me, and I shall point out by-and-by that is a fact that helps her, not that tells against her—there is, in my judgment, strong evidence that that chloroform, that fatal dose, was at some time or other in the glass which was afterwards found on the mantelpiece, and it seems to me very difficult to escape from the conclusion, which-

Adelaide Bartlett.

ever way it makes, that the chloroform which caused the man's death somehow found its way into the glass, and somehow from the glass into his stomach. There is also strong reason to think, from the medical testimony, that the chloroform, although it may have been swallowed when he was not recumbent, worked its serious and fatal effect while he was lying down. How much, or how little, he swallowed we cannot tell, and no human being can ever know. The statistics are not sufficiently extensive, the knowledge on the subject is not sufficiently accurate, and how much or how little will constitute a fatal dose is a matter on which we can only speculate. It seems that, under circumstances the precise nature of which is unascertained, a much smaller dose will do it than the writers have recorded in most instances, and very likely a smaller dose might do it than is recorded in any instance. As far as I remember, the smallest recorded dose which is supposed to have killed a person is either 2 ounces or one ounce and a half. That was the American case—the case of a person who died—a very remarkable case, because, if that case had not happened, death from so small a dose would have been supposed to be almost impossible. That was the case of a young man who took chloroform—committed suicide; he was insensible in three minutes, and died in an hour; and one can understand, I think, that very large doses are apt to defeat their own ends if taken with suicidal intent, because they make the patient sick, and then the stuff is got rid of. Much more than that as to the cause of death the evidence does not tell us, except this, that, if you are to act on the original theory of the prosecution, another difficulty arises. I suppose that, notwithstanding the slight discussion which the Attorney-General started this morning as to some other probability, you will refuse to take (as I should refuse) into your own mind at the last hour any but the supposition on which this battle has been fought, if I may use an expression which might to some minds convey the notion of a spirit very different from that in which this case has been conducted. I do not suppose you will consent to approach this subject as against the prisoner from any other hypothesis than that originally put forward, that to which all the medical evidence was directed, and on which alone the examination and cross-examination of the medical witnesses who have thrown all the light they can on the subject has been conducted, and therefore I say nothing more about that suggestion which fell from the learned Attorney-General this morning, except that I ask you, in the name of justice, to refuse, as I do, to have anything to do with it at the last hour of the investigation. This much more, then, we have, gentlemen—and it is the sum of all the evidence as to partial insensibility and the swallowing of chloroform by a person in that state—the attempt would be surrounded by so many difficulties, and open to

Charge to the Jury.

Mr Justice Wills

so many chances of failure, that no skilled man would venture upon it unless he were a madman. But I am bound also to say this, that the observation would have far greater weight if we were dealing with the case of a person possessed of minute and technical knowledge, and aware of its difficulties. Everybody knows that "Fools rush in where angels fear to tread," and the ignorant and presumptuous will sometimes attempt that which no human being who understood the conditions of the problem would think of trying, and will sometimes blunder into success. But, if she did succeed in that fashion, it is not too much to say it was a most extraordinary piece—I was going to say of good, but I had better say—of cruel fortune, because the conditions and chances are all against it. And that really seems to me about all we can learn from the medical testimony as to this part of the case. The fact undoubtedly has an important bearing on the case, though not so important as if we were dealing with the case of a Lamson or a Palmer. I could not help thinking, when the learned Attorney-General mentioned them, that the parallel was not a fair one, because they were people who had studied these things and were fully aware of everything done, said, and written with regard to the occult poisons they used; and it occurred to me at the time that, when the proper occasion came, I must call your attention to that difference, and not allow you to pursue that parallel in the case of this prisoner, because it would be a most disastrous parallel for her. On the other hand, it constantly happens that facts cut both ways, and so here the very ignorance of the prisoner in this matter diminishes, but does not take away altogether, the strength of the observation that, if this be a case of murder, an experiment has been successfully attempted which not one of those eminent physiologists and chloroformists called before you (if you can imagine that the foul fiend had put it into their hearts to commit murder) would have dreamed of attempting, because they would know that the chances of failure (not chances of detection merely, but chances of actual failure) were so preponderating. There seems to be a double difficulty. In the first place, no living adult person has yet been experimented upon to whom chloroform has been successfully administered so as to produce anæsthesia during sleep; in the second place, if that difficulty be overcome, the chances are that the power of swallowing would be gone.

These eminent medical men, however, tell us that they believe, nevertheless, in the possibility of such administration, and that extended experience will justify their belief; but up to the present time a boy of fifteen or sixteen is the oldest person to whom chloroform has been administered during sleep, although it has been tried, as Dr. Tidy has told you, under circumstances of exceptional facility. It is only in a few cases of boys under sixteen years of age that the attempt has been successful. And, supposing

Adelaide Bartlett.

that initial difficulty got over, there is a great difficulty in choosing the right moment for the rest of the operation, for the interval is very short during which alone it is possible. The right moment must be hit, or else the anæsthesia will be carried so far that the power of using the muscles which must be used in swallowing will be gone. And therefore it must be by a lucky concatenation of circumstances, all contributing to one end, that this thing must be done if it is to be done at all, and that is one of the great difficulties—and a very formidable one—in the way of the theory of murder.

The learned Attorney-General said, rightly, in my judgment, that no hypothesis can be put that is not attended with difficulties so great that, if it stood by itself and apart from surrounding circumstances, one would say it could hardly be true; and yet we know that Bartlett's death was caused by swallowing liquid chloroform, and therefore it must have been caused by chloroform either criminally administered to him or not criminally administered to him. There is no escaping from this dilemma. If you take the evidence on either head alone, you would say the thing could not be done. Yet it has been done, and one of the two impossible theories must be right. You, therefore, will have to choose between the two theories, unless, indeed, you are really unable to do so. If, not merely avoiding a disagreeable conclusion because it costs effort, but honestly and after every effort to arrive at a definite conclusion, you are compelled in the end to say, " We cannot decide this question," then the case for the Crown is not made out.

I must trouble you with some further remarks as to perhaps the material element of this case, and one which undoubtedly, in my opinion, presses more strongly than almost any other against the prisoner, and that is the history of that chloroform bottle. Let me say this before I approach it, that, putting for a moment out of sight the theory of criminal administration and admitting the possibility of non-criminal administration, a possibility has occurred to me which I confess I am surprised has not occurred to others also. It may be that it has been prompted and brought home to me by that experience of my own life to which I referred a few minutes ago, and which is one of the sources of accumulated experience which is for what it is worth at your service just as much as any other piece of information which I have gathered in my life. I know what none of these gentlemen probably do know. And we are now dealing merely with a speculation, dealing with that which is within the knowledge of no one, for on the theory of non-criminal administration the prisoner knows no more about it than any one else. Her conduct afterwards, and her conduct before, may or may not be such as to urge you powerfully to think that it was criminal; but, assuming that it was non-criminal, she can throw no light on it, and therefore we are in the region of

Charge to the Jury.

Mr Justice Wills

speculation, where my speculation is as good as my friend Mr. Clarke's, or Dr. Leach's, or anybody else's, and I know what possibly nobody else concerned in this trial knows as I do—the craving for that which will secure sleep which people who are suffering from sleeplessness undergo; and I know the uncommon strength of mind, will, and resolution which it takes to resist that impulse. Fortunately for myself, I soon became aware that one had better undergo any misery than resort to the fatal practice of taking narcotics, but it takes a very strong-minded man to come to that decision, and to act upon it, because the sufferings of that state of mind are greater than any person who has not gone through such an experience can imagine.

Now, assume for a moment, and before coming to the very serious question how that bottle of chloroform could have got within his reach, that it could have got innocently within his reach, and that he knew it was there. We have heard that morphia had been injected, and that morphia had failed. He had tried chloral hydrate, and what I should venture, notwithstanding Dr. Leach's opposite opinion, to say would be a pretty stiff dose. He had tried chlorodyne. Those things had all failed. It does strike me as a thing not only possible, but scarcely improbable, that a restless man, eager and anxious for sleep, and with that craving for the means of procuring sleep which seizes on the sleepless—it does strike me as possible that he might get hold of the bottle and pour some into a glass and drink it. It does strike me as possible that a man doing that in the dark might not be very nice about the quantity, and might pour more in than he intended to pour. Now, assuming—I hope I have not gone out of the way to make this suggestion, but it seems to me that, assuming the possibility of non-criminal administration, we have a more reasonable explanation than that of suicide which the learned counsel was instructed to present to you; and I make this suggestion the more readily, and the more do I feel it my duty to make it, because it will be my bounden duty to point out by-and-by how almost absolutely absurd to me seems the notion of suicide under the circumstances suggested in the defence of the learned counsel. Of course, if the explanation, whether of the one kind or the other, rested upon anything that had come from her mouth, and as to which she had, or ought to have had, the means of knowledge, it would be against her if she had failed and it were proposeed to substitute something else for her explanation. But, seeing that we are dealing now with what is pure speculation, her speculation, supposing she is not a guilty woman, is no better or worse than anybody else's; and Dr. Leach's is no better or worse than anybody else's; and mine is no better or worse than anybody else's—except as in so far to your judgment and experience the one or the other may seem the more rational and the more consistent with probability.

Adelaide Bartlett.

Mr Justice Wills

All this, however, leaves still behind the question which I am now going to approach—to my mind, by far the most important part of this inquiry—and that is, what is the history of that chloroform bottle? You know Dyson undoubtedly procured the chloroform in driblets. Dyson had his own motives for wishing to keep that matter secret. I cannot tell what they were; I can only speculate. He said he thought the chemist would not believe that the person for whom he was going to get it would be a proper person to be entrusted with it, because she would not be likely to have the proper medical knowledge. It is quite possible by that time the Rev. George Dyson may have had the thought of his spiritual superintendent before his mind, and was conscious that things had gone quite far enough between himself and Mrs. Bartlett, and it is quite possible that he thought the less he said about Mrs. Bartlett's connection with anything he was doing the better. I mean, he may have had this kind of feeling quite apart from any notion of his being mixed up with any criminal use of chloroform, because we must put any notion of that sort out of sight once for all. We are not going to let the Crown transfer a man from the dock to the witness-box for the purpose of letting him give evidence, and then, for the purpose of making a case against the prisoner, to admit the faintest suspicion of anything beyond folly, though folly carried to a perilous extent, in Mr. Dyson's conduct. But Dyson procured the chloroform, and he said he handed it to her on the Thames Embankment. Here, again, you know, I should be very sorry to form any conclusion in my own mind adverse to Mrs. Bartlett on the suspicion that it was really handed to her on the Thames Embankment. I do not see any reason for believing it to be true because it suits the Rev. George Dyson to say so. The Rev. George Dyson had to make out the best case he could for himself about the chloroform, and he told the story not for the first time when he came before you in the witness-box, but he had pinned himself to everything that was essential in it when he had a very strong suspicion that there was a fatal entanglement gathering round himself, and wished at any cost to extricate himself from its folds, and I can see in his conduct no trace of any chivalry which would induce him to suffer any possible chance against himself for the sake of not making things worse against Mrs. Bartlett. He did afford the means of testing that part of his story, which was an important one, because, if he did give it to her on the Embankment, it was a circumstance of undoubted suspicion, one calculated to raise suspicion in everybody's mind, though a suspicion which we must discard in this case, because it would be a suspicion that would implicate him in a kind of criminality which we are bound to discard. But there was a means of testing the truth of that statement. He said that a person named Hackett was at Bartlett's when he was calling there, and before he and Mrs. Bartlett strolled

Charge to the Jury.

Mr Justice Wills

on to the Embankment, and that he was not there when he came
back again. Hackett has not been called, and this is not a case
where anything that could be got at should be left out; and I should
therefore discard everything about this part of his story, except
the fact that chloroform in a bottle was handed to her—a bottle
something like the 6-ounce bottle produced before us.

Now, if that chloroform were administered to Bartlett non-
criminally—and I use that phrase purposely in order to include
every variety of suicide and accident, and every other case for
which the prisoner would not be responsible—if that were administered to him non-criminally, it is very difficult to deal with it on
any other supposition than that the bottle must have found its way
to the mantelpiece, as, indeed, she says it did, and then from the
mantelpiece to that glass where the smell was afterwards perceived.
A very strong fact in her favour, to my mind—I say it at once,
but I will recur to it afterwards—is that there had been no attempt
to clean out that glass. It is a fact which strikes my own mind
as one of considerable weight, and one that ought not to be lost
sight of. Assume, therefore—I am still keeping to the theory of
non-criminal administration—that the bottle must have been, as
she says it was, on the chimneypiece in the course of the evening
before she settled off to sleep, and that he took the chloroform. I
see no difficulty if it were so taken—accidentally, so far as she was
concerned—in supposing that he could have so far lifted himself
up as to have taken it without disturbing her, whether he was bent
on suicide, or bent, more probably as it seems to me, on allaying
his restless craving for sleep. I see no difficulty in understanding
that he could raise himself up sufficiently without disturbing the
sleeper at the foot of his bed. But, then, if anything is proved in
this case, it is proved, so far as human proof can go, that soon after
four o'clock in the morning that bottle was not there. I put aside
as of inferior weight the evidence of Doggett, because his search
was not exhaustive; he missed the bottle of chlorodyne which was
on the other side of the room; but Dr. Leach searched and did not
see it. The glass which must have been made use of in connection
with it was still in its proper place, and was found by Doggett;
he smelt it; he sniffed at it; and he gave that piece of evidence
which, I think, is an important piece of evidence in her favour—
he smelt the smell of paregoric or ether. It had brandy in it, no
doubt, but the smell was, beyond all doubt, the smell of the chloroform—that smell lingered about it. It is true that crime is
seldom armed at all points; its designs generally break down at
some place where you least expect it; but if that woman's hand
poured that chloroform out of that glass into that man's throat,
she must have been strangely constituted, according to the instincts
of criminals in general, if she was not possessed with the desire of
obliterating the traces of what had been in the glass.

389

Adelaide Bartlett.

Mr Justice Wills

And it is not as if there could be any suggestion of a formed design in her mind to allow death by chloroform to be attributed to accidental administration. It is clear that from no point of view was that her plan, and therefore you cannot suggest this was a clever thought, that it would be better to let the smell linger there in order that the notion might gather ground that he had taken it accidentally. If any such notion as that had been in her mind, she would not have lingered twenty-six days before giving vent to it. And she never did give vent to it, and therefore you cannot get rid in that way of the fact; and it does seem to me strangely unlike the conduct of any criminal in any case of which I have had experience to betray no anxiety to get rid of every trace of the actual method in which administration had taken place.

That is in her favour—very much in her favour. On the other hand, you know it is difficult beyond measure to account for the disappearance of that bottle if all was right; if all was wrong, one can understand it. There were drawers in the room behind, and there was her pocket. We can never know for certain in which of those two places it was. A sort of curious fatuity seems to have hung over the case at its earlier stages. The coroner's officer—a grown-up policeman—who was sent there on 4th January to aid in the discovery of truth, went away from that house without taking the ordinary precaution of searching the drawers, and therefore we shall never know for certain, because we have nothing to guide us but her statement, whether the way in which that bottle got out of the house was that it was in her pocket on 1st January, or that she had put it into the drawer on that night or on the morning of 1st January, and before she called the people up, and left it there until the seals were taken off the room. Now, you know, gentlemen, if that man took that poison non-criminally, the bottle must have been on the mantelshelf, and it must have been on the mantelshelf at a tolerably late period of the night. What is the fact? That about half-past four in the morning that bottle had disappeared, and all we know for certain of it is that it was never seen again.

With regard to Dr. Leach, I desire to speak of his evidence with every respect which a sense of duty will allow me. I am sorry for him to have been placed in a position of exceptional difficulty, and one must make great allowance for a man who is evidently possessed of a self-consciousness that not even the solemnity of this inquiry could still for a moment, and which undoubtedly detracts from the value of his evidence, because one never knew where facts ended and inferences began, and one never knew when one was getting the unvarnished efforts of memory or the impressions of a not very strong-headed man painfully haunted by the idea that he is the central personage in a drama of surpassing interest. It is one of the great difficulties, one of the circum-

390

Charge to the Jury.

Mr Justice Wills

stances which has made this investigation exceptionally difficult, that, for reasons of a kind very different from those which apply to Dyson, you cannot trust, without correcting it by your own judgment, the impressions or statements of Dr. Leach. But I have no doubt whatever that Dr. Leach means to tell the truth; I do not suppose anybody in this Court thinks he means to do otherwise; and without attributing to him the genius of a detective in a French novel, and without supposing that he is gifted with anything beyond an average degree of human intelligence, surely his instinct must have told him, when that man was lying dead before him mysteriously from some cause that he knew nothing to suggest, and when he could find nothing to account for the death—surely he must have been strangely constituted if he did not feel it to be one of his first duties to ascertain with care whether there was anything close at hand, or under the touch of immediate observation, which could account for this dreadful mystery. And if there is one thing that Dr. Leach is clear about, it is that he did look for bottles; he found the chlorodyne, which had escaped the observation of Mr. Doggett; and if there is one thing he is clear about, it is that this bottle was not there.

What had become of it? The only account we have respecting it is that given by Mrs. Bartlett herself on 26th January, when, according to Dr. Leach, she told him that she put it in the drawer in the other room some hours later than his visit—she believed about breakfast time. But where was it in the meantime? Why on earth should it be gone from that mantelpiece, and gone from any place where it could be readily found? Now, gentlemen, I watched with more care and more anxiety yesterday the learned counsel's address on this point than I did on any other. He could not give any satisfactory explanation. I should be unworthy to sit here—I should be useless for the purpose for which I have been appointed, if I did not make this observation to you. I am well aware whither it points, and I am well aware of the momentous character of this part of the inquiry, but it is a question which you have to face; you will have to ask yourselves, when you retire to that room, what happened to that bottle? I can give you no help. All we know is that which I have stated; to which must be added that to Dr. Leach—I suppose on the occasion when she made the statement that he afterwards reduced into writing in the sensational document we have heard so much of—she said it had been on the mantelpiece. That is to say, that it was on the chimney-piece either when he made his search or when he was sent for, and he says, " I cannot tell which, but I can hardly think she said it was there when I was there, because she knew that I had looked for everything."

Now, if it had been moved from the mantelpiece, or wherever else it was standing, there was but one person who could do that;

Adelaide Bartlett.

and, if so, you have this most remarkable conversation carried on between Dr. Leach and that person, who must have had that chloroform bottle in her possession at the very time it was taking place. " I discussed," said Dr. Leach, " the various alkaloids, and I said, ' This little bottle of chlorodyne, how did he come to have this? ' " " Oh," she says, " he washed his teeth with it at night." " Then he may have swallowed some of it." " He could not have done that, because he only put it on his gums." " Well, then," says Dr. Leach, " if that is so, we ought to find traces of it, he must have spat it out "; " and I went and looked," he said, using an unnecessary periphrasis to describe the chamber-pot, and he did not find it there. Chlorodyne and chloroform are things that smell more or less alike, so much alike that Dr. Leach himself said of the chloroform in the stomach, " Well, they must have mistaken chlorodyne for chloroform." How strange, when there was this anxious discussion to ascertain the cause of death, how strange that the person who had a large bottle of fatal stuff closely resembling in properties and smell the chlorodyne under discussion, should have said nothing about it. Of course, gentlemen—I may say this in anticipation, though it will come more naturally later—if you can accept the explanation given to Dr. Leach on the 26th, there is a reason for it, because if you can accept that account there are certain principles of modesty and reserve and delicacy which might very well have prevented any woman, except under extreme necessity, telling the story which was detailed to Dr. Leach. And, as it seems to me, a vast deal in this case must depend, after all is said and done, on what you think of that story; because, admit its possible truth, and it equally explains away the false statements said to have been made to Mr. Dyson when he was asked to procure chloroform. There would be the same reason in both cases for suppressing the real purpose for which it was obtained, and the same reason for assigning some motive other than the true one.

Well, now, on this same 1st of January we come again to a circumstance which is much pleasanter for me to dwell upon; it is undoubtedly a most extraordinary piece of conduct if this woman was guilty of administering chloroform to this man. Who was it who pressed for the immediate post-mortem examination? You know there is no doubt about this; it does not depend on Dr. Leach's anxiety to construct a drama which shall look as if it came out of a sensational novel, or upon anything except perfectly satisfactory testimony. Dr. Leach's telegrams to Dr. Green are the most conclusive proof that she was anxious, and that that anxiety was acted on, to procure the immediate examination of the body. Now, grant that she knew nothing about chloroform, grant that she might know little about its medical properties, there are very few men and women so ignorant in this country as not to know that an immediate examination would increase the chances

Charge to the Jury.

Mr Justice Wills

of detection. We are not dealing with the case of an ignorant or stupid person, but of a person of considerable education, and I should think of considerable intelligence. Few guilty persons would show an anxiety to precipitate an examination of that kind. It is common enough, when the thing is inevitable, to offer no difficulties and to throw no obstacles in the way, because many persons are intelligent enough to know that, when it comes to that point, the best thing they can do is to act like honest people. But it would have been so easy to say, without exciting the smallest suspicion, " Cannot you leave it till to-morrow? " or say, " You can have it as soon as you like; but I should think the day after tomorrow would do." And no human being would have thought of suspecting anything because that line was taken. But there is nothing of the kind; it is her active interference which precipitates the post-mortem examination. And it is a fact of extreme gravity and importance, to the full benefit of which, in this time of difficulty, she is entitled, and if words of mine can add anything to the weight of the powerful observations made by Mr. Clarke yesterday upon this point, they shall not be wanting. I wish to give my emphatic expression of cordial agreement with all that he said upon that subject. It was not her fault, and it was not her doing, that that man's body was not opened and examined within a very few hours after his death; and I cannot persuade myself that, however little she may have known about chloroform—it is plain, if her statement to Dr. Leach is to be taken as an expression of how much she knew, that it was very little—there is any person of average intelligence, of her time of life, in this country who does not know that a post-mortem examination, in a case of this kind, is worth double or treble as much if performed a few hours after death as it is worth if delayed any considerable time. This, therefore, is a point of extreme importance in her favour.

The Court adjourned for a short time.

Gentlemen of the jury, I had got to the very important point when the post-mortem was decided upon. The next day the post-mortem took place, and the post-mortem disclosed the fact that there were grounds for suspecting that chloroform was the cause of death. Those grounds were communicated to Mrs. Bartlett; and shortly afterwards the resolution was announced to seal up the rooms, and to treat the place as in the possession of the officers of justice. And then Mrs. Bartlett offered her keys to Dr. Leach, and told him to look in the drawer or drawers for her hat, and he brought the drawer to her. She has said since that at that time the bottle of chloroform was in the chest of drawers. There were two drawers; you remember Dr. Leach said so. In the second of them he did not look. As I have pointed out before, of the history

393

Adelaide Bartlett.

of that bottle we have no trace. We have no evidence except Mrs. Bartlett's own statement. She went away from the house; she left her bag behind her, and everything else; and she left with the kiss of her husband's father on her cheek—a kiss which, I think, might well have been spared, seeing that he was at the same moment searching her pockets, and feeling her cloak, to see whether she took anything away with her. At all events, that conduct of his prevents the suspicion of her having taken anything away with her on that occasion which was not already in her pocket. As I pointed out, that bottle may have been either in the drawer or in her pocket, and where exactly it was no human being can tell.

That night Mr. Dyson took her to Mrs. Matthews, and, according to Mr. Dyson, some conversation took place on the way about the chloroform; and I can hardly help thinking that some conversation of that kind must have taken place, and for this reason— Mr. Dyson knew that he had bought chloroform, and had handed chloroform to her, and he knew that the smell of chloroform had been detected in the contents of this man's stomach; and Mr. Dyson, whatever he is, is no fool, and he must have put this and that together, and he must have begun already to feel uneasy about his own share in the transaction. He had his own special reasons for being uneasy, for there is no reason to suppose that at that time she knew he had told lies to procure the chloroform; he had talked about the chloroform, but there is no reason to suppose that she knew how he had procured it; therefore it was natural enough that Mr. Dyson should have had with her some such conversation as he alleges. I do not dwell upon what he said, or what he says she said in reply, because we are more or less getting evidence from a tainted source, from a man who, when he gave his account, was wanting to relieve himself from any suspicion in the matter. But we do know this—so great was his uneasiness that on the Sunday morning, as he went to his church, he sanctified the Sabbath by throwing away these bottles in the place he afterwards pointed out to a police constable, and where a bottle was found. There is no doubt about his telling the truth upon this point. On the 4th, Monday morning, he was early at Dr. Leach's, and was inquiring of him, we do not know exactly what, but it was no doubt something more about the post-mortem and the appearances of the deceased. He went from there to Mrs. Matthews, to see Mrs. Bartlett; and there took place that remarkable scene which has been alluded to more than once. He was engaged in conversation alone with Mrs. Bartlett when Mrs. Matthews came in. She found Mrs. Bartlett, the prisoner, in a state of excitement and, as she says, stamping about the floor, and she had heard the stamping before she had come in. She asked what it meant, and, after a considerable time, Mrs. Bartlett said it was over a piece of paper or a piece of poetry which Mr. Dyson had been troubling her about. Mrs. Matthews left the room, but

394

Charge to the Jury.

Mr Justice Wills

she came in again, and she came in at a very critical point in the conversation, where Mr. Dyson was saying, " But did not you tell me that Edwin was not likely to live long? " Whereupon the prisoner said, " No, I did not." And thereupon Mr. Dyson said, " Oh, my God! " and bowed his head on the piano. Now, I feel a very strong conviction myself that we do not know the whole of the story, and do not know precisely what did pass on that occasion to lead up to this exclamation—because I cannot understand the connection between the denial on her part that she had told him that Edwin was not likely to live long, and this expression of his, " Oh, my God! " We want the key to it ; perhaps it does not suit Mr. Dyson's purpose to give it us. But it is plain that at that time Mr. Dyson was challenging her with having told him that her husband was not likely to live long, and that she denied it ; and then Mrs. Matthews advised Mr. Dyson to leave, and as he left the room he said, " I am a ruined man ! " I have no doubt that the account of that interview given by Mrs. Matthews had a very material effect upon the decision that was come to by the Attorney-General, and the counsel associated with him, in determining to offer no evidence against Mr. Dyson, because undoubtedly the tenor of it is greatly in his favour upon the critical point which they had to consider in determining whether they would proceed further against him or not.

He returned the same evening, and on that occasion, according to himself—and looking here again at a subsequent part of the case, I think there is no reason to doubt that he is telling the truth—he expressed his determination to make a clean breast of it, and to tell the share that he had had in procuring this drug. On the 4th the coroner's officer took possession of the bottles which had been sealed up, including no less than thirty-six bottles of Dr. Leach's stuff which this unhappy man had taken, and carried them off to the analyst, Dr. Stevenson. He there left the matter, making no search, and so depriving us of the advantage of knowing what the contents of the room were at that time. The next day Mr. Dyson and the prisoner do not seem to have met, and nothing seems to have taken place of any importance.

On Wednesday, the 6th, Mr. Dyson went in the morning with some letters which Mr. Wood had given him to take to Mrs. Bartlett—some letters of the deceased's—and Mrs. Matthews, Mrs. Bartlett, and Mr. Dyson went together to Victoria Station, and before three o'clock in the afternoon they were with Dr. Leach. Dr. Leach saw Mrs. Bartlett, and had a long interview with her. Mrs. Matthews says that she and Mr. Dyson were left alone for about an hour. In the course of that interview Dr. Leach pressed Mrs. Bartlett to account for the period which elapsed between the time she and her husband went to rest and the time when Dr. Leach was summoned in the morning ; and Dr. Leach, who was more full of his

Adelaide Bartlett.

own impressions than anything else which he had to tell us about, says that he thought the account satisfactory; but he cannot tell us one single word of what it was. I see no reason to suppose that it was anything more than what she had told him before. Then they went home; she had had her keys returned to her; the servant says she visited the rooms; and she herself told both Mrs. Matthews and Dr. Leach that upon that occasion, on the way home to Herne Hill, where she was stopping with Mrs. Matthews, she took advantage of the opportunity the railway journey afforded her to pour out the chloroform and get rid of it, and that then she threw the bottle away into a pond on the Common, and, having done that, returned home. And that is the whole of the information we possess as to what became of the bottle. It undoubtedly never was seen by any one else after the night when this fatal occurrence took place. That same evening of the 6th Mr. Dyson fixed the position by announcing to Mr. Matthews his intention of making a clean breast of the whole affair at the inquest. Mr. Matthews said, what was not, I think, at all unnatural under the circumstances, "Wait. The contents of the stomach have gone to be analysed; wait and see if there is any necessity for you to make any further disclosure; see what the cause of death is, and hold your peace for the present."

On Thursday, the 7th, the inquest took place. Not very much evidence was given then, and it was adjourned for four weeks, until 4th February, to await the result of the analyst's examination, and on that occasion Mr. Dyson dined with the prisoner at a confectioner's, and, as he says, they had a talk in which he persisted in his determination to inform the coroner and the world generally of his share in the purchase of this chloroform. And I suppose it is probable that he did so; what he did agrees with what he says, and everything seems to bear it out. Friday, the 8th, was the day of the funeral, and on Saturday, the 9th, in the afternoon, Mr. Dyson, Mrs. Matthews, and Mrs. Bartlett went home together from Mr. Matthews's business premises in the city, and then it was that Mr. Dyson's last conversation with Mrs. Bartlett took place. Mr. Dyson did not like the turn things were taking, and he kept harping upon this purchase of the chloroform. As I pointed out before, he had undoubtedly special reasons of his own for feeling great anxiety, because he would have been a fool indeed if he had not been conscious that the falsehoods he had told when he was procuring the chloroform would be very likely to tell with fatal effect against him should any serious case be made out against Mrs. Bartlett. And then he said, "Suppose it was found out that he died from the effects of chloroform, and suppose it was found out that I gave you the chloroform?" Then she said, with every appearance of honest indignation—there is no doubt about that— "Well, you may as well say at once, if you mean it, that I gave

396

Charge to the Jury.

Mr Justice Wills

him the chloroform; say so, if you think so, and do not mince
matters." And then he said, " I am not prepared to go that
length; but supposing it were so—putting it hypothetically—my
position would be a very serious one, and I should be a ruined
man." Then they parted, and had nothing more to do with one
another.

You remember, gentlemen, that the inquest was adjourned till
4th February. On 11th January that conversation took place with
Mrs. Matthews which I have already read twice to you, where Mrs.
Matthews said, " Why did you tell Mr. Dyson these lies? " and
the prisoner said, " Well, I could not get him to believe what was
the truth, namely, that Edwin was likely to die soon; and so I
told him the lies." Mrs. Matthews said, " I did not know that
Edwin thought he was going to die soon." She said, " The fact
of the matter is, he thought so latterly."

Then on 20th January the prisoner had a conversation with
Mr. and Mrs. Matthews, in which she told them Dr. Leach had told
her chloroform could not have been inhaled. He seems always to
have been arguing the matter out when he met her instead of con-
tenting himself with facts—telling her chloroform could not have
been given by inhalation, because of this, that, and the other—the
post-mortem appearances and so forth—and she retailed this conversation with Dr. Leach to Mrs. Matthews.

The next date we have is 26th January, when the analysis
had taken place, and was substantially completed. Something of
what the chemists had to say had leaked out. It had come to Dr.
Leach's ears, and he said to her, " I have got some good news for
you; it is fortunate that no prussic acid has been discovered,
because I must tell you that, if it were otherwise, there are people
who would seriously accuse you of having poisoned him." Very
likely he was thinking of the father's suspicions. He added that
it was not prussic acid, but chloroform, that had been discovered;
whereupon she said, " Well, I wish it had been anything else."
Then she proceeded to tell him this extraordinary story—which I
hardly need read at length again, because it must be for ever fixed
in your memory—about the platonic union between herself and
her husband, broken only by the solitary act of coition, which
occurred on the Sunday afternoon, and resulted in the child, which
died at its birth. Between her and Dr. Leach we get this story
about the mystic union—about her being a wife and no wife; and,
undoubtedly, if you believe that, you may believe as a part of the
story the alleged intention to wave the chloroform in the husband's
face and so produce a cessation of his urgency. I do not know what
you think of the evidence you heard this morning. It is difficult
after that to elevate these people into the hero and heroine of an
extraordinary sensational romance. It looks much more as if we
had two persons to deal with abundantly vulgar and commonplace

Adelaide Bartlett.

in their habits and ways of life. After that disclosure, how can you for a moment follow in the track of Dr. Leach and believe that there was anything about this man to justify you in looking upon him as the extraordinary creature, almost belonging to another world, that Dr. Leach talks about, or to make it likely that the relations of this man and this woman were such as were never heard of before? When Dr. Leach's grounds come to be examined, they turn out to be none. Dr. Leach is one of those persons who likes to see a long way into a milestone. Apparently he is tickled with a story of romance and sensational incident, and he says to you, " Oh, I wish you could see the pictures that I have before my mind's eye! I wish you could see this man, and see these things which I saw but cannot communicate, which made it apparent to me that he might have had this non-sexual connection with the wife he had lived with and slept with in the same bed for so many years! "

Well, gentlemen, I do not know—I may be wrong in looking at the things of life from the common points of view, and one must try to avoid that error if there really is anything extremely exceptional in the case; but when I read, two or three weeks ago, that French letters had been found in this man's possession, I had a strong suspicion that, before the case was over, they would throw some light upon the matter. I little anticipated what it would be. It did occur to me that this story told to Dr. Leach was the poeticised version of the use of these French letters; further it did occur to me—and I was prepared to put it before you as a thing to be taken into your consideration—that the pocket of a man's trousers was not the place in which he would keep these articles for *domestic* use, and that they might point to something else in Mr. Bartlett's habits; but what we have heard to-day, if it is true— and what earthly reason is there to doubt its truth?—shows that if these things were destined for external use, as they very likely may have been, they were also used at home. And then what becomes of this morbid romance about the non-sexual connection, and what becomes of the man with such exalted ideas about matrimony that he thought the wife whom he elected for his companion too sacred to be touched? The whole foundation for that baseless illusion is swept away by the one sentence which you heard in the witness-box to-day. I am sorry to say it, gentlemen, but, unless I do, how can I discharge the duty that falls upon me of administering even-handed justice, careless as to results, or at least only thinking about results in so far as they tend to make me careful beyond measure of every step in the process by which they are arrived at? How can I let this vital part of the story pass without this criticism? And if the one little grain of truth which is generally to be found in any romance, in any story of falsehood, be found in these articles and in the use habitually made of them

Charge to the Jury.

Mr Justice Wills

between husband and wife, what becomes of the whole story of the use for which the chloroform was wanted? Does not it go by the board? I know not how to look at it from any other point of view, and, if that story be exploded, what, after all, are you left to face? Chloroform procured for an unexplained and an inexplicable purpose; death by chloroform; the bottle disappearing, and, by the statement of this woman herself, emptied and thrown away by her; and when at last the state of things has been set up which renders it no longer possible to keep silence, an explanation given, which is a tissue of romance such as, if the evidence of Annie Walker be accepted, could deceive no one but the ecstatic person to whom it was originally detailed.

Gentlemen, this is the stress of the case against Mrs. Bartlett. I am anxious not to make too much of this disappearance of the bottle. The conduct of people who once suppose that a state of circumstances has arisen, or is going to arise, which may place them under suspicion, is apt to be the same whether they are guilty or innocent, because, when once such a state of things is set up, the same class of motives may operate with the innocent as with the guilty, and I am always myself careful to point out to a jury—careful to mark, in the exercise of my own judgment—the moment at which that kind of influence arises, because I am satisfied, from long experience, that the stress which is put upon subsequent conduct is oftentimes unduly great. And, therefore, take all that has been said and can be said about the disappearance of the bottle, and about the lack of satisfactory explanation, with every grain of allowance of that kind; but after all you are faced with these facts, which there is no getting out of—chloroform handed to her; chloroform in her possession; chloroform killing the man; the bottle of chloroform disappearing, and no account of it save the one we have been discussing. That account, no doubt, is extremely material if you can believe it, because it would dispose of every circumstance of suspicion as to the purchase of the chloroform and as to the subsequent silence about it; but it is for you to say whether you can possibly, consistently with your oaths and consistently with your consciences, accept it, or whether you must not look at it as the expression, in adorned and imaginative language, of the simple and vulgar fact that they had come to the determination to have no more children, and that their intercourse from that time forward was upon that footing—either by the occupation of separate beds as in Claverton Street, or by the other means which I will not characterise—and whether, in that event, the statement made to Dr. Leach is anything more than an amplified and etherealised version of that vulgar fact.

Gentlemen, if you think you ought not to believe it—if, in the face of Almighty God, before whom we are performing this solemn duty, you feel that you cannot do so, you must not flinch from

Adelaide Bartlett.

the consequences. Give to the prisoner the full advantage of those circumstances of exceptional weight to which I have drawn your attention, and which I will not recapitulate—not because I wish you not to give them their full effect, but because I know they are present to your minds. Give her the full benefit of all such considerations. But remember, after all, we are dealing with the case of a married woman who had fallen into a perilous friendship with a man who was not her husband, whose husband could have been, in the latter portion of his life, no attractive object, either mentally or physically, and as to the most important circumstances connected with whose disappearance from this world the only explanation you have been enabled to get is one which, as it seems to me, cannot stand in the presence of these vulgar facts.

If you think it can stand, by all means take a different view. I am not the jury; you are the jury. The last thing that would ever occur to my mind would be to feel a sense of embarrassment or annoyance, or a shadow of regret, if you were able to take a different view of facts from that which presents itself to my mind. Upon some points I am sure we shall be agreed—upon all those which I have pointed out as making in this woman's favour —such, for instance, as her own conduct and the difficulty of the operation involved in the theory of murder. Strong they are, undoubtedly. Upon all these, I am sure you agree with me in what I have said. If you think, as to other matters upon which it has been my sacred duty, in the interests of society and of justice, to point out considerations of a different aspect, that you ought to differ from me, if you think I have strained them, if you think I have not made sufficient allowance for phases of life which I have not understood, if you think that anywhere or in any way I have erred on the side of severity, the last thing that would occur to my mind would be to feel any tinge of regret that you should have done so. But you must do your duty; and if you think that, after all is said and done, the facts are too cogent, and that, when you come to balance the probabilities and the improbabilities, your minds are really in no suspense—in no such doubt as would induce you, in the serious and grave transactions of your own lives, to pause or hesitate—then it would be your bounden duty to act upon your convictions, however painful the consequences may be. If your state of mind should fall short of that; if either you can concur in the emphatic appeal by the learned counsel for the defence to acquit his client because you believe her innocent, or if, falling short of that state of mind, you still are unable, after facing the question like men, and after looking at these difficulties from all sides, to make up your minds, and you remain in a state of honest and conscientious doubt, why, then, in that case also, the prisoner would be entitled to her acquittal.

Charge to the Jury.

Gentlemen, my task is done. I can add nothing, I think, to the observations which I have felt it my duty to lay before you to assist you in this matter. It is not by minute attention to every triviality that a question of this kind can be decided. One must, after all, investigate this as one should investigate every other case, upon the broad lines of the well-known principles of human nature, upon the broad lines of the common play of human passions and affection, and upon the broad lines of manly, honest, good sense; and if any other lines than these be followed, whether it be in one direction or the other, an irreparable mischief will be done to society and to the country and the life of which we form a part.

I now dismiss you to your task. Should there be any of these documents that you may wish to consult, you will tell me, and they shall be handed to you. I imagine that the matters which rest upon them are so completely on the fringe of this case, and have so infinitely little weight in comparison with the momentous questions to which the latter portion of my address to you has been directed, that in all probability you will scarcely care to see them. They are at your disposal if you wish it. And now, gentlemen, be pleased to retire to perform your task in this difficult and anxious business.

> The jury retired to consider their verdict at seven minutes to three. They returned into Court at five minutes to four.

Mr. JUSTICE WILLS—Gentlemen, you have asked me two questions on matters of fact, and I thought it more proper that my answers should be given in public.

The first question you have asked me is, what the evidence is as to the time Mr. and Mrs. Doggett went to bed on 1st January. I should say, from my recollection, there is no evidence of the time they went to bed on the night of the 31st, though the servant went to bed after midnight. I shall be corrected if I am wrong, but I think there is no evidence of the time when Mr. and Mrs. Doggett went to bed.

The second question is, whether Dr. Leach searched one drawer or two. What he specifically said was, that he did not search the second drawer, but the first drawer he brought in unsearched, bodily, and then Mrs. Bartlett took her hat out of it. The second drawer he did not open.

Mr. POLAND—Mr. and Mrs. Doggett are here, my lord, if you wish to ask them.

Mr. JUSTICE WILLS—I can ask them the question, certainly. One of them will do. Mr. Doggett, what time did you go to bed on the night of 31st December?

Adelaide Bartlett.

The FOREMAN—Or the morning of the 1st?

Mr. DOGGETT—Between twenty-five minutes and half-past twelve, my lord, as near as I can fix it. It was quite twenty minutes, and past—twenty-five.

Mr. JUSTICE WILLS—Those are the answers, gentlemen. Do you wish to retire again?

The FOREMAN—Yes, my lord.

> The jury again retired at ten minutes past four. They returned into Court at five o'clock.

The CLERK OF THE COURT—Gentlemen, have you agreed upon your verdict?

The FOREMAN—We have.

The CLERK OF THE COURT—Do you find the prisoner, Adelaide Bartlett, guilty or not guilty?

The FOREMAN—We have well considered the evidence, and, although we think grave suspicion is attached to the prisoner, we do not think there is sufficient evidence to show how or by whom the chloroform was administered.

The CLERK OF THE COURT—Then you say that the prisoner is not guilty, gentlemen?

The FOREMAN—Not guilty.

> At the announcement of the verdict there was immense cheering in the Court and outside.

Mr. JUSTICE WILLS—This conduct is an outrage. A Court of justice is not to be turned into a theatre by such indecent exhibitions. Gentlemen, it only remains for me to express my grateful sense of the undivided attention which you have given to this case, and the cheerfulness with which you have submitted to inevitable privation and the disturbance of your usual habits and family intercourse.

I hope we shall not be insulted again by an exhibition of the character just witnessed, which is disgraceful to those who take part in it, and who forget that the occasion is the most solemn upon which men can be called on to perform a public duty. I may add that it is permitted to me to give practical effect to my sense of the recognition due to your services by directing that, for five years to come, each one of you shall be free from the obligation of serving again.

MADE AND PRINTED IN GREAT BRITAIN
BY
WILLIAM HODGE AND COMPANY, LIMITED
EDINBURGH AND GLASGOW